A BIBLIOGRAPHY OF
# Geographical Education
# 1970–1997

# A BIBLIOGRAPHY OF
# Geographical Education
# 1970–1997

### Edited by
### Nick Foskett and Bill Marsden

THE GEOGRAPHICAL ASSOCIATION

# Acknowledgements

Apart from the direct contributors to the bibliography, we would also like to acknowledge the help of the following in submitting their own bibliographies and providing other information and advice: Alan Blyth, David Boardman, Rachel Bowles, Mike Bradford, Simon Catling, Graham Corney, Richard Daugherty, Peter Davies, Jane Dove, Gordon Elliott, Bob Gant, Bill Gould, Phil Gravestock, Doug Harwood, Trevor Higginbottom, Alan Jenkins, David Lambert, Paul Machon, Stuart Nundy, Eleanor Rawling, Malcolm Renwick, John Reynolds, Frances Slater, Chris Spencer, Harry Tolley, Roger Trend, Rex Walford, David Wright and, from overseas, Don Biddle, Rod Gerber, Hartwig Haubrich, Tammy Kwan, John Lidstone, Philip Stimpson and Joe Stoltman. We also thank James Convey for help in preparing sections of the bibliography.

Nick Foskett and Bill Marsden
*March 1998*

Frontispiece: Ian M. Spooner, University of Sheffield

ISBN 1 899085 55 6

First published 1998

Impression number 10 9 8 7 6 5 4 3 2 1

Year 2001 2000 1999 1998

Published by the Geographical Association, 160 Solly Street, Sheffield S1 4BF.

The Geographical Association is a registered charity: no. 313129.

The Publications Officer of the GA would be happy to hear from other potential authors who have ideas for geography books. You may contact the Publications Officer via the GA at the address above. The views expressed in this publication are those of the author and do not necessarily represent those of the Geographical Association.

Edited, indexed, designed and typeset by Asgard Publishing Services, Leeds

Printed and bound by ColorCraft, Hong Kong

# FOREWORD

More than twenty-five years ago, Clare Lukehurst and I attempted to list in one volume much that had been written in the United Kingdom on geography in education from 1870 to 1970. It was called *Geography in Education: A Bibliography of British Sources 1870–1970*. We did this on the occasion of the 22nd International Geographical Congress, held in Montreal and Quebec City in 1972. It was a first effort, which the Geographical Association published in that year, and which was presented to the members of the IGU Symposium on Geography in Education in Quebec. In 1998, the Geographical Association is publishing the present volume, again linked with an IGU Commission on Geographical Education initiative, entitled *A Bibliography of Geographical Education 1970–1997*, which updates and extends the previous bibliography.

Much has happened in the intervening years. In the early 1970s the conceptual revolution in geography was affecting school curricula, and curriculum development projects were attempting to effect reform in both geography and pedagogy. Since then the pace of change has continued to accelerate, and we have seen developments in the geography of perception, in humanistic geography and in geomorphology and climatology continue to advance our understanding of human and physical processes. To the traditional concerns of geography has been added the developing field of environmental education.

In any educational enterprise, the basis of the knowledge we teach needs to be understood. Thus geographers have made excursions into philosophical systems, and concepts such as positivism, phenomenology and post-modernism appear frequently in articles and books on geographical education.

In the day-to-day practice of teaching geography, there has been a rapid change in the teaching aids available to teachers and students. I am, for example, typing this foreword directly into a computer, an aid which was not at my disposal twenty-five years ago. Neither were databases, nor the numerous other software packages in geography that are now in use.

Perhaps of greater significance is the growth in the research in geographical education which has gone on in the last twenty-five years. To take a simple example, in 1970 there were probably no more than four general books in print on geographical education that had been published in the UK. Today there are far more. Further, there has been an explosion in the number of articles in specialised journals, and in the number of university theses, dissertations and short monographs in this field. This is a reflection of the increasing number of university tutors specialising in this area and of teachers who have pursued a higher degree and explored educational problems in geography.

It is therefore not surprising that a new bibliography is needed, nor that the classification of entries should be somewhat different from that of the 1972 bibliography. It is to the credit of the British Committee of the IGU Commission on Geographical Education that it has undertaken the not inconsiderable task of assembling all the items in this bibliography. To Professor Bill Marsden of the University of Liverpool and to Dr Nick Foskett of the University of Southampton go our thanks for collating and editing the huge number of entries which, for the 28-year span, greatly exceeds that collected for the hundred years from 1870 to 1970.

Norman Graves
Professor Emeritus of Geography Education
University of London Institute of Education

# CONTENTS

# INTRODUCTION

This bibliography is an initiative of the British Committee of the International Geographical Union Commission on Geographical Education (IGUCGE). Proposed when Michael Naish chaired the Committee, the project was approved at the IGU Congress at The Hague during 1996. Its broader inspiration was of course the previous compilation by Clare Lukehurst and Norman Graves, *Geography in Education: A Bibliography of British Sources 1870–1970*, published by the Geographical Association in 1972. This was followed by Jay and Todd's *The Dudley Stamp Memorial Index to Geography*, published in 1974, and covering the period 1901–1969. Our bibliography follows on from where those left off, and we are delighted that some continuity has been maintained, in that Norman Graves is one of the contributors to this bibliography, having been co-editor of the earlier volume.

In the foreword to the Lukehurst and Graves bibliography, Professor Wise pointed to the need to strengthen the influence of geographical education at the international level, and much has been achieved since 1972, not least through the efforts of four distinguished Chairs of the IGUCGE, namely Norman Graves, Joseph Stoltman, Hartwig Haubrich and Rod Gerber.

We believe that this new bibliography is just as essential as its predecessor was nearly thirty years ago. Some might argue that traditional printed bibliographies are no longer needed in this era of electronic publishing. But access to the relevant parts of ERIC and International ERIC, for example, while helpful, has convinced us how inadequate a resource base of references they are, not least for geographical education. Equally, the annual volumes of the *British Education Index*, and of the monthly *Content Pages in Education,* are extremely useful, but essentially cover only journal articles.

It has been difficult deciding what to include and exclude, and some of our decisions may appear arbitrary. We have avoided making judgements on the basis of academic quality. Broadly, the following have been consciously excluded:

♦ with a few exceptions, material on substantive geographical topics

♦ short articles in popular journals which we have judged to be ephemeral or parochial in interest

♦ school geography textbooks and other teaching materials

♦ contributions to the press

♦ reviews

♦ with a few exceptions, generic curriculum and other educational studies materials which are not specific to geography

♦ dissertations below Masters' degree level

♦ many materials produced internally by academic institutions and local authorities.

The bibliography is principally geared to the needs of British researchers, teachers and students, though we hope it will be equally useful to geographical educationists in other countries. With this in mind, the Committee decided that this bibliography, unlike the previous one, should extend beyond British sources, to cover overseas English-language material, particularly from Australia and the United States. We do not, however, claim that this overseas material is as comprehensively covered as that from British sources: we have concentrated on publications that are reasonably accessible to British readers, such as journals and books often found in university libraries. If you have problems getting hold of any of the materials cited, bear in mind the Inter-Library Loans service.

Including all that is available would in any case have expanded the bibliography beyond reasonable bounds. For example, there is an enormous amount of American material on topics such as geographical learning, of which we have only been able to include a sample. For fuller coverage there are extensive specialised bibliographies, cited here in Section E3. For many other countries the choice has been equally difficult and arbitrary.

We have naturally made a special effort in this IGU initiative to include IGU publications. Unfortunately many of these are not well known, nor readily available, though some may be found in university and other major libraries. If you find it difficult to access any of the IGU materials referred to here, you are invited to contact the editors via the Geographical Association, or the current Chair of the British Committee, Dr Ashley Kent, at the University of London Institute of Education.

While the bibliography is extensive, we recognise that there may be unintended omissions, and despite our best efforts to sort out inconsistencies, no doubt some anomalies remain. Please let the editors know if you notice significant inaccuracies or omissions, and we will incorporate changes in any future editions.

The categories in the list of contents (pages vi–viii) were considered very carefully and have been revised several times. Normally we have included each entry only once; some entries have been duplicated where they fitted into more than one section, but we have tried to keep duplication to a minimum.

It has been difficult to decide how specific to geographical education the entries should be: we found many grey areas. Taking the example of 'Geography and citizenship education' (Sub-section C1a), we decided, in accordance with our criteria, to exclude generic materials on citizenship education (except for some written by geographical educationists), but to include those on citizenship education which included some significant reference to geography.

We have made a special case for environmental education, however, because there is a massive overlap with geographical education, as exemplified by the journal *International Research in Geographical and Environmental Education (IRGEE)*, and because, in practice, geography teachers have been made heavily responsible for environmental education in British schools. We have therefore included a large generic section (D1) on environmental education, and another (D3) on the relatively neglected area of heritage education. But the literature on environmental education is enormous, so we have had to be selective.

Nick Foskett and Bill Marsden
*March 1998*

# Conventions adopted

## Abbreviations

Apart from a few well-known cases such as DES, DfEE, HMSO and SCAA, we decided not to use acronyms, to avoid the need to refer back constantly to a list of abbreviations. One exception is the frequently used, and cumbersome, title International Geographical Union Commission on Geographical Education, which we have abbreviated to IGUCGE. The other is the much-quoted *International Research in Geographical and Environmental Education* journal, for which we have used its familiar acronym *IRGEE*.

## Points of style

◆ Titles of books, journals and unpublished theses are given in italics.

◆ Titles of journal articles and book chapters are given within single quotes.

◆ Entries for books (and book chapters) include the place of publication and the publisher.

◆ Entries for unpublished theses include the academic institution to which the thesis was submitted.

◆ Entries for book chapters include the page references within the book.

◆ Entries for journal articles include the volume, part-volume (issue number) and page references.

◆ Foreign places of publication are given in the common English form (e.g. Munich rather than München) where one exists.

## Arrangement of entries

Within each sub-section, entries are arranged in alphabetical order of author/editor or group of co-authors/co-editors (commas, 'a', 'and' and 'the' are ignored).

For each author or group of authors, entries are given in chronological order of publication, with two exceptions:

◆ Articles by the same author(s) within the same journal volume, or chapters by the same author(s) within the same book, are arranged in page order.

◆ Entries by the same author for which the chronological order is unknown, e.g. journal volumes or books published in the same year, are arranged in alphabetical order of article, chapter or book title (whichever appears first within the entry).

## Numbering

The entries in the Lukehurst and Graves bibliography were numbered from 1 to 1402. It was decided to number the entries in this bibliography starting at 2000 in order to avoid any overlap, bearing in mind the possibility of producing a combined bibliography at some future date.

# EDITORS AND CONTRIBUTORS

**Bill Marsden** is Emeritus Professor of Education and Honorary Research Fellow in the Department of Education at the University of Liverpool. He has had overall responsibility for Parts A, C, D and E and has contributed to Sections B2 and B8.

**Nick Foskett** is Senior Lecturer in the School of Education, University of Southampton. He has had overall responsibility for Part B.

## Contributors

The following are the contributors to the sections (shown in parentheses) not covered by the editors:

**Graham Butt** (B10, C3, C6) is Senior Lecturer in Geographical Education at the University of Birmingham.

**Andrew Convey** (B1c, C5, E1–3) is Lecturer in Geography at the University of Leeds.

**Norman Graves** (E4–6) is Emeritus Professor of Geographical Education at the University of London Institute of Education.

**John Halocha** (C1, C4) is Lecturer in Humanities Education in the School of Education, University of Durham.

**Ashley Kent** (B12) is Head of the Department of Education, Environment and Economy at the University of London Institute of Education.

**Sheila Morris** (B9) was formerly Head of the World Studies Faculty at St Francis Xavier College, London.

**Michael Naish** (B6) is Emeritus Reader in Education at the University of London Institute of Education.

**Andrew Powell** (D1–2) is Senior Lecturer in Geography at Kingston University.

**Patrick Wiegand** (B1) is Senior Lecturer in Education at the University of Leeds and atlas adviser to Oxford University Press.

**Michael Williams** (B11, C2, C7) is Research Professor in the Department of Adult Continuing Education at the University of Wales Swansea.

# A. GEOGRAPHY AND EDUCATION

## 1. Methodological Texts in Geographical Education

2000    Bailey, P. (1972) *Teaching Geography*. Newton Abbot: David and Charles.

2001    Bailey, P. and Fox, P. (eds) (1996) *Geography Teachers' Handbook*. Sheffield: Geographical Association.

2002    Bale, J. (1987) *Geography in the Primary School*. London: Routledge and Kegan Paul.

2003    Bale, J., Graves, N. and Walford, R. (eds) (1973) *Perspectives in Geographical Education*. Edinburgh: Oliver and Boyd.

2004    Barker, E. (1974) *Geography and Younger Children*. London: University of London Press.

2005    Battersby, J. (1995) *Teaching Geography at Key Stage 3*. Cambridge: Chris Kington Publishing.

2006    Blyth, A., Cooper, K., Derricott, R., Elliott, G. G., Sumner, H. and Waplington, A. (1976) *Place, Time and Society 8–13: Curriculum Planning in History, Geography and Social Science*. Glasgow/Bristol: Collins/ESL, for the Schools Council.

2007    Blyth, A. and Krause, J. (1995) *Primary Geography: A Developmental Approach*. London: Hodder and Stoughton.

2008    Blyth, J. (1984) *Place and Time with Children Five to Nine*. London: Croom Helm.

2009    Boardman, D. (ed) (1985) *New Directions in Geographical Education*. London: Falmer Press.

2010    Boardman, D. (ed) (1986) *Handbook for Geography Teachers*. Sheffield: Geographical Association.

2011    Boden, P. (1976) *Developments in Geography Teaching*. London: Open Books.

2012    Bowles, R. (1995) *Practical Guides: Geography*. Leamington Spa: Scholastic Publications.

2013    Chambers, B. and Donert, K. (1996) *Teaching Geography at Key Stage 2*. Cambridge: Chris Kington Publishing.

2014    Convey, A. and Nolzen, H. (eds) (1997) *Geography and Education (Münchner Studien zur Didaktik der Geographie, Band 10)*. Munich: Lehrstuhl für Didaktik der Geographie der Universität München.

2015    Department of Education and Science (1972) *New Thinking in School Geography: Educational Pamphlet No. 59*. London: HMSO.

2016    Department of Education and Science (1974) *School Geography in the Changing Curriculum: Education Survey No. 19*. London: HMSO.

2017    Department of Education and Science (1978) *The Teaching of Ideas in Geography: Some Suggestions for the Middle and Secondary Years of Education*. London: HMSO.

2018    Department of Education and Science (1986) *Geography from 5 to 16: Curriculum Matters 7, an HMI Series.* London: HMSO.

2019    De Villiers, M. (ed) (1990) *Primary Geography Matters.* Sheffield: Geographical Association.

2020    De Villiers, M. (ed) (1991) *Primary Geography Matters: Inequalities.* Sheffield: Geographical Association.

2021    De Villiers, M. (ed) (1992) *Primary Geography Matters: Change in the Primary Curriculum.* Sheffield: Geographical Association.

2022    De Villiers, M. (ed) (1993) *Primary Geography Matters: Children's Worlds.* Sheffield: Geographical Association.

2023    De Villiers, M. (ed) (1995) *Developments in Primary Geography: Theory and Practice.* Sheffield: Geographical Association.

2024    Foley, M. and Janikoun, J. (1996) *The Really Practical Guide to Primary Geography.* Cheltenham: Stanley Thornes.

2025    Gilbert, E. W. (1972) *British Pioneers in Geography.* Newton Abbot: David and Charles.

2026    Graves, N. (1971) *Geography in Secondary Education.* Sheffield: Geographical Association.

2027    Graves, N. (ed) (1972) *New Movements in the Study and Teaching of Geography.* London: Temple Smith.

2028    Graves, N. (1975) *Geography in Education.* London: Heinemann.

2029    Graves, N. (1979) *Curriculum Planning in Geography.* London: Heinemann.

2030    Graves, N. (1980) *Geographical Education in Secondary Schools.* Sheffield: Geographical Association.

2031    Graves, N. (ed) (1982) *New UNESCO Source Book for Geography Teaching.* Harlow/Paris: Longman/The UNESCO Press.

2032    Graves, N., Naish, M., Slater, F., Kent, A. and Hilton, K. (1982) *Geography in Education Now: Bedford Way Papers 13.* London: University of London Institute of Education.

2033    Hacking, E. (1992) *Geography into Practice.* Harlow: Longman.

2034    Hall, D. (1976) *Geography and the Geography Teacher.* London: George Allen and Unwin.

2035    Hickman, G., Reynolds, J. and Tolley, H. (1973) *A New Professionalism for a Changing Geography.* London: Schools Council.

2036    Huckle, J. (ed) (1983) *Geographical Education: Reflection and Action.* Oxford: Oxford University Press.

2037    Jay, L. J. (1981) *Geography Teaching with a Little Latitude.* London: George Allen and Unwin.

2038    Kent, A. (ed) (1985) *Perspectives on a Changing Geography.* Sheffield: Geographical Association.

2039    Kent, A., Lambert, D., Naish, M. and Slater, F. (eds) (1996) *Geography in Education: Viewpoints on Teaching and Learning.* Cambridge: Cambridge University Press.

2040    Knight, P. (1993) *Primary Geography, Primary History.* London: David Fulton.

2041    Long, M. (ed) (1974) *Handbook for Geography Teachers.* London: Methuen.

2042 Lukehurst, C. T. and Graves, N. (eds) (1972) *Geography in Education: A Bibliography of British Sources 1870–1970*. Sheffield: Geographical Association.

2043 Marchant, E. C. (ed) (1971) *Education in Europe: The Teaching of Geography in Secondary Schools*. London/Strasbourg: George C. Harrap/Council of Europe.

2044 Marsden, W. E. (1976) *Evaluating the Geography Curriculum*. Edinburgh: Oliver and Boyd.

2045 Marsden, W. E. (1995) *Geography 11–16: Rekindling Good Practice*. London: David Fulton.

2046 Marsden, W. E. and Hughes, J. (eds) (1994) *Primary School Geography*. London: David Fulton.

2047 Martin, F. (1995) *Teaching Early Years Geography*. Cambridge: Chris Kington Publishing.

2048 Mills, D. (ed) (1988) *Geographical Work in Primary and Middle Schools*. Sheffield: Geographical Association.

2049 Molyneux, F. and Tolley, H. (1987) *Teaching Geography: A Teaching Skills Workbook*. London: Macmillan.

2050 Naish, M. (ed) (1992) *Geography and Education: National and International Perspectives*. London: University of London Institute of Education.

2051 Nicholson, H. N. (1993) *Inspirations for Geography*. Leamington Spa: Scholastic Publications.

2052 Palmer, J. (1994) *Geography in the Early Years*. London: Routledge.

2053 Rawling, E. (ed) (1980) *Geography into the 1980s*. Sheffield: Geographical Association.

2054 Rawling, E. and Daugherty, R. (eds) (1996) *Geography into the Twenty-first Century*. Chichester: John Wiley and Sons.

2055 Sebba, J. (1995) *Geography for All*. London: David Fulton.

2056 Slater, F. (1982) *Learning through Geography: An Introduction to Activity Planning*. London: Heinemann.

2057 Slater, F. (1993) *Learning through Geography*. Indiana, PA: National Council for Geographic Education.

2058 Tilbury, D. and Williams, M. (eds) (1997) *Teaching and Learning Geography*. London: Routledge.

2059 Tolley, H. and Orrell, K. (1977) *Geography 14–18: A Handbook for School-based Curriculum Development*. London: Macmillan.

2060 Walford, R. (ed) (1973) *New Directions in Geography Teaching*. London: Longman.

2061 Walford, R. (ed) (1981) *Signposts for Geography Teaching*. Harlow: Longman.

2062 Walford, R. (ed) (1991) *Viewpoints on Geography Teaching*. Harlow: Longman.

2063 Wiegand, P. (1992) *Places in the Primary School*. London: Falmer Press.

2064 Wiegand, P. (1993) *Children and Primary Geography*. London: Cassell.

2065 Wiegand, P. and Orrell, K. (eds) (1982) *New Leads in Geographical Education*. Sheffield: Geographical Association.

2066 Williams, M. (ed) (1996) *Understanding Geographical and Environmental Education: The Role of Research*. London: Cassell.

2067 Baxter, J. and Eyles, J. (1997) 'Evaluating qualitative research in social geography: establishing "rigour" in interview analysis', *Transactions of the Institute of British Geographers*, 22, 4, pp. 505–525.

2068 Biilmann, O., Williams, M. and Gerber, R. (1995) 'Conceptualising qualitative research in curriculum studies', *Curriculum Studies*, 3, 3, pp. 283–297.

2069 Downs, R. M. (1994) 'The need for research in geographic education: it would be nice to have some data' in Bednarz, R. S. and Peterson, J. (eds) *A Decade of Reform in Geographic Education: Inventory and Prospect.* Indiana, PA: National Council for Geographic Education, pp. 127–133.

2070 Gerber, R. and Williams, M. (eds) (1996) *Qualitative Research in Geographical Education.* Armidale, NSW: IGUCGE/University of New England Press.

2071 Ghaye, A. (1996) 'Improving practice through practitioner research' in Kent, A. Lambert, D., Naish, M. and Slater, F. (eds) *Geography in Education: Viewpoints on Teaching and Learning.* Cambridge: Cambridge University Press, pp. 344–370.

2072 Graves, N. (ed) (1984) *Research and Research Methods in Geographical Education.* London: IGUCGE/University of London Institute of Education.

2073 Graves, N. (1987) 'Research in geographical education', *New Zealand Journal of Geography*, 84, pp. 15–19.

2074 Graves, N. (1988) 'The changing nature of research in geographical education in the United Kingdom' in Gerber, R. and Lidstone, J. (eds) *Skills in Geographical Education Symposium '88, Volume 1.* Brisbane: IGUCGE/Brisbane College of Advanced Education, pp. 249–258.

2075 Graves, N., Kent, A., Lambert, D., Naish, M. and Slater, F. (1989) *Research in Geography Education: MA Dissertations 1968–1988.* London: University of London Institute of Education.

2076 Haubrich, H. (1992) 'Geographical education research 2000: some personal views', *IRGEE*, 1, 1, pp. 52–57.

2077 Hebden, R. and Fyfe, E. (1988) 'Research in geographical education in the United Kingdom' in Gerber, R. and Lidstone, J. (eds) *Developing Skills in Geographical Education.* Brisbane: IGUCGE/Jacaranda Press, pp. 286–297.

2078 Jay, L. J. and Todd, H. (1974) *The Dudley Stamp Memorial Index to Geography, Volumes 1–54: 1901–1969.* Sheffield: Geographical Association.

2079 Lee, A. (1992) 'Poststructuralism and educational research', *IRGEE*, 2, 1, pp. 1–12.

2080 Lergessner, D. A. (1972) 'Fundamental research and school geography', *Geographical Education*, 1, 4, pp. 375–391.

2081 Marbeau, L. (1992) 'The need for curriculum research in geography: the case of France' in Naish, M. (ed) *Geography and Education: National and International Perspectives.* London: University of London Institute of Education, pp. 80–94.

2082 Marsden, W. E. (1980) *Historical Perspectives on Geographical Education.* London: IGUCGE/University of London Institute of Education.

2083    Marsden, W. E. (1984) 'Research methods in the history of geographical education' in Graves, N. (ed) *Research and Research Methods in Geographical Education*. London: IGUCGE/University of London Institute of Education, pp. 1–28.

2084    Marsden, W. E. (1996) 'Geography' in Gordon, P. (ed) *A Guide to Educational Research*. London: Woburn Press, pp. 1–30.

2085    Marsden, W. E. (1996) 'Researching the history of geographical education' in Williams, M. (ed) *Understanding Geographical and Environmental Education*. London: Cassell, pp. 264–273.

2086    Naish, M. (1972) *Some Aspects of the Study and Teaching of Geography in Britain: A Review of Recent British Research*. Sheffield: Geographical Association.

2087    Naish, M. (1993) 'Never mind the quality – feel the width: how shall we judge the quality of research in geographical education?', *IRGEE*, 2, 1, pp. 64–65.

2088    Naish, M. (1994) 'Rationalising research approaches' in Haubrich, H. (ed) *Europe and the World in Geography Education (Geographiedidaktische Forschungen, Band 22)*. Nuremberg: IGUCGE, pp. 419–422.

2089    Naish, M. (1996) 'Action research for a new professionalism in geography education' in Kent, A., Lambert, D., Naish, M. and Slater, F. (eds) *Geography in Education: Viewpoints on Teaching and Learning*. Cambridge: Cambridge University Press, pp. 321–343.

2090    Schrettenbrunner, H. and van Westrhenen, J. (eds) (1992) *Empirical Research and Geography Teaching (Netherlands Geographical Studies, 142)*. Amsterdam: IGUCGE/Centrum voor Educatieve Geografie Vrije Universiteit Amsterdam.

2091    Slater, F. (1981) 'What is your view of people?: some comments on recently changing viewpoints in geographical research', *New Zealand Journal of Geography*, 71, pp. 6–9.

2092    Slater, F. (ed) (1989) *Language and Learning in the Teaching of Geography*. London: Routledge.

2093    Slater, F. (1994) 'Introduction: do our definitions exist?: research in geographical education' in Slater, F. (ed) *Reporting Research in Geographical Education: Monograph No. 1*. London: University of London Institute of Education.

2094    Slater, F. (1996) 'Illustrating research in geographical education' in Kent, A., Lambert, D., Naish, M. and Slater, F. (eds) *Geography in Education: Viewpoints on Teaching and Learning*. Cambridge: Cambridge University Press, pp. 291–320.

2095    Slater, F., Lambert, D. and Lines, D. (eds) (1997) *Education, Environment and Economy: Reporting Research in a New Academic Grouping (Bedford Way Papers)*. London: University of London Institute of Education.

2096    Stoddart, D. R. (1986) 'Geography, education and research' in Stoddart, D. R. *On Geography*. Oxford: Basil Blackwell, pp. 41–58.

2097    Stoltman, J. (ed) (1976) *International Research in Geographical Education*. Kalamazoo, MI: IGUCGE/Western Michigan University.

2098    Verduin-Muller, H. (1992) *Serving the Knowledge-based Society: Research on Knowledge Products (Netherlands Geographical Studies, 142)*. Amsterdam: IGUCGE/Centrum voor Educatieve Geografie Vrije Universiteit Amsterdam.

2099    Williams, M. (ed) (1996) *Understanding Geographical and Environmental Education: The Role of Research*. London: Cassell.

2100    Wolforth, J. (1980) 'Research in geographical education' in Choquette, R., Wolforth, J. and Villenure, M. (1980) *Canadian Geographical Education*. Ottawa: Canadian Association of Geographers/University of Ottawa Press.

## 3. The Geography of Education

2101    Bondi, L. (1987) 'Education, social needs and resource allocation: a study of primary schools in Manchester', *Area*, 19, 4, pp. 333–343.

2102    Bondi, L. (1987) 'School closures and local politics: the negotiation of primary school rationalisation in Manchester', *Political Geography Quarterly*, 6, 3, pp. 203–224.

2103    Bondi, L. and Matthews, M. H. (eds) (1988) *Education and Society: Studies in the Politics, Sociology and Geography of Education*. London: Routledge.

2104    Bradford, M. (1989) 'Educational change in the city' in Herbert, D. T. and Smith, D. M. (1989) *Social Problems and the City*. Oxford: Oxford University Press, pp. 142–158.

2105    Bradford, M. (1990) 'Education, attainment and the geography of choice', *Geography*, 76, 1, pp. 3–16.

2106    Bradford, M. (1991) 'School-performance indicators, the local residential environment, and parental choice', *Environment and Planning A*, 23, pp. 319–332.

2107    Bradford, M. (1993) 'Population change and education: school rolls and rationalisation before and after the 1988 Education Reform Act' in Chapman, T. (ed) *Population Matters: The Local Dimension*. London: Paul Chapman, pp. 64–82.

2108    Bradford, M. (1995) 'Diversification and division in the English education system: towards a post-Fordist model?', *Environment and Planning A*, 27, pp. 1595–1612.

2109    Bradford, M. and Burdett, F. (1989) 'Privatisation, education and the north–south divide' in Lewis, J. and Townsend, A. (eds) *The North–South Divide: Regional Change in Britain in the 1980s*. London: Paul Chapman, pp. 192–212.

2110    Bradford, M. and Burdett, F. (1989) 'Spatial polarisation of private education in England', *Area*, 21, 1, pp. 47–57.

2111    Brock, C. (1976) 'A role for geography in the service of comparative education', *Compare*, 6, 1, pp. 35–36.

2112    Brown, P. J. B. and Ferguson, S. S. (1982) 'Schools and population change in Liverpool' in Gould, W. T. S. and Hodgkiss, A. G. (eds) *The Resources of Merseyside*. Liverpool: Liverpool University Press, pp. 177–190.

2113    Burdett, F. (1988) 'A hard act to swallow?: the geography of education after the Great Reform Bill', *Geography*, 73, 3, pp. 208–215.

2114    Christian, C. M., Jakle, J. A. and Roseman, C. C. (1971) 'The prejudicial use of space: school assignment strategies in the United States', *Journal of Geography*, 70, 2, pp. 105–109.

2115    Coates, B. E. and Rawstron, E. M. (1971) 'Aspects of the geography of education' in Coates, B. E. and Rawstron, E. M. *Regional Variations in Britain: Studies in Social and Economic Geography*. London: Batsford, pp. 243–280.

2116    Coleman, B. I. (1972) 'The incidence of education in mid-century' in Wrigley, E. A. (ed) *Nineteenth-century Society: Essays in the Use of Quantitative Methods for the Study of Social Data*. Cambridge: Cambridge University Press, pp. 397–406.

2117 Dhanapal, D. and Ahmad, A. (1982) 'School provision in urban Delhi: a spatial perspective', *Indian Geographical Journal*, 57, 1, pp. 24–34.

2118 Dube, R. S. and Misra, R. P. (1981) 'Level of education: a versatile indicator of regional development', *Geographical Review of India*, 43, 3, pp. 278–300.

2119 Geipel, R. (1986) *Schools, Space and Social Policy: Educational Provision for the Children of Migrant Workers in Munich*. Liverpool: Liverpool University Press.

2120 Gould, W. T. S. (1971) 'Geography and educational opportunity in tropical Africa', *Tijdschrift voor Economische en Sociale Geografie*, 62, 2, pp. 82–89.

2121 Gould, W. T. S. (1978) *Guidelines for School Location Planning*. Washington, DC: The World Bank.

2122 Gould, W. T. S. (1982) 'Provision of primary schools and population redistribution' in Clarke, J. I. and Kosinski, L. A. (eds) *Redistribution of Population in Africa*. London: Heinemann, pp. 44–49.

2123 Gould, W. T. S. (1985) 'Circulation and schooling in East Africa' in Prothero, R. M. and Chapman, M. (eds) *Circulation in Third World Countries*. London: Routledge and Kegan Paul, pp. 262–278.

2124 Gould, W. T. S. (1986) 'Population analysis for the planning of primary schools in the Third World' in Gould, W. T. S. and Lawton, R. *Planning for Population Change*. London: Croom Helm, pp. 181–200.

2125 Herbert, D. T. (1976) 'Urban education: problems and policies' in Herbert, D. T. and Johnston, R. J. (eds) *Social Areas in Cities, Volume II: Spatial Perspectives on Problems and Policies*. London: John Wiley, pp. 123–158.

2126 Herbert, D. T. and Thomas, C. J. (1997) *Cities in Space: City as Place*. London: David Fulton, pp. 327–329.

2127 Hones, G. and Ryba, R. H. (1972) 'Why not a geography of education?', *Journal of Geography*, 71, 3, pp. 135–139.

2128 Kniveton, B. H. (1986) 'An investigation of parental protectiveness of young children travelling to school', *British Journal of Sociology of Education*, 7, 3, pp. 287–292.

2129 Marsden, W. E. (1976) 'The geographical component in studies in the history of education' in Maksakovsky, V. P. and Abramov, L. S. (eds) *Geographical Education, Geographical Literature and Dissemination of Geographical Knowledge*. Moscow/Oxford: IGUCGE/Pergamon Press, pp. 38–42.

2130 Marsden, W. E. (1977) 'Education and the social geography of nineteenth-century towns and cities' in Reeder, D. (ed) *Urban Education in the Nineteenth Century*. London: Taylor and Francis, pp. 193–230.

2131 Marsden, W. E. (1977) 'Historical geography and the history of education', *History of Education*, 6, 1, pp. 21–42.

2132 Marsden, W. E. (1980) 'Travelling to school: aspects of nineteenth-century catchment areas', *Geography*, 65, 1, pp. 19–26.

2133 Marsden, W. E. (1982) 'Diffusion and regional variation in elementary education in England and Wales 1800–1870', *History of Education*, 11, 3, pp. 173–194.

2134 Marsden, W. E. (1986) 'Education' in Langton, J. and Morris, R. J. (eds) *Atlas of Industrializing Britain 1780–1914*. London: Methuen, pp. 206–211.

2135    Marsden, W. E. (1987) 'Diffusion and regional disparity in educational provision in England and Wales 1800–1870' in Marsden, W. E. *Unequal Educational Provision in England and Wales: The Nineteenth-century Roots.* London: Woburn Press, pp. 25–59.

2136    Marsden, W. E. (1989) 'Late nineteenth-century disparities in educational provision in England and Wales' in Pope, R. (ed) *Atlas of British Social and Economic History since c. 1700.* London: Croom Helm, pp. 198–210.

2137    Marsden, W. E. (1995) 'Charles Booth and the social geography of education in late nineteenth-century London' in Englander, D. and O'Day, R. (eds) *Retrieved Riches: Social Investigation in Britain 1840–1914.* Aldershot: Scolar Press, pp. 241–263.

2138    Moulden, M. and Bradford, M. (1984) 'Influences on educational attainment: the importance of the local residential environment', *Environment and Planning A*, 16, pp. 49–66.

2139    Ryba, R. H. (1972) 'The geography of education and educational planning' in Adams, W. P. and Helleiner, F. M. (eds) *International Geography 1972: Volume 2.* Toronto: IGUCGE/University of Toronto Press, pp. 1060–1062.

2140    Ryba, R. H. (1976) 'Aspects of territorial inequality in education', *Comparative Education*, 12, 3, pp. 183–197.

2141    Ryba, R. H. (1976) 'Aspects of territorial inequality in education', *Compare*, 6, 1, pp. 27–34.

2142    Ryba, R. H. (1979) 'Territorial patterns of diversity in education', *Comparative Education*, 15, 3, pp. 151–257.

2143    Stephens, W. B. (1987) *Education, Literacy and Society 1830–70: The Geography of Diversity in Provincial England.* Manchester: Manchester University Press.

2144    Williamson, W. (1977) 'Patterns of educational inequality in West Germany', *Comparative Education*, 13, 1, pp. 29–44.

# 4. The Changing Nature of Geographical Education: Historical and Future Perspectives

2145    Ahier, J. (1988) *Industry, Children and the Nation: An Analysis of National Identity in School Textbooks.* London: Falmer Press.

2146    Ambrose, P. J. (1973) 'New developments in geography' in Walford, R. (ed) *New Directions in Geography Teaching: Papers from the 1970 Charney Manor Conference.* London: Longman, pp. 69–84.

2147    Bailey, P. (1982) 'School geography: a decade of change' in Dufour, B. (ed) *New Movements in the Social Sciences and Humanities.* London: Temple Smith, pp. 164–177.

2148    Bailey, P. (1988) 'Politics and practicalities: developing geography in the secondary school curriculum of England and Wales 1976–1988' in Gerber, R. and Lidstone, J. (eds) *Skills in Geographical Education Symposium '88, Volume 2.* Brisbane: IGUCGE/Brisbane College of Advanced Education, pp. 477–486.

2149    Balchin, W. (1993) *The Geographical Association: The First Hundred Years 1893–1993*, Sheffield: Geographical Association.

2150    Beddis, R. (1983) 'Geographical education since 1960: a personal view' in Huckle, J. (ed) *Geographical Education: Reflection and Action*. Oxford: Oxford University Press, pp. 10–19.

2151    Biddle, D. S. (1980) 'Paradigms and geography curricula in England and Wales 1882–1972' in Boardman, D. (ed) (1985) *New Directions in Geographical Education*. London: Falmer Press, pp. 11–33.

2152    Binns, T. (1991) 'Geography and education: UK perspective', *Progress in Human Geography*, 15, 1, pp. 57–63.

2153    Binns, T. (1992) 'At the chalk face: teaching geography in the United Kingdom' in Rogers, A., Viles, H. and Goudie, A. (eds) *The Student's Companion to Geography*. Oxford: Blackwell, pp. 333–339.

2154    Binns, T. (1993) 'Geography and education: UK perspective', *Progress in Human Geography*, 17, 1, pp. 101–110.

2155    Binns, T. (1995) 'Geography and education: UK perspective', *Progress in Human Geography*, 19, 4, pp. 541–550.

2156    Binns, T. (1996) 'School geography: the key questions for discussion' in Rawling, E. and Daugherty, R. (eds) *Geography into the Twenty-first Century*. Chichester: John Wiley and Sons, pp. 37–58.

2157    Boardman, D. (1983) 'Geography in British schools in the 1980s', *Journal of Geography*, 82, 2, pp. 64–71.

2158    Boardman, D. and McPartland, M. (1993) 'A hundred years of geography teaching', *Teaching Geography*, 18, 1, pp. 3–6.

2159    Boardman, D. and McPartland, M. (1993) 'From regions to models: 1944–1969', *Teaching Geography*, 18, 2, pp. 65–69.

2160    Boardman, D. and McPartland, M. (1993) 'Innovation and change: 1970–1982', *Teaching Geography*, 18, 3, pp. 117–120.

2161    Boardman, D. and McPartland, M. (1993) 'Towards centralisation: 1983–1993', *Teaching Geography*, 18, 4, pp. 159–162.

2162    Brook, G. A. and Brook, D. L. (1980) 'Trends in geographic education in British secondary schools', *Journal of Geography*, 79, 2, pp. 60–70.

2163    Bryan, P. E. (1970) *The Teaching of Geography in the Nineteenth Century as Illustrated through the Textbooks of the Time*, unpublished MEd dissertation. University of Edinburgh.

2164    Catling, S. (1979) 'Whither primary geography?: reflections on the HMI Report "Primary Education in England"', *Teaching Geography*, 5, 2, pp. 73–76.

2165    Catling, S. (1991) 'Geography in primary practice in a period of transition' in Walford, R. (ed) *Viewpoints on Geographical Education*. Harlow: Longman, pp. 95–102.

2166    Catling, S. (1992) 'Issues for the future of primary geography' in Naish, M. (ed) *Geography and Education: National and International Perspectives*. London: University of London Institute of Education, pp. 9–33.

2167    Catling, S. (1993) 'The whole world in our hands', *Geography*, 78, 4, pp. 340–358.

2168    Cleverley, P. (1985) 'Classroom hot spots change again', *Geography*, 70, 3, pp. 206–211.

2169    Coley, J. A. (1975) 'Geography in the middle school', *Teaching Geography*, 1, 2, pp. 65–66.

2170 Daugherty, R. and Rawling, E. (1996) 'New perspectives for geography: an agenda for action' in Rawling, E. and Daugherty, R. (eds) *Geography into the Twenty-first Century.* Chichester: John Wiley and Sons, pp. 359–377.

2171 Day, A. (1995) 'Geography: challenges for its next century', *Teaching Geography*, 20, 2, pp. 90–92.

2172 Digby, B. (1995) 'Education for change: new approaches to geography', *Streetwise*, 6, 3, pp. 13–15.

2173 Edwards, G. (1996) 'Alternative speculations on geographical futures: towards a post-modern perspective', *Geography*, 81, 3, pp. 217–224.

2174 Farmer, G. T. (1977) *Knowledge, Geography and Planned Change: Some Sociological Approaches Towards a Means of Changing Geographical Education*, unpublished MSc (Ed) dissertation. University of Southampton.

2175 Fitzgerald, B. P. (1973) 'Scientific method, quantitative techniques and the teaching of geography' in Walford, R. (ed) *New Directions in Geography Teaching.* London: Longman, pp. 85–94.

2176 Gilchrist, G. E. (1981) *Curriculum Development in Geography 1945–1970*, unpublished MEd dissertation. University of Liverpool.

2177 Goodson, I. F. (1983) 'Geography: aspects of subject history' in Goodson, I. F. *School Subjects and Curriculum Change: Case Studies in Curriculum History.* London: Croom Helm, pp. 60–88.

2178 Goodson, I. F. (1983) 'Subjects for study: aspects of a social history of the curriculum', *Journal of Curriculum Studies*, 15, 4, pp. 391–408.

2179 Goodson, I. F. (1984) 'Subjects for study: towards a social history of curriculum' in Goodson, I. F. and Ball, S. J. (eds) *Defining the Curriculum: Histories and Ethnographies.* London: Falmer Press, pp. 25–44.

2180 Goodson, I. F. (1988) 'Becoming a school subject' in Goodson, I. F. (1988) *The Making of Curriculum: Collected Essays.* London: Falmer Press, pp. 160–183.

2181 Gowing, D. (1973) 'A fresh look at objectives' in Walford, R. (ed) *New Directions in Geography Teaching.* London: Longman, pp. 152–160.

2182 Grady, A. D. (1972) *The Role of Geographical Societies in the Development of Geography in Britain from 1900 to 1914*, unpublished PhD thesis. Birkbeck College, University of London.

2183 Graves, N. (1974) 'Geographical education in Britain: crisis and opportunity', *Geographical Education*, 2, 2, pp. 147–158.

2184 Graves, N. (1976) 'The International Geographical Union's Commission on Geographical Education', *Geography*, 61, 2, pp. 95–96.

2185 Graves, N. (1977) 'Geography in education at the 23rd International Geographical Congress, USSR, 1976', *Journal of Geography in Higher Education*, 1, 1, pp. 76–77.

2186 Graves, N. (1979) 'Contrasts and contradictions in geographical education', *Geography*, 64, 4, pp. 259–267.

2187 Graves, N. (1980) 'Geography in education' in Brown, E. H. (ed) *Geography Yesterday and Tomorrow.* Oxford: Oxford University Press, pp. 100–113.

2188 Graves, N. (1980) 'Paul Vidal de la Blache and geographical education in France' in Marsden, W. E. (ed) *Historical Perspectives on Geographical Education.* London: IGUCGE/University of London Institute of Education, pp. 8–17.

2189    Graves, N. (1980) 'Geographical education in Britain', *Progress in Human Geography*, 4, 4, pp. 560–567.

2190    Graves, N. (1981) 'Geographical education', *Progress in Human Geography*, 5, 4, pp. 562–571.

2191    Graves, N. (1981) 'International aspects of geographical education', *Journal of Geography*, 80, 3, pp. 84–86.

2192    Graves, N. (1982) 'Aims, content and recent development of geographical education in England and Wales' in Haubrich, H. (ed) *International Focus on Geographical Education*. Brunswick: Georg Eckert Institute for International Textbook Research, pp. 92–99.

2193    Graves, N. (1982) 'Geographical education', *Progress in Human Geography*, 6, 4, pp. 563–575.

2194    Graves, N. (1982) 'Research in geographical education' in Graves, N., Naish, M., Slater, F., Kent, A. and Hilton, K. *Geography in Education Now: Bedford Way Papers 13*. London: University of London Institute of Education, pp. 52–60.

2195    Graves, N. (1985) 'Geography in education: a review' in Kent, A. (ed) *Perspectives on a Changing Geography*. Sheffield: Geographical Association, pp. 15–22.

2196    Graves, N. (1988) 'Curriculum developments in geography in the 1990s' in Gerber, R. and Lidstone, J. (eds) *Developing Skills in Geographical Education*. Brisbane: IGUCGE/Jacaranda Press, pp. 181–187.

2197    Graves, N. (1996) 'Curriculum development in geography: an ongoing process' in Kent, A., Lambert, D., Naish, M. and Slater, F. (eds) *Geography in Education: New Viewpoints on Teaching and Learning*. Cambridge: Cambridge University Press, pp. 72–99.

2198    Graves, N. (1996) 'The intellectual origins of late nineteenth-century and early twentieth-century British geography textbooks', *Paradigm*, 19, pp. 27–52.

2199    Graves, N. (1996) 'The nature of innovations in geographical education: an historical review' in van der Zijpp, T., van der Schee, J. and Trimp, H. (eds) *Innovation in Geographical Education: Proceedings of the 28th International Geographical Congress Commission on Geographical Education*. Amsterdam: IGUCGE/Centrum voor Educatieve Geografie Vrije Universiteit Amsterdam, pp. 241–246.

2200    Graves, N. (1997) 'Geographical education in the 1990s' in Tilbury, D. and Williams, M. (eds) *Teaching and Learning Geography*. London: Routledge, pp. 25–31.

2201    Graves, N. (1997) 'Network of authors and the nature of geography textbooks 1875–1925', *Paradigm*, 22, pp. 15–23.

2202    Grenyer, N. (1972) 'An introduction to recent developments in geography teaching: an annotated bibliography', *Geography*, 57, 4, pp. 333–336.

2203    Hall, D. (1982) 'Changing outlooks in geography' in Wiegand, P. and Orrell, K. (eds) *New Leads in Geographical Education*. Sheffield: Geographical Association, pp. 1–8.

2204    Hall, D. (1984) 'Knowledge in the geography classroom' in Fien, J., Gerber, R. and Wilson, P. (eds) *The Geography Teacher's Guide to the Classroom*. Melbourne: Macmillan, pp. 1–12.

2205    Hall, D. (1991) 'Charney revisited: twenty-five years of geographical education' in Walford, R. (ed) *Viewpoints on Geography Teaching*. Harlow: Longman, pp. 10–29.

2206    Haubrich, H. (1991) 'Centralisation or decentralisation of geography curricula: an international perspective', *Geography*, 76, 3, pp. 209–217.

2207   Hebden, R. (1988) 'Geography in the British education system' in Gerber, R. and Lidstone, J. (eds) *Skills in Geographical Education Symposium '88, Volume 2*. Brisbane: IGUCGE/Brisbane College of Advanced Education, pp. 508–517.

2208   Helburn, N. (1979) 'An American's perceptions of British geography', *Geography*, 64, 4, pp. 327–333.

2209   Hicks, D. (1993) 'Mapping the future: a geographical contribution', *Teaching Geography*, 18, 4, pp. 146–149.

2210   Hicks, D. (1995) *Visions of the Future: Why we Need to Teach for Tomorrow*. Stoke-on-Trent: Trentham Books.

2211   Hicks, D. (1995) 'Geographical futures: sketch-maps from the edge', *Geographical Education*, 8, 3, pp. 31–34.

2212   Huckle, J. (1983) 'The politics of school geography' in Huckle, J. (ed) *Geographical Education: Reflection and Action*. Oxford: Oxford University Press, pp. 143–154.

2213   Huckle, J. (1987) 'What sort of geography for what sort of curriculum?', *Area*, 19, 3, pp. 261–265.

2214   Hunter, L. (1996) 'Geography in the Scottish school curriculum' in Rawling, E. and Daugherty, R. (eds) *Geography into the Twenty-first Century*. Chichester: John Wiley and Sons, pp. 235–246.

2215   Jay, L. J. (1980) 'Douglas Freshfield's contribution to geographical education' in Marsden, W. E. (ed) *Historical Perspectives on Geographical Education*. London: IGUCGE/University of London Institute of Education, pp. 43–53.

2216   John, M. E. (1977) *A Review of Curriculum Development in Geography from 1944 to 1976 with Particular Reference to Secondary Schools in Wales*, unpublished MEd dissertation. University of Wales Cardiff.

2217   Johnson, S. P. (1977) *School Geography Textbooks 1803–1970: A Study of Textbook Development with Particular Reference to those Produced for English Secondary Schools*, unpublished MSc (Ed) dissertation. University of Southampton.

2218   Jones, D. I. (1973) *The Teaching of Geography: Aspects of its Development in Welsh Secondary Schools since 1917*, unpublished MEd dissertation. University of Wales Cardiff.

2219   Jones, S. (1976) 'The challenge of change in geography teaching', *Geography*, 61, 4, pp. 195–205.

2220   Jones, S., Rolfe, R. and Cleverley, P. (1981) 'Three schoolteachers reflect on geography 1970–1980' in Walford, R. (ed) *Signposts for Geography Teaching*. Harlow: Longman, pp. 83–94.

2221   Kent, A. (1997) 'Challenging geography: a personal view', *Geography*, 82, 4, pp. 293–303.

2222   King, R. (1989) 'Geography in the school curriculum: a battle won but not yet over', *Area*, 21, 2, pp. 127–136.

2223   Kirby, A. and Lambert, D. (1981) 'Seven reasons to be cheerful?... or school geography in youth, maturity and old age' in Walford, R. (ed) *Signposts for Geography Teaching*. Harlow: Longman, pp. 113–119.

2224   Knight, P. (1996) 'Subject associations: the cases of secondary phase geography and home economics 1976–94', *History of Education*, 25, 3, pp. 269–284.

2225    Long, M. (1974) 'Problems facing geography teachers' in Long, M. (ed) *Handbook for Geography Teachers*. London: Methuen, pp. 3–12.

2226    Machon, P. and Ranger, G. (1996) 'Change in school geography' in Bailey, P. and Fox, P. (eds) *Geography Teachers' Handbook*. Sheffield: Geographical Association, pp. 39–46.

2227    MacKewan, N. (1986) 'Phenomenology and the curriculum: the case of secondary school geography' in Taylor, P. H. (ed) *Recent Developments in Curriculum Studies*. London: NFER/Nelson, pp. 156–167.

2228    Maclean, K. (1975) 'George G. Chisholm: his influence on university and school geography', *Scottish Geographical Magazine*, 91, 2, pp. 70–78.

2229    Maddrell, M. C. (1997) 'Scientific discourse and the geographical work of Marion Newbigin', *Scottish Geographical Magazine*, 113, 1, pp. 33–41.

2230    Marsden, W. E. (1980) 'Sir Archibald Geikie (1835–1924) as geographical educationist' in Marsden, W. E. *Historical Perspectives on Geographical Education*. London: IGUCGE/University of London Institute of Education, pp. 54–65.

2231    Marsden, W. E. (1986) 'The Royal Geographical Society and geography in secondary education' in Price, M. H. (ed) *The Development of the Secondary Curriculum*. London: Croom Helm, pp. 182–213.

2232    Marsden, W. E. (1988) 'Continuity and change in geography textbooks: perspectives from the 1930s to the 1960s', *Geography*, 73, 4, pp. 327–343.

2233    Marsden, W. E. (1988) 'The early politicization of the geography curriculum in England' in Gerber, R, and Lidstone, J. (eds) *Skills in Geographical Education Symposium '88, Volume 1*. Brisbane: IGUCGE/Brisbane College of Advanced Education, pp. 309–321.

2234    Marsden, W. E. (1989) '"All in a good cause": geography, history and the politicization of the curriculum in nineteenth- and twentieth-century England', *Journal of Curriculum Studies*, 21, 6, pp. 509–526.

2235    Marsden, W. E. (1993) 'Geography: again a pivot of the primary curriculum', *Primary Geographer*, 12, pp. 18–19.

2236    Marsden, W. E. (1994) 'Places and peoples: continuity and change in primary geography' in Marsden, W. E. and Hughes, J. (eds) *Primary School Geography*. London: David Fulton Publishers, pp. 1–8.

2237    Marsden, W. E. (1997) 'From pre- to anti-modern: some visions of teaching geography for a better world' in Convey, A. and Nolzen, H. (eds) *Geography and Education (Münchner Studien zur Didaktik der Geographie, Band 10)*. Munich: Lehrstuhl für Didaktik der Geographie der Universität München, pp. 189–198.

2238    Marsden, W. E. (1997) 'On taking the geography out of geographical education: some historical pointers', *Geography*, 82, 3, pp. 241–252.

2239    Marsden, W. E. (1990) 'Politicizing geography and history curricula in England and Wales' in Aasen, P. (ed) *Historical Perspectives on Childhood*. Trondheim: Norwegian Centre for Child Research, pp. 36–63.

2240    Marsden, W. E. (1990) 'The role of geography in education in England and Wales', *GeoJournal*, 20, 1, pp. 25–31.

2241    Marsden, W. E. (1990) 'Rooting racism into the educational experience of childhood and youth in the nineteenth and twentieth centuries', *History of Education*, 19, 4, pp. 333–353.

2242    Marsden, W. E. (1992) 'The Graves years in geographical education' in Naish, M. (ed) *Geography and Education: National and International Perspectives*. London: University of London Institute of Education, pp. 193–300.

2243    Marsden, W. E. (1994) 'Geography: educational programs' in Husen, T. and Postlethwaite, T. N. (eds) *The International Encyclopaedia of Education*. Oxford: Pergamon Press, pp. 2465–2470.

2244    Marsden, W. E. (1996) 'The place of geography in the school curriculum: an historical overview, 1886–1976' in Tilbury, D. and Williams, M. (eds) *Teaching and Learning Geography*. London: Routledge, pp. 7–14.

2245    Masterton, T. H. (1975) 'Teaching geography in Scotland', *Teaching Geography*, 1, 1, pp. 15–18.

2246    Morgan, J. (1996) 'What a carve up!: new times for geography teaching' in Kent, A., Lambert, D., Naish, M. and Slater, F. (eds) *Geography in Education: Viewpoints on Teaching and Learning*. Cambridge: Cambridge University Press, pp. 50–70.

2247    Morgan, J. (1997) 'Geo-graphing: writing the wor(l)d in geography classrooms' in Slater, F., Lambert, D. and Lines, D. (eds) *Education, Environment and Economy: Reporting Research in a New Academic Grouping (Bedford Way Papers)*. London: University of London Institute of Education, pp. 57–70.

2248    Naish, M. (1974) 'Current trends in geography teaching' in Long, M. (ed) *Handbook for Geography Teachers*. London: Methuen, pp. 109–125.

2249    Naish, M. (1980) 'Geography into the 1980s' in Rawling, E. (ed) *Geography into the 1980s*. Sheffield: Geographical Association, pp. 61–66.

2250    Naish, M. (1982) 'Geography in the curriculum: beyond the "Great Debate"' in Graves, N., Naish, M., Slater, F., Kent, A. and Hilton, K. *Geography in Education Now: Bedford Way Papers 13*. London: University of London Institute of Education, pp. 9–17.

2251    Naish, M. (1992) 'Geography in the secondary curriculum' in Naish, M. (ed) *Geography and Education: National and International Perspectives*. London: University of London Institute of Education, pp. 34–50.

2252    Naish, M. (1996) 'The geography curriculum: a martyr to epistemology?' in Gerber, R. and Lidstone, J. *Developments and Directions in Geographical Education*. Clevedon: Channel View Publications, pp. 63–76.

2253    Naish, M. (1997) 'Geography and education: knowledge and control' in Convey, A. and Nolzen, H. (eds) *Geography and Education (Münchner Studien zur Didaktik der Geographie, Band 10)*, Munich: Lehrstuhl für Didaktik der Geographie der Universität München, pp. 199–207.

2254    Newby, P. T. (1980) 'The benefits and costs of the quantitative revolution', *Geography*, 65, 1, pp. 13–18.

2255    Nicholls, A. D. (1972) 'The influence of the "new geographies" on the content and curricula of geography in British schools' in Adams, W. P. and Helleiner, F. M. (eds) *International Geography 1972, Volume 2*. Toronto: IGUCGE/University of Toronto Press, pp. 1056–1057.

2256    Owen, E. E. (1975) *The Nature and Development of Geography Teaching in Secondary Schools in Scotland*, unpublished PhD thesis. University of Edinburgh.

2257    Owen, R. (1971) *Geography in the Schools of England and France, 1800–1939, with Special Reference to Secondary Schools*, unpublished MLitt thesis. University of Bristol.

2258 Ploszajska, T. S. (1996) 'Cloud cuckoo land?: fact and fantasy in geographical readers, 1870–1944', *Paradigm*, 20, pp. 2–13.

2259 Ploszajska, T. S. (1996) 'Constructing the subject: geographical models in English schools, 1870–1944', *Journal of Historical Geography*, 22, 4, pp. 388–398.

2260 Ploszajska, T. S. (1996) *Geographical Education, Empire and Citizenship 1870–1944*, unpublished PhD thesis. University of London.

2261 Proctor, N. (1974) *Tradition and Innovation in Geography Teaching: A Study of English Schools, 1900–1970*, unpublished MEd dissertation. University of Leicester.

2262 Proctor, N. (1986) 'The pioneers of geography: a new and currently relevant perspective', *Transactions of the Institute of British Geographers*, 11, 1, pp. 75–85.

2263 Rawling, E. (1991) 'Innovations in the geography curriculum 1970–90: a personal view' in Walford, R. (ed) *Viewpoints on Geography Teaching*. Harlow: Longman, pp. 33–38.

2264 Rawling, E. (1993) 'School geography: towards 2000', *Geography*, 78, 2, pp. 110–116.

2265 Rawling, E. (1996) 'School geography: some key issues for higher education', *Journal of Geography in Higher Education*, 20, 3, pp. 305–322.

2266 Robinson, R. (1985) 'Ten years of change: influences on school geography 1972–1982' in Boardman, D. (ed) *New Directions in Geographical Education*. London: Falmer Press, pp. 35–53.

2267 Scarfe, N. V. (1980) 'James Fairgrieve, 1870–1953: pioneer geographical educationist' in Marsden, W. E. (ed) *Historical Perspectives on Geographical Education*. London: IGUCGE/University of London Institute of Education, pp. 32–42.

2268 Slater, F. (1976) '"A huge world-embracing network of links": some comparisons of curriculum change in geography', *New Era*, 57, pp. 23–25.

2269 Slater, F. (1994) 'Education through geography: knowledge, understanding, values and culture', *Geography*, 79, 2, pp. 147–163.

2270 Slater, F. (1995) 'Geography into the future', *Geographical Education*, 8, 3, pp. 4–6, 63.

2271 Smith, P. R. (1987) 'Geographical education in schools: the continuing debate', *Area*, 19, 3, pp. 255–261.

2272 Storm, M. (1983) 'The geography curriculum in the 1980s' in Huckle, J. (ed) *Geographical Education: Reflection and Action*. Oxford: Oxford University Press, pp. 132–142.

2273 Storm, M. (1989) 'Geography in schools: the state of the art', *Geography*, 74, 4, pp. 289–298.

2274 Tapsfield, A. (1991) 'A geographical agenda for the 1990s' in Walford, R. (ed) *Viewpoints on Geography Teaching*. Harlow: Longman, pp. 125–127.

2275 Thomas, P. R. (1970) 'Education and the new geography', *Geography*, 55, 3, pp. 274–280.

2276 Tidswell, V. (1990) 'Capes, concepts and conscience: continuity in the curriculum', *Geography*, 75, 4, pp. 302–312.

2277 Turner, A. and Catling, S. (1982) 'A new consensus in primary geography', *Teaching Geography*, 8, 1, pp. 24–26.

2278    Underwood, B. L. (1971) *The Relationship between Aims in Geographical Teaching and General Educational Aims, 1871–1971*, unpublished MA (Ed) dissertation. University of Sussex.

2279    Vaughan, J. E. (1972) 'Aspects of teaching geography in England in the early nineteenth century', *Paedagogica Historica*, 12, pp. 128–147.

2280    Vaughan, J. E. (1980) 'William Hughes, FRGS (1818–1876) as geographical educationist' in Marsden, W. E. (ed) *Historical Perspectives on Geographical Education*. London: IGUCGE/University of London Institute of Education, pp. 66–79.

2281    Walford, R. (1977) 'Geographical education in Britain', *Progress in Human Geography*, 1, 4, pp. 503–509.

2282    Walford, R. (1982) 'British school geography in the 1980s: an easy test?', *Journal of Geography in Higher Education*, 6, 2, pp. 151–158.

2283    Walford, R. (1984) 'Geography and the future', *Geography*, 69, 3, pp. 193–208.

2284    Walford, R. (1989) 'On the frontier with the new model army: geography publishing from the 1960s to the 1990s', *Geography*, 74, 4, pp. 308–320.

2285    Walford, R. (1991) 'The eighties: geography in context' in Walford, R. (ed) *Viewpoints on Geography Teaching*. Harlow: Longman, pp. 1–9.

2286    Walford, R. (1993) 'Mackinder, the GA in wartime and the National Curriculum', *Geography*, 78, 2, pp. 117–123.

2287    Walford, R. (1995) 'Geographical textbooks 1930–1990: the strange case of the disappearing text', *Paradigm*, 18, pp. 1–11.

2288    Walford, R. (1996) 'Geography 5–19: retrospect and prospect' in Rawling, E. and Daugherty, R. (eds) *Geography into the Twenty-first Century*. Chichester: John Wiley and Sons, pp. 131–143.

2289    Walford, R. (1996) 'Promoting geography as a school subject through pupil-centred activity and research' in van der Schee, J., Schoenmaker, G., Trimp, H. and Westrhenen, H. (eds) *Innovation in Geographical Education (Netherlands Geographical Studies, 208)*. Utrecht/Amsterdam: IGUCGE/Centrum voor Educatieve Geografie Vrije Universiteit Amsterdam, pp. 159–166.

2290    Walford, R. and Haggett, P. (1995) 'Geography and geographical education: some speculations for the 21st Century', *Geography*, 80, 1, pp. 3–13.

2291    Walford, R. and Williams, M. (1985) 'Geography and the school curriculum: the recent role of the Geographical Association', *Area*, 17, 4, pp. 317–321.

2292    Wheeler, K. (1971) 'Geography' in Whitfield, R. C. (ed) *Disciplines of the Curriculum*. Maidenhead: McGraw Hill, pp. 80–92.

2293    Williams, M. (1987) 'Theory and practice in secondary school geography in England and Wales' in Haubrich, H. (ed) *International Trends in Geographical Education*. Freiburg: IGUCGE/Pädagogische Hochschule Freiburg, pp. 79–93.

2294    Williams, M. and Catling, S. (1985) 'Geography in primary education', *Geography*, 70, 3, pp. 243–245.

2295    Wise, M. (1977) 'Geography in universities and schools', *Geography*, 62, 4, pp. 249–258.

2296    Wise, M. (1986) 'The Scott Keltie Report 1885 and the teaching of geography in Great Britain', *Geographical Journal*, 152, 3, pp. 367–382.

2297    Wise, M. (1992) 'International geography: the IGU Commission on Education' in Naish, M. (ed) *Geography and Education: National and International Perspectives*. London: University of London Institute of Education, pp. 233–246.

2298    Wise, M. (1993) 'The campaign for geography in education: the work of the Geographical Association 1893–1993', *Geography*, 78, 2, pp. 101–109.

2299    Wise, M. (1997) 'The school atlas, 1885–1915', *Paradigm*, 23, pp. 1–11.

2300    Wright, D. (1996) 'A curriculum palimpsest: continuity and change in UK geography textbooks, 1820–1870', *Paradigm*, 21, p. 32–38.

# 5. Justification of Geography in the Curriculum

2301    Bailey, P. (1986) 'A geographer's view: contributions of geography to the school curriculum', *Geography*, 71, 3, pp. 193–205.

2302    Bailey, P. (1986) 'Geography in the school curriculum', *Teaching Geography*, 11, 2, pp. 64–67.

2303    Bailey, P. and Binns, T. (eds) (1987) *A Case for Geography*. Sheffield: Geographical Association.

2304    Bennetts, T. (1985) 'Geography from 5 to 16: a view from the inspectorate', *Geography*, 70, 4, pp. 299–314.

2305    Boardman, D. (1986) 'Geography in the secondary school curriculum' in Boardman, D. (ed) *Handbook for Geography Teachers*. Sheffield: Geographical Association, pp. 1–26.

2306    Brown, C. (1981) 'The geography curriculum of the primary school', *Curriculum*, 2, 1, pp. 41–45.

2307    Bunce, V. (1986) 'Underrated but invaluable: the image of secondary school geography in the 1980s', *Geography*, 71, 4, pp. 325–332.

2308    Catling, S. (1987) 'The child is a geographer: criteria for geographical content in the primary school curriculum' in Bailey, P. and Binns, T. (eds) *A Case for Geography*. Sheffield: Geographical Association, pp. 18–25.

2309    Catling, S. (1989) 'What is primary geography?', *Primary Geographer*, 1, pp. 4–5.

2310    Catling, S. (1993) 'Specialising in geography: how might geography appear in the primary curriculum?', *Primary Geographer*, 15, pp. 9–10.

2311    Clark, L. (1970) 'Geography and curriculum development', *Scottish Geographical Magazine*, 86, 2, pp. 83–90.

2312    Coates, B. E. and Williams, M. (1981) 'Geography in the school curriculum 5-16', *Geography*, 66, 3, pp. 179–180.

2313    Cracknell, J. R. (1976) 'Geography in junior schools', *Geography*, 61, 3, pp. 150–156.

2314    Cracknell, R. (1979) 'Putting geography back into the primary curriculum: wasn't John Dewey right?', *Teaching Geography*, 4, 3, pp. 115–117.

2315    Daugherty, R. (1981) 'Geography and the school curriculum debate' in Walford, R. (ed) *Signposts for Geography Teaching*. Harlow: Longman, pp. 119–128.

2316    Daugherty, R. and Walford, R. (1980) 'A framework for the school curriculum: an initial response on behalf of the Geographical Association', *Geography*, 65, 3, pp. 232–235.

2317    Geographical Association (1981) *Geography in the School Curriculum 5-16*. Sheffield: Geographical Association.

2318    Graves, N. and Moore, T. (1972) 'The nature of geographical knowledge' in Graves, N. (ed) *New Movements in the Study and Teaching of Geography*. London: Temple Smith, pp. 17-28.

2319    Gwilliam, P. (1984) 'Experiential learning: a role for geography in the primary school', *Teaching Geography*, 10, 1, pp. 16-18.

2320    Her Majesty's Inspectorate (1978) 'Geography in the school curriculum: a discussion paper', *Teaching Geography*, 4, 2, pp. 76-78.

2321    Jenkins, S. (1992) 'Four cheers for geography', *Geography*, 77, 3, pp. 193-197.

2322    Joseph, K. (1985) 'Geography in the school curriculum', *Geography*, 70, 4, pp. 290-298.

2323    Marsden, W. E. (1989) 'Primary school geography: the question of balance' in Campbell, J. and Little, V. (eds) *Humanities in the Primary School*. London: Falmer Press, pp. 87-106.

2324    Marsden, W. E. (1993) 'Breadth, balance and connection in the primary curriculum: bridge-building, past and present' in Campbell, R. J. (ed) *Breadth and Balance in the Primary Curriculum*. London: Falmer Press, pp. 122-136.

2325    Mills, D. (1988) 'Geography and some recent statements on its place in the curriculum' in Mills, D. (ed) *Geographical Work in Primary and Middle Schools*. Sheffield: Geographical Association, pp. 19-23.

2326    Mills, D. (1988) 'The place of geography in the 3-13 curriculum' in Mills, D. (ed) *Geographical Work in Primary and Middle Schools*. Sheffield: Geographical Association, pp. 24-28.

2327    Morgan, W. (1987) 'Making opportunities for primary school geography', *Teaching Geography*, 12, 4, pp. 149-151.

2328    Morris, J. W. (1972) 'Geography in junior schools', *Trends in Education*, 28, pp. 14-23.

2329    Naish, M. (1997) 'The scope of school geography: a medium for education' in Tilbury, D. and Williams, M. (eds) *Teaching and Learning Geography*. London: Routledge, pp. 49-58.

2330    Pinchemel, P. (1982) 'The aims and values of geographical education' in Graves, N. (ed) *New UNESCO Source Book for Geography Teaching*. Harlow/Paris: Longman/UNESCO Press, pp. 1-15.

2331    Proctor, N. (1984) 'Geography and the common curriculum', *Geography*, 69, 1, pp. 38-45.

2332    Rawling, E. (1987) 'Geography 11-16: criteria for geographical content in the secondary school curriculum' in Bailey, P. and Binns, T. (eds) *A Case for Geography*. Sheffield: Geographical Association, pp. 26-33.

2333    Rawling, E., Williams, M., Ward, H. and Binns, T. (1988) 'Comments from the Geographical Association on the HMI Discussion Paper *Geography from 5 to 16*', *Geography*, 73, 1, pp. 41-46.

2334    Storm, M. (1989) 'The five basic questions for primary geography', *Primary Geographer*, 2, p. 4.

2335    Underwood, B. L. (1976) 'Aims in geographical education', *Cambridge Journal of Education*, 6, 3, pp. 151-156.

2336　Walford, R. (1985) 'Sir Keith speaks to the GA', *Teaching Geography*, 11, 1, pp. 20–23.

2337　Walford, R. (1996) 'A strategy for meeting curriculum challenge to geography' in van der Zijpp, T., van der Schee, J. and Trimp, H. (eds) *Innovation in Geographical Education: Proceedings of the 28th International Geographical Congress Commission on Geographical Education*. Amsterdam: IGUCGE/Centrum voor Educatieve Geografie Vrije Universiteit, Amsterdam, pp. 351–355.

2338　Walford, R. and Williams, M. (1982) 'Recent involvement of the Geographical Association in the curriculum debate', *Geography*, 67, 1, pp. 71–75.

2339　Williams, M. (1985) 'The Geographical Association and the Great Debate', *Geography*, 70, 2, pp. 129–137.

2340　Williams, M. and Walford, R. (1986) 'Geography and the school curriculum: the recent role of the Geographical Association', *Area*, 17, 4, pp. 317–321.

2341　Wynne, T. E. (1973) 'Geography and the curriculum' in Bale, J., Graves, N., and Walford, R. (eds) *Perspectives in Geographical Education*. Edinburgh: Oliver and Boyd, pp. 250–257.

# 6. Geography in the National Curriculum of England and Wales

2342　Bailey, P. (1989) 'A place in the sun: the role of the Geographical Association in establishing geography in the National Curriculum of England and Wales', *Journal of Geography in Higher Education*, 13, 2, pp. 149–157.

2343　Bailey, P. (1989) 'Geography, new subject, new curricular conditions' in Wiegand, P. and Rayner, M. (eds) *Curriculum Progress 5–16: School Subjects and the National Curriculum Debate*. London: Falmer Press, pp. 175–189.

2344　Bailey, P. (1991) *Securing the Place of Geography in the National Curriculum of English and Welsh Schools: A Study in the Politics and Practicalities of Curriculum Reform*. Sheffield: Geographical Association.

2345　Bailey, P. (1992) 'Geography and the National Curriculum: a case hardly won', *Geographical Journal*, 158, 1, pp. 66–74.

2346　Bale, J. (1984) 'Geography teaching, post-modernism and the National Curriculum' in Walford, R. and Machon, P. (eds) *Challenging Times: Implementing the National Curriculum in Geography*. Cambridge: Cambridge Publishing Services, pp. 95–97.

2347　Bennetts, T. (1994) 'The Dearing Report and its implications for geography', *Teaching Geography*, 19, 2, pp. 60–63.

2348　Bennetts, T. (1994) 'The draft proposals for geography: a personal response', *Teaching Geography*, 19, 4, pp. 160–161.

2349　Bennetts, T. (1994) 'Reflections on the development of geography in the National Curriculum' in Walford, R. and Machon, P. (eds) *Challenging Times: Implementing the National Curriculum in Geography*. Cambridge: Cambridge Publishing Services, pp. 6–12.

2350　Bland, K. (1989) 'Implications of the National Curriculum: a primary perspective', *Teaching Geography*, 14, 3, pp. 114–115.

2351　Blatch, Baroness (1993) 'Geography and the National Curriculum', *Geography*, 78, 4, pp. 359–366.

2352   Blyth, A. (1990) 'Place, time and society in the national primary curriculum', *Social Science Teacher*, 20, 1, pp. 11–12.

2353   Boardman, D. (ed) (1995) 'National Curriculum: geography at Key Stage 3', *Teaching Geography*, 20, 2 (special edition), pp. 56–89.

2354   Burden, J. (1992) 'The impact of National Curriculum geography at Key Stage 3', *Teaching Geography*, 17, 3, pp. 154–157.

2355   Butt, G. (1992) 'Geography' in Ribbins, P. (ed) (1992) *Delivering the National Curriculum: Subjects for Secondary Schooling*, Harlow: Longman, pp. 157–175.

2356   Butt, G. (1997) *An Investigation into the Dynamics of the National Curriculum Geography Working Group (1989–1990)*, unpublished PhD thesis. University of Birmingham.

2357   Butt, G. (1997) 'Instilling values into a centralised geography National Curriculum' in Naish, M. (ed) *Values in Geography Education: Proceedings*. London: IGUCGE/University of London Institute of Education, pp. 111–116.

2358   Carter, R. (1994) 'The GA responds to the draft proposals for geography', *Teaching Geography*, 19, 4, pp. 158–159.

2359   Catling, S. (1989) 'Anticipation and opportunities: geography in the National Curriculum', *Teaching Geography*, 14, 3, pp. 98–102.

2360   Catling, S. (ed) (1989) *Some Issues for Geography within the National Curriculum*. Sheffield: Geographical Association.

2361   Catling, S. (1990) 'A primary perspective: the views of primary teachers on the Geography Working Group's Interim Report', *Primary Geographer*, 4, p. 12.

2362   Catling, S. (1990) 'Subjecting geography to the National Curriculum', *Curriculum Journal*, 1, 1, pp. 77–89.

2363   Catling, S. (1991) 'Geography in primary practice in a period of transition' in Walford, R. (ed) *Viewpoints on Geography Teaching*. Harlow: Longman, pp. 95–102.

2364   Catling, S. (1994) 'Primary geography "after Dearing"', *Primary Geographer*, 17, pp. 14–16.

2365   Catling, S. (1994) 'Back to the bare necessities', *Primary Geographer*, 19, pp. 12–13.

2366   Clarke, K. (1992) 'Geography in the National Curriculum', *Teaching Geography*, 17, 1, pp. 28–30.

2367   Couldridge, E. (1995) 'The implementation of the National Curriculum in geography: selected findings of a 1992 study of ten secondary schools in a shire county' in Slater, F. (ed) *Reporting Research in Geography Education, Monograph No. 2*. London: University of London Institute of Education, pp. 41–60.

2368   Curriculum and Assessment Authority for Wales (1994) *Geography in the National Curriculum in Wales: Proposals for Consultation*. Cardiff: ACAC.

2369   Curriculum Council for Wales (1990) *National Curriculum Geography: CCW Advisory Paper 8: Comments on the Proposals of the Secretary of State for Wales*. Cardiff: CCW.

2370   Curriculum Council for Wales (1991) *Geography in the National Curriculum (Wales)*. Cardiff: CCW.

2371   Curriculum Council for Wales (1991) *Geography in the National Curriculum: Non-statutory Guidance for Teachers*. Cardiff: CCW.

2372    Curriculum Council for Wales (1993) *An Enquiry Approach to Learning Geography at Key Stages 2 and 3*. Cardiff: CCW.

2373    Daugherty, R. (ed) (1989) *Geography in the National Curriculum: A Viewpoint from the Geographical Association*. Sheffield: Geographical Association.

2374    Daugherty, R. (1989) 'Learning to live with a National Curriculum', *Geography*, 74, 4, pp. 299–307.

2375    Daugherty, R. (1989) 'What will they do next?: helping to shape a National Curriculum', *Teaching Geography*, 14, 4, pp. 146–148.

2376    Daugherty, R. and Lambert, D. (1994) 'Teacher assessment and geography in the National Curriculum', *Geography*, 79, 4, pp. 339–349.

2377    Davies, S. (1995) 'The implementation of National Curriculum history and geography in a small country primary school in Wales', *Welsh Journal of Education*, 4, 2, pp. 59–68.

2378    Department for Education (1995) *Geography in the National Curriculum: England*. London: HMSO.

2379    Department of Education and Science/Welsh Office (1989) *National Curriculum Geography Working Group: Interim Report*. London: DES.

2380    Department of Education and Science/Welsh Office (1990) *Geography for Ages 5–16: Proposals of the Secretary of State for Education and Science and Secretary of State for Wales*. London: DES.

2381    Department of Education and Science (1991) *Geography in the National Curriculum: England*. London: DES/HMSO.

2382    Derricott, R. (1994) 'Subjects as resources: from a Schools Council project to National Curriculum geography' in Marsden, W. E. and Hughes, J. (eds) *Primary School Geography*. London: David Fulton, pp. 9–22.

2383    Dixon, A. (1991) 'Primary geography: a pink curriculum?', *Forum*, 33, 2, pp. 51–52.

2384    Dowgill, P. (1996) 'Reporting pupils' experience of the National Curriculum geography' in Gerber, R. and Williams, M. (eds) *Qualitative Research in Geographical Education*. Armidale, NSW: IGUCGE/University of New England Press, pp. 57–72.

2385    Dunkerley, S. M. (1994) 'The implementation of National Curriculum geography in one primary school' in Slater, F. (ed) *Reporting Research in Geographical Education, Monograph No. 1*. London: University of London Institute of Education, pp. 39–51.

2386    Fry, P. and Schofield, A. (1993) *Teachers' Experiences of National Curriculum Geography in Year 7*. Sheffield: Geographical Association.

2387    Gayford, C. (1990) 'Environmental education in the National Curriculum: an update', *Environmental Education and Information*, 9, 1, pp. 11–13.

2388    Geographical Association (1993) 'National Curriculum: the GA writes to Sir Ron Dearing', *Teaching Geography*, 18, 4, pp. 155–157.

2389    Geographical Association (1994) 'The Dearing Review: the GA continues the dialogue', *Teaching Geography*, 19, 1, pp. 15–17.

2390    Geographical Association (1995) 'National Curriculum: geography at Key Stage 3', *Teaching Geography*, 20, 2, pp. 56–92.

2391   Geographical Association (1995) 'National Curriculum Special: your complete guide to coping with the new National Curriculum geography at Key Stages 1 and 2', *Primary Geographer*, 21, pp. 4–46.

2392   Graves, N., Kent, A., Lambert, D. and Slater, F. (1990) 'National Curriculum: first impressions', *Teaching Geography*, 15, 1, pp. 2–5.

2393   Graves, N., Kent, A., Lambert, D., Naish, M. and Slater, F. (1990) 'Evaluating the Final Report', *Teaching Geography*, 15, 4, pp. 147–151.

2394   Hall, D. (1990) 'The National Curriculum and the two cultures: towards a humanistic perspective', *Geography*, 75, 4, pp. 313–324.

2395   Hall, D. (1994) 'Postgraduate understanding and awareness of the specifics and professional dimensions of the new National Curriculum in England and Wales' in Haubrich, H. (ed) *Europe and the World in Geography Education (Geographiedidaktische Forschungen, Band 22)*. Nuremberg: IGUCGE, pp. 297–324.

2396   Hawkey, K. (1993) 'Implementation of National Curriculum history and geography at Key Stage 3: a case study', *Curriculum*, 14, 2, pp. 140–145.

2397   Hewitt, M. (1989) 'Accentuate the positive', *Teaching Geography*, 14, 3, pp. 104–105.

2398   Hicks, D. (1990) 'Lessons from a global education: avoiding a nationalistic curriculum', *Education 3–13*, 18, 3, pp. 39–45.

2399   Hopkin, J. (1991) 'Geography at the secondary level', *Forum*, 33, 2, pp. 53–54.

2400   Lambert, D. (1994) 'Geography in the National Curriculum: a cultural analysis' in Walford, R. and Machon, P. (eds) *Challenging Times: Implementing the National Curriculum in Geography*. Cambridge: Cambridge Publishing Services, pp. 88–94.

2401   Lambert, D. (1994) 'The National Curriculum: what shall we do with it?', *Geography*, 79, 1, pp. 65–76.

2402   Lloyd, K. (1994) 'Place and practice: the current state of geography in the primary curriculum', *Primary Geographer*, 17, pp. 7–9.

2403   Marsden, W. E. (1991) 'Primary geography and the National Curriculum' in Gorwood, B. T. (ed) *Changing Primary Schools (Aspects of Education 45)*. Hull: University of Hull Institute of Education, pp. 38–54.

2404   Marsden, W. E. (1997) 'Continuity after the National Curriculum', *Teaching Geography*, 22, 2, pp. 68–70.

2405   Morgan, W. (1990) 'A space for place in the primary curriculum', *Education Today*, 40, 4, pp. 43–46.

2406   Morgan, W. (1992) 'Windows on the world' in De Villiers, M. (ed) *Primary Geography Matters: Change in the Primary Curriculum*. Sheffield: Geographical Association, pp. 13–19.

2407   Morgan, W. (1994) 'Making a place for geography: the Geographical Association's initiatives and the Geography Working Group's experience' in Marsden, W. E. and Hughes, J. (eds) *Primary School Geography*. London: David Fulton, pp. 23–36.

2408   Morgan, W. (1995) 'Four years of Key Stage 2 geography', *Teaching Geography*, 20, 3, pp. 108–111.

2409   Morgan, W. (ed) (1995) 'National Curriculum Special', *Primary Geographer*, 21 (special edition), pp. 3–46.

2410 **Morris, J. S.** (1992) '"Back to the future": the impact of political ideology on the design and implementation of geography in the National Curriculum', *Curriculum Journal*, 3, 1, pp. 75–85.

2411 **Naish, M.** (ed) (1990) *Experiences of Centralisation: An International Study of the Impacts of Centralised Education Systems upon Geography Curricula.* London: IGUCGE/University of London Institute of Education.

2412 **Naish, M.** (ed) (1992) *Monitoring the Implementation of Geography in the Primary National Curriculum.* Sheffield: Geographical Association.

2413 **Naish, M.** (1992) *Primary Schools and National Curriculum Geography.* London: IGUCGE/University of London Institute of Education.

2414 **Naish, M.** (1993) 'Over the top!: implementing NCG in the primary school' in De Villiers, M. (ed) *Primary Geography Matters: Children's Worlds.* Sheffield: Geographical Association, pp. 19–27.

2415 **National Curriculum Council** (1990) *Geography 5–16 in the National Curriculum: Consultation Report.* York: NCC.

2416 **National Curriculum Council** (1991) *Geography: Non-statutory Guidance.* York: NCC.

2417 **National Curriculum Council** (1993) *An Introduction to Teaching Geography at Key Stages 1 and 2.* York: NCC.

2418 **National Curriculum Council** (1993) *An Introduction to Teaching Geography at Key Stage 3.* York: NCC.

2419 **Proctor, N.** (1988) 'Government control of the curriculum: some archive and recent evidence', *British Educational Research Journal*, 14, 2, pp. 155–166.

2420 **Proctor, N.** (1990) 'The good, the bad and the ugly: interim report of the National Curriculum Geography Working Group', *Education*, 175, 12, pp. 289–290.

2421 **Ranger, G.** (1994) 'All change or no change?', *Teaching Geography*, 19, 3, pp. 116–117.

2422 **Rawling, E.** (1991) 'Making the most of the National Curriculum', *Teaching Geography*, 16, 3, pp. 130–131.

2423 **Rawling, E.** (1992) 'The making of a national geography curriculum', *Geography*, 77, 4, pp. 292–309.

2424 **Rawling, E.** (1994) 'Dearing and the National Curriculum: what next for geography' in Walford, R. and Machon, P. (eds) *Challenging Times: Implementing the National Curriculum in Geography.* Cambridge: Cambridge Publishing Services, pp. 98–99.

2425 **Rawling, E.** (1995) 'What's new?', *Teaching Geography*, 20, 2, pp. 59–61.

2426 **Rawling, E.** (1996) 'The impact of the National Curriculum on school-based curriculum development in geography' in Kent, A., Lambert, D., Naish, M. and Slater, F. (eds) *Geography in Education: Viewpoints on Teaching and Learning.* Cambridge: Cambridge University Press, pp. 100–132.

2427 **Rawling, E.** (1996) 'A school geography curriculum for the twenty-first century?: the experience of the National Curriculum in England and Wales' in Stoltman, J. (ed) *International Developments in Geographical Education: Preparing for the Twenty-first Century* (*International Journal of Social Education*, 10, 2; special edition). Muncie, IN: Ball State University, pp. 1–21.

2428 **Rawling, E.** and **Westaway, J.** (1995) 'The National Curriculum: background and timetable for change', *Primary Geographer*, 21, pp. 8–9.

2429 Roberts, M. (1991) 'On the eve of the geography National Curriculum: implications for secondary schools', *Geography*, 76, 4, pp. 331–342.

2430 Roberts, M. (1995) 'Interpretations of the geography National Curriculum: a common curriculum for all?', *Journal of Curriculum Studies*, 27, 2, pp. 187–205.

2431 Robinson, R. (1990) 'It may not be too late...', *Teaching Geography*, 15, 4, pp. 152–155.

2432 Robinson, R. (1992) 'Facing the future: not the National Curriculum', *Teaching Geography*, 17, 1, pp. 31–32.

2433 School Curriculum and Assessment Authority (1994) *Geography in the National Curriculum: Draft Proposals*. London: SCAA.

2434 School Curriculum and Assessment Authority (1997) *Expectations in Geography at Key Stages 1 and 2*. London: SCAA.

2435 Slater, F. (1990) 'Policies for education and the National Curriculum for geography in England and Wales', *New Zealand Journal of Geography*, 90, pp. 12–19.

2436 Smith, P. R. (1997) 'Standards achieved: a review of geography in primary schools in England, 1995/96', *Primary Geographer*, 31, pp. 4–5.

2437 Speak, C. and Wiegand, P. (eds) (1993) *International Understanding through Geography: International Understanding and the National Curriculum*. Sheffield: Geographical Association.

2438 Storm, M. (1989) 'Geography and the National Curriculum', *Teaching Geography*, 14, 3, pp. 103–104.

2439 Unwin, T. (1992) 'Geography in the educational system of England and Wales' in Unwin, T. (1992) *The Place of Geography*. Harlow: Longman, pp. 11–17.

2440 Walford, R. (1989) 'Geography and the National Curriculum', *Teaching Geography*, 14, 1, pp. 33–34.

2441 Walford, R. (1989) 'Geography and the National Curriculum: a chronicle and a commentary', *Area*, 21, 2, pp. 161–166.

2442 Walford, R. (1991) 'The eighties: geography in context' in Walford, R. (ed) *Viewpoints on Geography Teaching*. Harlow: Longman, pp. 1–9.

2443 Walford, R. (1991) 'Geography and the National Curriculum', *Education Today*, 41, 1, pp. 27–31.

2444 Walford, R. (1991) 'National Curriculum: burden or opportunity?', *Teaching Geography*, 16, 1, p. 32.

2445 Walford, R. (1991) '"What say you, Simon Catling?": a commentary on "subjecting geography to the National Curriculum"', *Curriculum Journal*, 2, 1, pp. 79–83.

2446 Walford, R. (1992) 'Creating a National Curriculum: a view from the inside' in Hill, A. D. (ed) *International Perspectives on Geographical Education*. Boulder, CO/Skokie, IL: IGUCGE/Rand, McNally and Co., pp. 89–100.

2447 Walford, R. (1993) 'Geography' in King, A. and Reiss, M. *The Multicultural Dimension of the National Curriculum*. London: Falmer Press, pp. 91–108.

2448 Walford, R. (1995) 'Geography in the National Curriculum of England and Wales: rise and fall?', *Geographical Journal*, 161, 2, pp. 192–198.

2449 Walford, R. (1997) 'The great debate and 1988' in Tilbury, D. and Williams, M. (eds) *Teaching and Learning Geography*. London: Routledge, pp. 15–24.

2450    Walford, R. and Machon, P. (eds) (1994) *Challenging Times: Implementing the National Curriculum in Geography.* Cambridge: Cambridge Publishing Services.

2451    Welsh Office (1995) *Geography in the National Curriculum: Wales.* Cardiff: HMSO.

2452    Wiegand, P. (1990) 'Geography: the National Curriculum proposals', *Child Education,* 67, 9, pp. 34–35.

2453    Wiegand, P. (1995) 'Geography' in Anning, A. (ed) *A National Curriculum for the Early Years.* Milton Keynes: Open University Press, pp. 75–84.

2454    Williams, M. (1994) 'National Curriculum, national identity and geographical education' in Haubrich, H. (ed) *Europe and the World in Geographical Education (Geographiedidaktische Forschungen, Band 22).* Nuremberg: IGUCGE, pp. 67–77.

2455    Wilson, C. (1990) 'National Curriculum Geography Working Group', *Teaching Earth Sciences,* 15, 1, pp. 18–23.

2456    Winter, C. (1996) 'Challenging the dominant paradigm in the geography National Curriculum: reconstructing place knowledge', *Curriculum Studies,* 4, 3, pp. 367–384.

# B. GEOGRAPHY IN THE CURRICULUM

## 1. Learning and Teaching in Geography

### (a) Graphicacy

2457    Amlund, J. T., Gaffney, J. and Kulhavy, R. W. (1985) 'Map feature content and text recall of good and poor readers', *Journal of Reading Behaviour*, 17, 4, pp. 317–330.

2458    Allen, G. L., Kirasic, K. C., Siegel, A. W. and Herman, J. F. (1979) 'Developmental issues in cognitive mapping: the selection and utilisation of environmental landmarks', *Child Development*, 50, pp. 1062–1070.

2459    Bailey, P. (1979) 'Teaching and learning from landscape and map', *Cartographic Journal*, 16, 1, pp. 21–23.

2460    Balchin, W. (1985) 'Graphicacy comes of age', *Teaching Geography*, 11, 1, pp. 8–9.

2461    Billett, S. and Matusiak, C. (1988) 'Nursery children as map makers', *Education 3–13*, 16, 1, pp. 41–45.

2462    Blades, M. and Spencer, C. (1985) 'Using maps in pre-school education', *Child Education*, 62, pp. 26–27.

2463    Blades, M. and Spencer, C. (1986) 'The implications of psychological theory and methodology for cognitive cartography', *Cartographica*, 23, 4, pp. 1–13.

2464    Blades, M. and Spencer, C. (1986) 'Map use in the environment, and educating children to use maps', *Environmental Education and Information*, 5, 3, pp. 187–204.

2465    Blades, M. and Spencer, C. (1986) 'On the starting grid: the use of grid references by under-fives', *Child Education*, 63, pp. 27–28.

2466    Blades, M. and Spencer, C. (1987) 'Map use by three and four year old children exploring mazes', *British Journal of Developmental Psychology*, 5, 1, pp. 19–24.

2467    Blades, M. and Spencer, C. (1987) 'Young children's recognition of environmental features from aerial photographs and maps', *Environmental Education and Information*, 6, 3, pp. 189–198.

2468    Blades, M. and Spencer, C. (1987) 'How do people use maps to navigate through the world?', *Cartographica*, 24, 3, pp. 64–75.

2469    Blades, M. and Spencer, C. (1987) 'Map use by young children', *Geography*, 71, 1, pp. 47–52.

2470    Blades, M. and Spencer, C. (1987) 'Young children's strategies when using maps with landmarks', *Journal of Environmental Psychology*, 7, 3, pp. 201–218.

2471    Blades, M. and Spencer, C. (1988) 'How do children find their way through familiar and unfamiliar environments?', *Environmental Education and Information*, 7, 1, pp. 1–14.

2472   Blades, M. and Spencer, C. (1989) 'Young children's ability to use co-ordinate references', *Journal of Genetic Psychology*, 150, pp. 5–18.

2473   Blades, M. and Spencer, C. (1989) 'Young children's wayfinding: the pedestrian use of landmarks in urban environments and on maps', *Man-Environment Systems*, 17, pp. 105–112.

2474   Blades, M. and Spencer, C. (1990) 'The development of 3–6 year olds' map-using ability: the relative importance of landmarks and map alignment', *Journal of Genetic Psychology*, 151, pp. 181–194.

2475   Blades, M. and Spencer, C. (1994) 'The development of children's ability to use spatial representations', *Advances in Child Development and Behavior*, 25, pp. 157–197.

2476   Blaut, J. M. (1991) 'Natural mapping', *Transactions of the Institute of British Geographers*, 16, 1, pp. 55–74.

2477   Blaut, J. M., Downs, R. M. and Liben, L. S. (1997) 'Forum: the mapping abilities of young children', *Annals of the Association of American Geographers*, 87, 1, pp. 152–180.

2478   Blaut, J. M., McCleary, G. S. and Blaut, A. S. (1970) 'Environmental mapping in young children', *Environment and Behaviour*, 2, pp. 335–349.

2479   Blaut, J. M. and Stea, D. (1974) 'Mapping at the age of three', *Journal of Geography*, 73, 7, pp. 5–9.

2480   Bluestein, N. and Acredolo, L. P. (1979) 'Developmental changes in map reading skills', *Child Development*, 50, pp. 691–697.

2481   Board, C. (1981) 'Cartographic communication', *Cartographica*, 18, 2, pp. 42–78.

2482   Boardman, D. (1983) *Graphicacy and Geography Teaching*. London: Croom Helm.

2483   Boardman, D. (1985) 'Spatial concept development and primary school map work' in Boardman, D. (ed) *New Directions in Geographical Education*. London: Falmer Press, pp. 119–134.

2484   Boardman, D. (1985) 'Cartographic communication with topographic maps' in Boardman, D. (ed) *New Directions in Geographical Education*. London: Falmer Press, pp. 135–152.

2485   Boardman, D. (1989) 'The development of graphicacy: children's understanding of maps', *Geography*, 74, 4, pp. 321–331.

2486   Catling, S. (1978) 'The child's spatial conception and geographic education', *Journal of Geography*, 77, 1, pp. 24–28.

2487   Catling, S. (1979) 'Maps and cognitive maps: the young child's perception', *Geography*, 64, 4, pp. 288–296.

2488   Catling, S. (1980) 'Map use and objectives for map learning', *Teaching Geography*, 6, 1, pp. 15–17.

2489   Catling, S. (1996) 'Technical interest in curriculum development: a programme of map skills' in Williams, M. (ed) *Understanding Geographical and Environmental Education: The Role of Research*. London: Cassell, pp. 93–111.

2490   Chilton, J. S. (1982) *The Identification and Examination of the Nature of Selected Problems Experienced by Secondary Pupils in Developing Graphicate Skills*, unpublished MA dissertation. University of London Institute of Education.

2491 Cohen, R. (ed) (1985) *The Development of Spatial Cognition*. Hillsdale, NJ: Laurence Erlbaum.

2492 Dale, P. F. (1971) 'Children's reactions to maps and aerial photographs', *Area*, 3, 3, pp. 170–177.

2493 Devereux, P. (1982) *Environmental Knowledge and Map Learning in Boys aged 11 to 16*, unpublished MA dissertation. University of London Institute of Education.

2494 Downs, R. M. and Liben, L. S. (1988) 'Through a map darkly: understanding maps as representations', *Genetic Epistemologist*, 16, pp. 11–18.

2495 Downs, R. M. and Stea, D. (eds) (1973) *Image and Environment: Cognitive Mapping and Spatial Behavior*. Chicago, IL: Aldine.

2496 Downs, R. M. and Stea, D. (1977) *Maps in Minds: Reflections on Cognitive Mapping*. New York: Harper and Row.

2497 Eastman, J. R. (1985) 'Graphic organization and memory structures for map learning', *Cartographica*, 22, 1, pp. 1–20.

2498 Freundschuh, S. (1990) 'Can young children use maps to navigate?', *Cartographica*, 27, 1, pp. 54–66.

2499 Gärling, T., Böök, A. and Lindberg, E. (1984) 'Cognitive mapping of large scale environments: the interrelationship of action plans, acquisition and orientation', *Environment and Behaviour*, 16, 1, pp. 3–34.

2500 Gerber, R. (1981) 'Young children's understanding of the elements of maps', *Teaching Geography*, 6, 3, pp. 128–133.

2501 Gerber, R. (1982) 'An international study of children's perception and understanding of type used on atlas maps', *Cartographic Journal*, 19, 2, pp. 115–121.

2502 Gerber, R. (1985) 'Competence and performance in cartographic language' in Boardman, D. (ed) *New Directions in Geographical Education*. London: Falmer Press, pp. 153–170.

2503 Gerber, R. (1987) 'A form–function analysis of school atlases', *Cartographica*, 24, 1, pp. 144–159.

2504 Gerber, R. (1992) 'Is mapping in schools reflecting developments in cartography and geographical information?' in Naish, M. (ed) *Geography and Education: National and International Perspectives*. London: University of London Institute of Education, pp. 194–211.

2505 Gerber, R. and Wilson, P. (1979) 'Spatial reference systems and mapping with eleven-year-olds', *Geographical Education*, 3, 3, pp. 387–397.

2506 Gersmehl, P. J. and Andrews, S. K. (1986) 'Teaching the language of maps', *Journal of Geography*, 85, 6, pp. 267–270.

2507 Gilmartin, P. P. and Patton, J. C. (1984) 'Comparing the sexes on spatial abilities: map-use skills', *Annals of the Association of American Geographers*, 74, 4, pp. 605–619.

2508 Goldberg, J. and Kirman, J. M. (1990, 'Sex-related differences in learning to interpret Landsat images and in road map reading in young adolescents', *Journal of Geography*, 89, 1, pp. 15–25.

2509 Gould, P. and White, R. (1974) *Mental Maps*. Harmondsworth: Penguin Books.

2510 Griffin, T. L. C. (1983) 'Problem solving on maps: the importance of user strategies', *Cartographic Journal*, 20, 2, pp. 101–109.

B. GEOGRAPHY IN THE CURRICULUM

2511    Harnapp, V. and King, D. (1991) 'A new look at making raised-relief maps in the classroom', *Journal of Geography*, 90, 5, pp. 241–244.

2512    Harrison, D. A. (1978) 'Cognitive maps of a Canadian five-year-old', *Teaching Geography*, 4, 2, pp. 65–67.

2513    Hatcher, B. (1983) 'Putting young cartographers "on the map"', *Childhood Education*, 59, pp. 311–315.

2514    Hawkins, M. L. (1977) 'Map and globe skills in elementary school textbooks', *Journal of Geography*, 76, 7, pp. 261–265.

2515    Hayes, D. A. (1993) 'Freehand maps are for teachers and students alike', *Journal of Geography*, 92, 1, pp. 13–15.

2516    Heamon, A. J. (1973) 'The maturation of spatial ability in geography', *Educational Research*, 16, 1, pp. 63–66.

2517    Hennings, G. (1981) 'Understanding time–space relationships through map construction in the elementary grades', *Journal of Geography*, 81, 3, pp. 129–55.

2518    Jones, M. (1990) *An Image of Great Britain: The Educational Value of Large Area Cognitive Maps*, unpublished MA dissertation. University of London Institute of Education.

2519    Kinnear, P. R. and Wood, M. (1987) 'Memory for topographic contour maps', *British Journal of Psychology*, 78, 3, pp. 395–402.

2520    Kitchin, R. M., Blades, M. and Golledge, R. G. (1997) 'Understanding spatial concepts at the geographic scale without the use of vision', *Progress in Human Geography*, 21, 2, pp. 225–242.

2521    Levine, M., Marchon, I. and Hanley, G. (1984) 'The placement and misplacement of you-are-here maps', *Environment and Behavior*, 16, 2, pp. 139–157.

2522    Liben, L. S. and Downs, R. M. (1989) 'Understanding maps as symbols: the development of map concepts in children' in Reese, H. (ed) *Advances in Child Development*. New York: Academic Press, pp. 145–201.

2523    Lloyd, R. (1989) 'Cognitive maps: encoding and decoding information', *Annals of the Association of American Geographers*, 79, 1, pp. 101–124.

2524    MacCabe, C. L. (1988) 'Student sketch maps as a surrogate for geographic knowledge' in Gerber, R. and Lidstone, J. (eds) *Skills in Geographical Education Symposium '88, Volume 2*. Brisbane: IGUCGE/Brisbane College of Advanced Education, pp. 627–664.

2525    MacEachren, A. M. (1986) 'Map use and map making education: attention to sources of geographic education', *Cartographic Journal*, 23, 2, pp. 115–122.

2526    MacEachren, A. M. (1991) 'The role of maps in spatial knowledge acquisition', *Cartographic Journal*, 28, 2, pp. 152–162.

2527    MacEachren, A. M. (1992) 'Application of environmental learning theory to spatial knowledge acquisition from maps', *Annals of the Association of American Cartographers*, 82, 2, pp. 245–274.

2528    MacEachren, A. M. (1995) *How Maps Work*. New York: Guilford Press.

2529    McGee, C. (1982) 'Children's perception of symbols on maps and aerial photographs', *Geographical Education*, 4, 2, pp. 51–59.

2530    McGeorge, C. (1976) *Graphicacy in the Curriculum: A Conceptual and Critical Analysis*, unpublished MA dissertation. University of London Institute of Education.

2531    Martland, J. R. (1994) 'New thinking in mapping' in Marsden, W. E. and Hughes, J. (eds) *Primary School Geography*. London: David Fulton, pp. 37–49.

2532    Martland, J. R. and Walsh, S. E. (1997) 'A workshop: "I know where I am and I know where I am going!"', *Cartographica*, 32, 2, pp. 57–63.

2533    Matthews, M. H. (1980) 'The mental maps of children: images of Coventry's city centre', *Geography*, 65, 3, pp. 169–179.

2534    Matthews, M. H. (1984) 'Cognitive mapping abilities of young boys and girls', *Geography*, 69, 4, pp. 327–336.

2535    Matthews, M. H. (1984) 'Cognitive maps: a comparison of graphic and iconic techniques', *Area*, 16, 1, pp. 33–40.

2536    Matthews, M. H. (1984) 'Environmental cognition of young children: images of journey to school and home area', *Transactions of the Institute of British Geographers*, 9, 1, pp. 89–105.

2537    Matthews, M. H. (1986) 'Gender, graphicacy and geography', *Educational Review*, 38, 3, pp. 259–271.

2538    Matthews, M. H. (1987) 'Gender, home range, and environmental cognition', *Transactions of the Institute of British Geographers*, 12, 1, pp. 43–56.

2539    Matthews, M. H. (1992) *Making Sense of Place: Children's Understanding of Large-scale Environments*. Hemel Hempstead: Harvester Wheatsheaf.

2540    Metz, H. M. (1990) 'Sketch maps: helping students get the big picture', *Journal of Geography*, 89, 3, pp. 114–118.

2541    Meyer, J. M. W. (1973) 'Map skills instruction and the child's developing cognitive abilities', *Journal of Geography*, 72, 6, pp. 27–35.

2542    Monmonier, M. (1991) *How to Lie with Maps*. Chicago: University of Chicago Press.

2543    Mosenthal, P. B. and Kirsch, I. S. (1990) 'Understanding thematic maps', *Journal of Reading*, 34, 2, pp. 136–140.

2544    Murray, D. and Spencer, C. (1979) 'Individual differences in the drawing of cognitive maps: the effects of geographical mobility, strength of mental imagery and basic graphic ability', *Transactions of the Institute of British Geographers*, 4, 3, pp. 385–391.

2545    Noyes, L. (1979) 'Are some maps better than others?', *Geography*, 64, 4, pp. 303–306.

2546    Noyes, L. (1980) 'The positioning of type on maps: the effect of surrounding material on word recognition', *Human Factors*, 22, 3, pp. 353–360.

2547    Ottosson, T. (1988) 'What does it take to read a map?', *Cartographica*, 25, 4, pp. 28–35.

2548    Overton, J. M. (1982) *Some Influences on the Standards of Graphicacy amongst 15–16 Year Old Pupils in Secondary Schools*, unpublished MSc (Ed) dissertation. University of Southampton.

2549    Pearson, J. (1994) 'First maps', *Child Education*, 10, pp. 31–37.

2550    Petchenik, B. (1987) 'Fundamental considerations about atlases for children', *Cartographica*, 24, 1, pp. 16–23.

2551    Phillips, R. J. (1979) 'An experiment with contour lines', *Cartographic Journal*, 16, 2, pp. 72–76.

2552    Phillips, R. J., de Lucia, A. and Skelton, N. (1975) 'Some objective tests of the legibility of relief maps', *Cartographic Journal*, 12, 1, pp. 39–46.

2553   Phillips, R. J., Noyes, E. and Audley, R. J. (1978) 'Searching for names on maps', *Cartographic Journal*, 15, 2, pp. 72–77.

2554   Potash, L. M., Farrell, J. P. and Jeffrey, T. (1978) 'A technique for assessing map relief legibility', *Cartographic Journal*, 15, 1, pp. 28–35.

2555   Potegal, M. (ed) (1982) *Spatial Abilities: Development and Psychological Foundations*. New York: Academic Press.

2556   Muir, S. P. (1985) 'Understanding and improving students' map reading skills', *Elementary School Journal*, 86, 2, pp. 207–216.

2557   Muir, S. P. and Cheek, H. N. (1991) 'Assessing spatial development: implications for map skill instruction', *Social Education*, 55, 5, pp. 316–319.

2558   Presson, C. C. (1982) 'The development of map-reading skills', *Child Development*, 53, pp. 196–199.

2559   Renshaw, P. H. (1979) *The Perception of Atlas Maps: A Preliminary Investigation among Secondary School Pupils in Botswana*, unpublished MSc (Ed) dissertation. University of Southampton.

2560   Rhodes, B. (1994) 'Learning curves ... and map contours', *Teaching Geography*, 19, 3, pp. 111–115.

2561   Robinson, A. and Petchenik, B. (1975) 'The map as a communication system', *Cartographic Journal*, 12, 1, pp. 7–15.

2562   Rice, G. H. (1990) 'Teaching students to become discriminating map users', *Social Education*, 54, 6, pp. 393–397.

2563   Sandford, H. A. (1980) 'Directed and free search of the school atlas map', *Cartographic Journal*, 17, 2, pp. 83–92.

2564   Sandford, H. A. (1980) 'Map design for children', *Bulletin of the Society of University Cartographers*, 14, pp. 39–48.

2565   Saveland, R. N. (1978) 'Free-hand small-scale maps: activities for cognitive mapping', *Journal of Geography*, 77, 7, pp. 277–279.

2566   Sawyer, K. E. (1982) *An Investigation into Factors Influencing the Map Using Abilities in Children of 7–11 Years*, unpublished MPhil thesis. University of Southampton.

2567   Siegel, A. W. and Schadler, J. (1977) 'Young children's cognitive maps of their classroom', *Child Development*, 48, pp. 388–394.

2568   Spencer, C. and Blades, M. (1986) 'Pattern and process: a review essay on the relationship between behavioural geography and environmental psychology', *Progress in Human Geography*, 10, 3, pp. 230–248.

2569   Spencer, C., Blades, M. and Morsley, K. (1989) *The Child in the Physical Environment*. Chichester: John Wiley.

2570   Spencer, C. and Darvizeh, Z. (1981) 'The case for developing a cognitive environmental psychology that does not underestimate the abilities of young children', *Journal of Environmental Psychology*, 1, 1, pp. 21–31.

2571   Spencer, C. and Darvizeh, Z. (1983) 'Young children's place descriptions, maps and route finding: a comparison of nursery school children in Iran and Britain', *International Journal of Early Childhood*, 15, 1, pp. 26–31.

2572    Spencer, C. and Darvizeh, Z. (1984) 'The importance of landmarks in the child's wayfinding through the large-scale environment', *Environmental Education and Information*, 3, 2, pp. 97–105.

2573    Spencer, C. and Dixon, J. (1983) 'Mapping the development of feelings about the city: a longitudinal study of new residents' affective maps', *Transactions of the Institute of British Geographers*, 8, 3, pp. 373–383.

2574    Spencer, C., Harrison, N. and Darvizeh, Z. (1980) 'The development of iconic mapping ability in young children', *International Journal of Early Childhood*, 12, 2, pp. 57–64.

2575    Spencer, C., Mitchell, S. and Wisdom, J. (1984) 'Evaluating environmental education in nursery and primary schools', *Environmental Education and Information*, 3, 1, pp. 16–32.

2576    Spencer, C. and Weetman, M. (1981) 'The microgenesis of cognitive maps: a longitudinal study of new residents of an urban area', *Transactions of the Institute of British Geographers*, 6, 3, pp. 375–385.

2577    Tierney, G. (1985) *The Development of Spatial Cognition and Ability in the Primary and Secondary School*, unpublished MA dissertation. University of London Institute of Education.

2578    Trifonoff, K. M. (1995) 'Going beyond location: thematic maps in the early elementary grades', *Journal of Geography*, 94, 2, pp. 368–374.

2579    Underwood, J. D. M. (1981) 'Influencing the perception of contour lines', *Cartographic Journal*, 18, 2, pp. 116–119.

2580    van Dijk, H., van der Schee, J., Trimp, H. and van der Zijpp, T. (1994) 'Map skills and geographical knowledge', *IRGEE*, 3, 1, pp. 68–80.

2581    Verhetsel, A. (1994) 'The world in our heads: an experimental tuition programme focusing on students' ability to represent and structure spatially', *IRGEE*, 3, 2, pp. 35–44.

2582    Walker, R. J. (1978) *An Investigation into the Development of Map Using Abilities in Primary School Children*, unpublished MA dissertation. University of London Institute of Education.

2583    Walker, R. J. (1980) 'Map using abilities of five to nine year old children', *Geographical Education*, 3, 4, pp. 545–554.

2584    Weeden, P. (1997) 'Learning through maps' in Tilbury, D. and Williams, M. (eds) *Teaching and Learning Geography*. London: Routledge, pp. 168–179.

2585    Wiegand, P. (1991) 'A model for the realisation of a school atlas', *Geography*, 76, 1, pp. 50–58.

2586    Wiegand, P. (1995) 'Young children's freehand maps of the world', *IRGEE*, 4, 1, pp. 19–28.

2587    Wiegand, P. (1996) 'Constructing cartographic knowledge' in van der Zijpp, T., van der Schee, J. and Trimp, H. (eds) *Innovation in Geographical Education: Proceedings of the 28th International Geographical Congress Commission on Geographical Education*. Amsterdam: IGUCGE/Centrum voor Educatieve Geografie Vrije Universiteit Amsterdam, pp. 84–88.

2588    Wiegand, P. (1996) 'A constructivist approach to children's understanding of thematic maps' in van der Schee, J., Schoenmaker, G., Trimp, H. and van Westrhenen, H. (eds) *Innovation in Geographical Education (Netherlands Geographical Studies, 208)*. Utrecht/Amsterdam: IGUCGE/Centrum voor Educatieve Geografie Vrije Universiteit Amsterdam, pp. 57–65.

2589    Wiegand, P. and Stiell, B. (1996) 'Children's estimations of the sizes of the continents', *Educational Studies*, 22, 1, pp. 57–68.

2590    Wiegand, P. and Stiell, B. (1996) 'Communication in children's picture atlases', *Cartographic Journal*, 33, 1, pp. 17–25.

2591    Wiegand, P. and Stiell, B. (1996) 'Lost continents?: children's understanding of the location and orientation of the Earth's land masses', *Educational Studies*, 22, 3, pp. 383–394.

2592    Wiegand, P. and Stiell, B. (1997) 'Children's relief maps of model landscapes', *British Educational Research Journal*, 23, 2, pp. 179–192.

2593    Wilczynska-Woloszyn, M. M. (1988) 'Realistic images in developing map reading skill' in Gerber, R. and Lidstone, J. (eds) *Skills in Geographical Education Symposium '88, Volume 2*. Brisbane: IGUCGE/Brisbane College of Advanced Education, pp. 695–706.

2594    Wise, N. and Kon, J. H. (1990) 'Assessing geographic knowledge with sketch maps', *Journal of Geography*, 89, 3, pp. 123–129.

2595    Wood, M. (1972) 'Human factors in cartographic communication', *Cartographic Journal*, 9, 2, pp. 123–132.

2596    Wood, D. and Fels, J. (1986) 'Designs on signs: myth and meaning in maps', *Cartographica*, 23, 3, pp. 54–103.

2597    Wood, D. (1994) *The Power of Maps*. London: Routledge.

## (b) Children's learning

2598    Angier, N. Q. (1989) *An Investigation of the Effectiveness of Piagetian Derived Teaching Methods in Teaching the Interpretation of Contour Lines to Second Year Pupils*, unpublished MA dissertation. University of London Institute of Education.

2599    Anooshian, L. J., Hartman, S. R. and Scharf, J. S. (1982) 'Determinants of young children's search strategies in a large-scale environment', *Developmental Psychology*, 18, 4, pp. 608–616.

2600    Anooshian, L. J. and Kromer, M. K. (1986) 'Children's spatial knowledge of their school campus', *Developmental Psychology*, 22, 6, pp. 854–860.

2601    Arnold, P., Sarge, A. and Worrall, L. (1995) 'Children's knowledge of the earth's shape and its gravitational field', *International Journal of Science Education*, 17, 5, pp. 635–641.

2602    Aron, R. H., Francek, M. A., Nelson, B. D. and Bisard, W. J. (1994) 'Atmospheric misconceptions', *Science Teacher*, 61, 1, pp. 31–33.

2603    Baker, R. R. (1981) *Human Navigation and the Sixth Sense*. New York: Simon and Schuster.

2604    Balderstone, D. (1994) *An Evaluation of the Impact of a Range of Learning Experiences in Concept Acquisition in Physical Geography*, unpublished MA dissertation. University of London Institute of Education.

2605    Bar, V. (1989) 'Children's views about the water cycle', *Science Education*, 73, 4, pp. 481–500.

2606    Batchelor, R. J. (1987) *An Investigation into Some Aspects of Spatial Learning Problems in Geographical Education*, unpublished MA dissertation. University of London Institute of Education.

2607    Batterham, D., Stanistreet, M. and Boyes, E. (1996) 'Kids, cars and conservation: children's ideas about the environmental impact of motor cars', *International Journal of Science Education*, 18, 3, pp. 347–54.

2608    Beatty, W. W. and Troster, A. I. (1987) 'Gender differences in geographical knowledge', *Sex Roles*, 16, 11/12, pp. 565–590.

2609    Bland, K. (1983) *The Concept of Distance in Geography: Its Relationship with Cognitive Development and the School Curriculum*, unpublished MA dissertation. University of London Institute of Education.

2610    Blaut, J. M. and Stea, D. (1971) 'Studies of geographic learning', *Annals of the Association of American Geographers*, 61, 2, pp. 387–393.

2611    Bogdin, D. F. R. (1980) *An Investigation into the Understanding of Selected Concepts Experienced in Geographical Field Studies by Pupils aged 15+ to 17+*, unpublished MA dissertation. University of London Institute of Education.

2612    Boyes, E. and Stanistreet, M. (1992) 'Students' perceptions of global warming', *International Journal of Environmental Studies*, 42, pp. 287–300.

2613    Boyes, E. and Stanistreet, M. (1993) 'The "greenhouse effect": children's perceptions of causes, consequences and cures', *International Journal of Science Education*, 15, 5, pp. 531–552.

2614    Boyes, E. and Stanistreet, M. (1994) 'The ideas of secondary school children concerning ozone layer damage', *Global Environmental Change*, 4, 4, pp. 311–324.

2615    Boyes, E. and Stanistreet, M. (1996) 'Threats to the global atmospheric environment: the extent of pupil understanding', *IRGEE*, 5, 3, pp. 186–195.

2616    Butt, G. (1997) 'Language and learning in geography' in Tilbury, D. and Williams, M. (eds) *Teaching and Learning Geography*. London: Routledge, pp. 154–167.

2617    Carlstein, T., Parkes, D. and Thrift, N. (eds) (1978) *Timing Space and Spacing Time*. London: Edward Arnold.

2618    Carswell, R. J. B. and Wescott, H. M. (1974) 'Comparative use of a picture and written material in social studies', *Cartographic Journal*, 11, 2, pp. 122–123.

2619    Castner, H. W. (1990) *Seeking New Horizons: A Perceptual Approach to Geographic Education*. Montreal/Kingston: McGill/Queen's University Press.

2620    Castner, H. W. (1995) *Discerning New Horizons: A Perceptual Approach to Geographic Education*. Indiana, PA: National Council for Geographic Education.

2621    Castner, H. W. (1996) 'Maps, concepts and themes in geographic education' in van der Zijpp, T., van der Schee, J. and Trimp, H. (eds) *Innovation in Geographical Education: Proceedings of the 28th International Geographical Congress Commission on Geographical Education*. Amsterdam: IGUCGE/Centrum voor Educatieve Geografie Vrije Universiteit Amsterdam, pp. 54–58.

2622    Clare, P. H. (1977) *A Consideration of the Place of Mathematical Concepts in the Teaching and Learning of Geography at Secondary School Level*, unpublished MSc (Ed) dissertation. University of Southampton.

2623 Cross, J. A. (1987) 'Factors associated with students' place location knowledge', *Journal of Geography*, 86, 2, pp. 59–63.

2624 Dove, J. (1996) 'Do polar bears live in Antarctica?', *Journal of Biological Education*, 31, 1, pp. 3–6.

2625 Dove, J. (1996) 'Student misconceptions on the greenhouse effect, ozone layer, depletion and acid rain', *Environmental Education Research*, 2, 1, pp. 89–100.

2626 Downs, R. M., Liben, L. S. and Daggs, D. G. (1988) 'On education and geographers: the role of cognitive developmental theory in geographical education', *Annals of the Association of American Geographers*, 78, 4, pp. 680–700.

2627 Ellis, A. K. (1974) 'Concept and skill development in a primary geography unit utilizing alternative learning progressions', *Journal of Geography*, 73, 1, pp. 20–26.

2628 Gale, N., Golledge, R. G., Pellegrino, J. W. and Doherty, S. (1990) 'The acquisition and integration of route knowledge in an unfamiliar environment', *Journal of Environmental Psychology*, 10, 1, pp. 3–25.

2629 Gärling, T., Böök, A., Lindberg, E. and Nilsson, T. (1981) 'Memory for the spatial layout of the everyday physical environment: factors affecting rate of acquisition', *Journal of Psychology*, 1, pp. 263–277.

2630 Gerber, R. (1984) 'The diagnosis of student learning in geography' in Fien, J., Gerber, R. and Wilson, P. (eds) *The Geography Teacher's Guide to the Classroom*. Melbourne: Macmillan, pp. 185–196.

2631 Ghaye, A. (1978) *The Identification and Arrangement of Certain Geographical Concepts for the 11–14 Year Age Range*, unpublished MA dissertation. University of London Institute of Education.

2632 Golledge, R. G., Gale, N., Pellegrino, J. W. and Doherty, S. (1992) 'Spatial knowledge acquisition by children: route learning and relational distances', *Annals of the Association of American Geographers*, 82, 2, pp. 223–244.

2633 Golledge, R. G., Smith, T. R., Pellegrino, J. W., Doherty, S. and Marshall, S. P. (1985) 'A conceptual model and empirical analysis of children's acquisition of spatial knowledge', *Journal of Environmental Psychology*, 5, 2, pp. 125–152.

2634 Greaves, E., Stanistreet, M., Boyes, E. and Williams, T. (1993) 'Children's ideas about rainforests', *Journal of Biological Education*, 27, 3, pp. 189–194.

2635 Hall, D. (1984) 'Knowledge in the geography classroom' in Fien, J., Gerber, R. and Wilson, P. (eds) *The Geography Teacher's Guide to the Classroom*. Melbourne: Macmillan, pp. 1–12.

2636 Hart, R. (1979) *Children's Experience of Place*. New York: Irvington.

2637 Hartland, D. (1992) *An Investigation into the Development of Environmental Cognition and Knowledge in Primary Schoolchildren*, unpublished MA dissertation. University of London Institute of Education.

2638 Harvey, J. (ed) (1980) *Cognition, Social Behaviour and Environment*. Hillsdale, NJ: Laurence Erlbaum.

2639 Harwood, D. and Jackson, P. (1993) 'Why did they build this hill so steep?: problems in assessing primary children's understanding of physical landscape features in the context of the UK National Curriculum', *IRGEE*, 2, 2, pp. 64–79.

2640 Harwood, D. and McShane, J. (1996) 'Young children's understanding of nested hierarchies of place relationships', *IRGEE*, 5, 1, pp. 3–28.

2641  Haslam, J. (1992) *A Study of the Effect of Restricted Environmental Experience on Spatial Representation and Environmental Knowledge in Boys aged 8 to 13 Years*, unpublished MA dissertation. University of London Institute of Education.

2642  Jones, F. A. (1985) *Child Space*, unpublished MA dissertation. University of London Institute of Education.

2643  Jones, W. H. (1980) *Language, Thinking and Learning in Geography: The Importance of Classroom Talk*, unpublished MSc (Ed) dissertation. University of Southampton.

2644  Kaminske, V. (1997) 'Geographical concepts: their complexity and their grading', *IRGEE*, 6, 1, pp. 4–26.

2645  Kilburn, E. B. (1974) *A Critical Assessment of the Concept of Reality in Geography in Education*, unpublished MA dissertation. University of London Institute of Education.

2646  Kirby, J. R. (1993, 'Collaborative and competitive effects of verbal and spatial processes', *Learning and Instruction*, 3, pp. 201–214.

2647  Leat, D. (1997) 'Cognitive acceleration in geographical education' in Tilbury, D. and Williams, M. (eds) *Teaching and Learning Geography*. London: Routledge, pp. 143–153.

2648  Leat, D. (1997) *Thinking through Geography*. Cambridge: Chris Kington Publishing.

2649  Leat, D. and Chandler, S. (1996) 'Using concept mapping in geography teaching', *Teaching Geography*, 21, 3, pp. 108–112.

2650  Leather, A. D. (1987) 'Views of the nature and origin of earthquakes and oil held by eleven to seventeen year olds', *Geology Teaching*, 12, 3, pp. 102–108.

2651  Liben, L. S., Patterson, A. H. and Newcombe, N. (eds) (1981) *Spatial Representation across the Life Span: Theory and Application*. New York: Academic Press.

2652  Lidstone, J. (1984) 'Teaching geography in the mixed ability classroom' in Fien, J., Gerber, R. and Wilson, P. (eds) *The Geography Teacher's Guide to the Classroom*. Melbourne: Macmillan, pp. 197–207.

2653  Lillo, J. (1994) 'An analysis of the annotated drawings of the internal structure of the earth made by students aged 10–15 from primary and secondary schools in Spain', *Teaching Earth Sciences*, 19, 3, pp. 83–87.

2654  Lyle, S. (1997) 'Children aged 9–11 making meaning in geography', *IRGEE*, 6, 2, pp. 111–123.

2655  Matthews, M. H. (1985) 'Environmental capability of the very young: some implications for environmental education in primary schools', *Educational Review*, 37, 3, pp. 227–39.

2656  Matthews, M. H. (1985) 'Young children's representations of the environment: a comparison of techniques', *Journal of Environmental Psychology*, 5, 3, pp. 261–278.

2657  May, T. (1996) 'Children's ideas about rivers', *Primary Geographer*, 25, pp. 12–13.

2658  Mays, P. (1985) *Teaching Children through the Environment*. London: Hodder and Stoughton.

2659  Molyneux, F. and Tolley, H. (1987) *Teaching Geography: A Teaching Skills Workbook*. London: Macmillan.

2660  Moore, G. T. and Golledge, R. G. (1976) *Environmental Knowing*. Stroudsburg, PA: Dowden, Hutchinson and Ross.

2661  Moore, R. (1986) *Childhood's Domain*. London: Croom Helm.

2662    Naish, M. (1977) 'The development of children's thinking in school geography', *Teaching Geography*, 3, 2, pp. 81–83.

2663    Nelson, B. D., Aron, R. H. and Francek, M. A. (1992) 'Clarification of selected misconceptions in physical geography', *Journal of Geography*, 91, 2, pp. 76–80.

2664    Nussbaum, J. (1979) 'Children's conceptions of the earth as a cosmic body: a cross age study', *Science Education*, 63, 1, pp. 83–93.

2665    Nussbaum, J. and Novak, J. D. (1976) 'An assessment of children's concepts of the earth using structured interviews', *Science Education*, 60, 4, pp. 535–550.

2666    Palmer, J. (1993) 'From Santa Claus to sustainability: emergent understanding of concepts and issues in environmental science', *International Journal of Science Education*, 15, 5, pp. 487–495.

2667    Parke, S. (1990) *A Study of the Quality of Adolescents' Thinking in Geography*, unpublished MA dissertation. University of London Institute of Education.

2668    Proctor, N. (1987) 'Concepts or skills?: a question of focus', *Teaching Geography*, 12, 5, pp. 224–225.

2669    Purnell, K. and Sollman, R. (1993) 'The application of quantitative load theory to improve the learning of spatial information', *IRGEE*, 2, 2, pp. 80–91.

2670    Qualter, A., Francis, C., Boyes, E. and Stanistreet, M. (1995) 'The greenhouse effect: what do primary children think?', *Education 3–13*, 23, 2, pp. 28–31.

2671    Rand, D., Towler, J. and Price, D. (1976) 'Geographic knowledge as measured by Piaget's spatial stages' in Stoltman, J. (ed) *International Research in Geographical Education*. Kalamazoo, MI: IGUCGE/Western Michigan University, pp. 61–78.

2672    Robertson, M. (1994) 'The influence of place on adolescents' responses to environmental stimuli', *IRGEE*, 3, 2, pp. 3–21.

2673    Robertson, M. (1995) 'Adolescents, place experience and visual intelligence: implications for educators', *IRGEE*, 4, 2, pp. 65–84.

2674    Ross, K. E. K. and Shuell, T. J. (1993) 'Children's beliefs about earthquakes', *Science Education*, 77, 2, pp. 191–205.

2675    Rhys, W. (1972) 'The development of logical thinking' in Graves, N. (ed) *New Movements in the Study and Teaching of Geography*. London: Temple Smith, pp. 93–106.

2676    St Peter, P. H. and Lenegran, D. A. (1993) 'The five fundamental themes of geography as advance organisers in instructional design', *IRGEE*, 2, 1, pp. 51–63.

2677    Sandford, H. A. (1972) 'Perceptual problems' in Graves, N. (ed) *New Movements in the Study and Teaching of Geography*. London: Temple Smith, pp. 83–92.

2678    Sharp, J. G., Mackintosh, M. and Seedhouse, P. (1995) 'Some comments on children's ideas about earth structure, volcanoes, earthquakes and plates', *Teaching Earth Sciences*, 20, 1, pp. 28–30.

2679    Slater, F. (1970) 'Learning theory and geography teaching', *New Zealand Journal of Geography*, 48, pp. 12–16.

2680    Slater, F. (1973) 'The relationship between levels of learning in geography, Piaget's theory of intellectual development and Bruner's teaching hypothesis' in Biddle, D. S. and Deer, C. E. (eds) *Readings in Geographical Education: Selections from Australian and New Zealand Sources, Volume 2: 1966–1972*. Sydney: Whitcombe and Tombs/Australian Geography Teachers' Association, pp. 77–87.

2681    Slater, F. (1982) *Learning through Geography*. London: Heinemann.

2682    Slater, F. (1982) 'Literacy, numeracy and graphicacy in geographical education' in Graves, N., Naish, M., Slater, F., Kent, A. and Hilton, K. (1982) *Geography in Education Now: Bedford Way Papers 13*. London: University of London Institute of Education, pp. 18–27.

2683    Slater, F. (ed) (1989) *Language and Learning in the Teaching of Geography*. London: Routledge.

2684    Slater, F. (1994) 'Education through geography: knowledge, understanding, values and culture', *Geography*, 79, 2, pp. 147–163.

2685    Speak, C. (1988) 'Children's conceptual development seen through their drawings' in Gerber, R. and Lidstone, J. G. (eds) *Skills in Geographical Education Symposium '88, Volume 1*. Brisbane: IGUCGE/Brisbane College of Advanced Education, pp. 112–125.

2686    Spencer, C. (1994) 'Environmental cognition' in *The Encyclopedia of Human Behavior, Volume 2*. San Diego: Academic Press, pp. 255–264.

2687    Spencer, C. and Blades, M. (1993) 'Children's understanding of places: the world at hand', *Geography*, 78, 4, pp. 367–373.

2688    Spencer, C., Blades, M. and Morsley, K. (1989) *The Child in the Physical Environment*. Chichester: John Wiley.

2689    Spencer, C. and Darvizeh, Z. (1981) 'The case for developing a cognitive environmental psychology that does not underestimate the abilities of young children', *Journal of Environmental Psychology*, 1, 1, pp. 21–31.

2690    Spencer, C. and Darvizeh, Z. (1981) 'Techniques for the assessment of young children's environmental cognition', *Environmental Education and Information*, 1, 4, pp. 275–284.

2691    Stepans, J. and Kuehn, C. (1985) 'Children's conceptions of weather', *Science and Children*, 23, 10, pp. 44–47.

2692    Stephens, A. (1984) *Learning A-level Geography: A Student's Perspective*, unpublished MA dissertation. University of London Institute of Education.

2693    Stoltman, J. (1976) 'Territorial concept development: a review of the literature' in Stoltman, J. (ed) *International Research in Geographical Education*, Kalamazoo, MI: IGUCGE/Western Michigan University, pp. 1–15.

2694    Stoltman, J. (1988) 'The effects of self-directed atlas study upon student learning in geography' in Gerber, R. and Lidstone, J. (eds) *Skills in Geographical Education Symposium '88, Volume 2*. Brisbane: IGUCGE/Brisbane College of Advanced Education, pp. 675–684.

2695    Strommen, E. (1995) 'Lions and tigers and bears, oh my!: children's conceptions of forests and their inhabitants', *Journal of Research in Science Teaching*, 32, 7, pp. 683–698.

2696    Sullivan, B. J. (1981) *Distance: An Elusive Concept for Pupils and Teachers*, unpublished MSc (Ed) dissertation. University of Southampton.

2697    Teh, G. and Fraser, B. (1995) 'Associations between student outcomes and geography classroom environment', *IRGEE*, 4, 1, pp. 3–18.

2698    Thomas, S. and McGahan, H. (1997) 'Geography: it makes you think', *Teaching Geography*, 22, 3, pp. 114–118.

2699 Tilbury, D. and Turner, K. (1996) 'Levels of understanding: the case of acid rain', *Teaching Geography*, 21, 3, pp. 118–122.

2700 Venness, T. (1972) 'The contribution of psychology' in Graves, N. (ed) *New Movements in the Study and Teaching of Geography*. London: Temple Smith, pp. 75–82.

2701 Verhetsel, A. (1994) 'The world in our heads: an experimental tuition programme focusing on students' ability to represent and structure spatially', *IRGEE*, 3, 2, pp. 35–44.

2702 Waller, G. and Harris, P. L. (1988) 'Who's going where?: children's route descriptions for peers and younger children', *British Journal of Developmental Psychology*, 6, pp. 137–143.

2703 Walmsley, D. J. and Epps, D. R. (1988) 'Do humans have an innate sense of direction?', *Geography*, 73, 1, pp. 31–40.

2704 Warwick, P. (1987) 'How do children "see" geographical pictures?', *Teaching Geography*, 12, 2, pp. 118–119.

2705 Wiegand, P. (1991) 'The known world of the primary school', *Geography*, 76, 2, pp. 143–149.

2706 Wiegand, P. (1992) *Places in the Primary School: Knowledge and Understanding of Places in Key Stages 1 and 2*. London: Falmer Press.

2707 Wiegand, P. (1996) 'Learning with atlases and globes' in Bailey, P. and Fox, P. (eds) *Geography Teachers' Handbook*. Sheffield: Geographical Association, pp. 125–137.

2708 Wiegand, P. and Dickinson, J. (1996) 'Draw me a map of the British Isles', *Primary Geographer*, 30, pp. 20–21.

2709 Wiegand, P. and Stiell, B. (1997) 'The development of children's sketch maps of the British Isles', *Cartographic Journal*, 34, 1, pp. 13–22.

2710 Wiegand, P. and Stiell, B. (1997) 'Mapping the place knowledge of teachers in training', *Journal of Geography in Higher Education*, 21, 2, pp. 187–198.

2711 Wilson, P. and Goodwin, M. (1981, 'How do twelve and ten year old students perceive rivers?', *Geographical Education*, 4, 1, pp. 5–16.

2712 Wood, T. F. (1987) 'Thinking in geography', *Geography*, 72, 4, pp. 289–299.

## (c) Language

2713 Banks, V. and Hackman, S. (1993) 'English and geography liaison', *Teaching Geography*, 18, 2, pp. 105–107.

2714 Butt, G. (1991) *An Investigation into the Effects of Audience-centred Teaching on Children's Writing in Geography*, unpublished MA dissertation. University of London Institute of Education.

2715 Butt, G. (1993) 'The effects of audience-centered teaching on children's writing in geography', *IRGEE*, 2, 1, pp. 11–25.

2716 Butt, G. (1997) 'Language and learning in geography' in Tilbury, D. and Williams, M. (eds) *Teaching and Learning Geography*. London: Routledge, pp. 154–167.

2717 Carter, R. (ed) (1991) *Talking about Geography: The Work of Geography Teachers on the National Oracy Project*. Sheffield: Geographical Association.

2718  Catling, S. (ed) (1989) *Some Issues for Geography within the National Curriculum.* Sheffield: Geographical Association.

2719  Chambers, G., Speak, C. and Wiegand, P. (1993) 'The National Curriculum: modern foreign languages and geography' in Speak, C. and Wiegand, P. (eds) *International Understanding through Geography.* Sheffield: Geographical Association, pp. 18–21.

2720  Clark, G. (1985) 'Arguing a case in geography', *Teaching Geography,* 11, 1, pp. 31–33.

2721  Church, A. and Bull, P. (1995) 'Evaluating and assessing student oral presentations: a limited but effective role for employers in the geography curriculum', *Journal of Geography in Higher Education,* 19, 2, pp. 196–202.

2722  Convey, A. and Convey, F. M. (1996) 'Appropriate language competence for geographers: Anglo-French perspectives' in van der Zijpp, T., van der Schee, J. and Trimp, H. (eds) *Innovation in Geographical Education: Proceedings of the 28th International Geographical Congress Commission on Geographical Education.* Amsterdam: IGUCGE/Centrum voor Educatieve Geografie Vrije Universiteit Amsterdam, pp. 19–24.

2723  Cummings, R. (1984) *Pupil Talk in Groups during a CAL Simulation Game,* unpublished MA dissertation. University of London Institute of Education.

2724  Gerber, R. and Stewart-Dore, N. (1984) 'Strategies for improving reading and learning in geography lessons', *Teaching Geography,* 9, 5, pp. 216–222.

2725  Gersmehl, P. J. and Young, J. E. (1992) 'Images, analysis and evaluation: a linguistic basis for a regional geography course' in Hill, A. D. (ed) *International Perspectives on Geographical Education.* Boulder, CO/Skokie, IL: IGUCGE/Rand, McNally and Co., pp. 229–240.

2726  Hamilton, J. (1994) 'Sing the target language: from Pilton to Tokyo: a journey through the earth's crust', *Language Learning Journal,* 10, pp. 16–18.

2727  Hay, I. (1994) 'Justifying and applying oral presentations in geographical education', *Journal of Geography in Higher Education,* 18, 1, pp. 43–55.

2728  Hay, I. and Delaney, E. J. (1994) '"Who teaches, learns": writing groups in geographical education', *Journal of Geography in Higher Education,* 18, 3, pp. 317–334.

2729  Jenkins, A. and Pepper, D. (1988) 'Teaching oral and groupwork skills in geography' in Gerber, R. and Lidstone, J. (eds) *Developing Skills in Geographical Education.* Brisbane: IGUCGE/Jacaranda Press, pp. 147–151.

2730  Jones, W. H. (1980) *Language, Thinking and Learning in Geography: The Importance of Classroom Talk,* unpublished MSc (Ed) dissertation. University of Southampton.

2731  Leang, M. J. (1986) *Pupil Judgement of the Readability of Selected 16+ Geography Textbooks in Relation to Objective Measures,* unpublished MA dissertation. University of London Institute of Education.

2732  Lester, A. and Slater, F. (1996) 'Reader, text, metadiscourse and argument' in van der Schee, J., Schoenmaker, G., Trimp, H. and van Westrhenen, H. (eds) *Innovation in Geographical Education (Netherlands Geographical Studies, 208).* Utrecht/Amsterdam: IGUCGE/Centrum voor Educatieve Geografie Vrije Universiteit Amsterdam, pp. 115–125.

2733  Lewis, D. (1987) 'What do your pupils write?', *Teaching Geography,* 12, 2, pp. 60–63.

2734  McKenzie, J. (1983) *Readability and the Provision of Geography Materials in Comprehensive Schools,* unpublished MSc (Ed) dissertation. University of Southampton.

2735    McKenzie, V. (1982) *Language across the Curriculum and its Impact on Geographical Education in an Outer London Borough*, unpublished MA dissertation. University of London Institute of Education.

2736    Marsden, W. E. (1979) 'The language of the geography textbook: an historical appraisal', *Westminster Studies in Education*, 2, pp. 53–65.

2737    Milburn, D. (1972) 'Children's vocabulary' in Graves, N. (ed) *New Movements in the Study and Teaching of Geography*. London: Temple Smith, pp. 107–120.

2738    Mills, D. (1988) 'Talking, reading, writing and geographical work' in Mills, D. (ed) *Geographical Work in Primary and Middle Schools*. Sheffield: Geographical Association, pp. 42–27.

2739    Norton, D. E. (1993) 'Circa 1492 and the integration of literature, reading, and geography (engaging children in literature)', *Reading Teacher*, 46, 7, pp. 610–614.

2740    Platten, L. (1995) 'Talking geography: an investigation into young children's understanding of geographical terms, part 1', *International Journal of Early Years Education*, 3, 1, pp. 74–92.

2741    Platten, L. (1995) 'Talking geography: an investigation into young children's understanding of geographical terms, part 2', *International Journal of Early Years Education*, 3, 3, pp. 69–84.

2742    Roberts, M. (1986) 'Talking, reading and writing' in Boardman, D. (ed) *Handbook for Geography Teachers*. Sheffield: Geographical Association, pp. 68–78.

2743    Sawicka, E. (1996) 'Developing skills' in Bailey, P. and Fox, P. (eds) *Geography Teachers' Handbook*. Sheffield: Geographical Association, pp. 95–106.

2744    School Curriculum and Assessment Authority (1997) *Geography and the Use of Language*. London: SCAA.

2745    Sharp, N. (1989) 'How to teach oral and groupwork skills in geography', *Journal of Geography in Higher Education*, 13, 2, pp. 207–209.

2746    Shepherd, I. and Bleasdale, S. (1993) 'Student reading and course readers in geography', *Journal of Geography in Higher Education*, 17, 2, pp. 103–121.

2747    Slater, F. (ed) (1989) *Language and Learning in the Teaching of Geography*. London: Routledge.

2748    Stephenson, B. (1984) 'Language in the geography classroom' in Fien, J., Gerber, R. and Wilson, P. (eds) *The Geography Teacher's Guide to the Classroom*. Melbourne: Macmillan, pp. 13–28.

2749    Stimpson, P. (1994) 'Making the most of discussion', *Teaching Geography*, 17, 1, pp. 11–14.

2750    Walford, R. (1981) 'Language, ideologies and geography teaching' in Walford, R. (ed) *Signposts for Geography Teaching*. Harlow: Longman, pp. 215–222.

2751    Walker, D. (1996) 'Put it in writing: using maps to stimulate writing in geography classrooms', *Journal of Geography*, 95, 4, pp. 158–161.

2752    Westoby, G. (1996) 'Making reading "easier" in geography', *Teaching Geography*, 21, 3, pp. 113–117.

2753    Williams, M. (1981) *Language Teaching and Learning Geography*. London: Ward Lock.

2754    Younger, M. (1988) 'Oral assessment in GCSE geography', *Teaching Geography*, 13, 3, pp. 117–119.

## (d) Teaching styles

2755   Bale, J. (1987) 'Classroom styles' in Bale, J. *Geography in the Primary School.* London: Routledge and Kegan Paul, pp. 105–138.

2756   Boardman, D. (1988) 'The public inquiry as a teaching approach' in Gerber, R. and Lidstone, J. (eds) *Developing Skills in Geographical Education.* Brisbane: IGUCGE/Jacaranda Press, pp. 94–102.

2757   Butt, G. (1993) 'The effects of audience-centered teaching on children's writing in geography', *IRGEE*, 2, 1, pp. 11–25.

2758   Gilchrist, G. (1992) 'Flexible learning: the way forward for geography?', *Teaching Geography*, 17, 3, pp. 173–175.

2759   Harris, L. D. (1977) 'Lecturing from the atlas: an experiment in teaching', *Journal of Geography*, 76, 6, pp. 211–214.

2760   Kelly, C. R. M. (1995) *Working in Groups: A Study into the Effectiveness of Students Working in Groups*, unpublished MA dissertation. University of London Institute of Education.

2761   Kent, A. (ed) (1986) *Alternative Teaching Strategies for Geography.* London: University of London Institute of Education.

2762   Laws, K. (1988) 'An approach to data collection and teaching processing skills in geography' in Gerber, R. and Lidstone, J. (eds) *Developing Skills in Geographical Education.* Brisbane: IGUCGE/Jacaranda Press, pp. 39–43.

2763   Lidstone, J. (1984) 'Teaching geography in the mixed ability classroom' in Fien, J., Gerber, R. and Wilson, P. (eds) *The Geography Teacher's Guide to the Classroom.* Melbourne: Macmillan, pp. 197–207.

2764   Lyman, L. and Foyle, H. (1991) 'Teaching geography using cooperative learning', *Journal of Geography*, 90, 5, pp. 223–26.

2765   Molyneux, F. and Tolley, H. (1987) *Teaching Geography: A Teaching Skills Workbook.* London: Macmillan.

2766   Nairn, K. (1995) 'Quiet students in geography classrooms: some strategies for inclusion', *New Zealand Journal of Geography*, 100, pp. 24–31.

2767   Naish, M. (1988) 'Teaching styles in geographical education' in Gerber, R. and Lidstone, J. (eds) *Developing Skills in Geographical Education.* Brisbane: IGUCGE/Jacaranda Press, pp. 11–19.

2768   Phillips, A. (1982) *An Investigation into the Behaviour of Pupils when Taught by Two Different Teaching Styles*, unpublished MA dissertation. University of London Institute of Education.

2769   Rawling, E. (1986) 'Approaches to teaching and learning' in Boardman, D. (ed) *Handbook for Geography Teachers.* Sheffield: Geographical Association, pp. 56–67.

2770   Roberts, M. (1996) 'Teaching styles and strategies' in Kent, A., Lambert, D., Naish, M. and Slater, F. (eds) *Geography in Education: Viewpoints on Teaching and Learning.* Cambridge: Cambridge University Press, pp. 231–259.

2771    Roberts, M. (1996) 'An exploration of the role of the teacher within enquiry based classroom activities' in van der Schee, J., Schoenmaker, G. and Trimp, H. (eds) *Innovation in Geographical Education (Netherlands Geographical Studies, 208)*. Utrecht/Amsterdam: IGUCGE/Centrum voor Educatieve Geografie Vrije Universiteit Amsterdam, pp. 91–102.

2772    Roberts, M. (1996) 'Whose enquiry?: an investigation into the role of the teacher within a problem solving geography lesson' in van der Zijpp, T., van der Schee, J. and Trimp, H. (eds) *Innovation in Geographical Education: Proceedings of the 28th International Geographical Congress Commission on Geographical Education*. Amsterdam: IGUCGE/Centrum voor Educatieve Geografie Vrije Universiteit Amsterdam, pp. 79–83.

2773    Shapland, H. (1977) 'Group teaching is not the prerogative of mixed ability classes', *Teaching Geography*, 2, 4, pp. 150–151.

2774    Shevill, M. (1985) 'Teaching study skills in lower secondary school projects', *Teaching Geography*, 10, 4, pp. 164–166.

2775    Slater, F. (1976) 'Student perception of teaching style in geography: an exploratory study in London, UK' in Stoltman, J. (ed) *International Research in Geographical Education*. Kalamazoo, MI: IGUCGE/Western Michigan University, pp. 115–126.

2776    Slater, F. (1988) 'Teaching style?: a case study of postgraduate teaching students observed' in Gerber, R. and Lidstone, J. (eds) *Developing Skills in Geographical Education*. Brisbane: IGUCGE/Jacaranda Press, pp. 20–26.

2777    Springford, A. (1992) 'Flexible learning: what does it mean for geography teaching?', *Teaching Geography*, 17, 4, pp. 176–178.

2778    Steinbrink, J. (1976) 'Researching instructional style and classroom environments' in Stoltman, J. (ed) *International Research in Geographical Education*. Kalamazoo, MI: IGUCGE/Western Michigan University, pp. 89–114.

2779    Stoltman, J. (1976) 'Student perception of teacher style: the effects of the High School Geography Project' in Stoltman, J. (ed) *International Research in Geographical Education*. Kalamazoo, MI: IGUCGE/Western Michigan University, pp. 89–114.

2780    Stoltman, J. (1976) 'An international perspective on teacher classroom style' in Stoltman, J. (ed) *International Research in Geographical Education*. Kalamazoo, MI: IGUCGE/Western Michigan University, pp. 225–240.

2781    Trimp, H. (1988) 'Teaching styles and computer assisted learning in geography' in Gerber, R. and Lidstone, J. (eds) *Developing Skills in Geographical Education*. Brisbane: IGUCGE/Jacaranda Press, pp. 44–52.

## (e) Differentiation and progression

2782    Bailey, P. (1980) 'Progression', *Teaching Geography*, 5, 4, p. 146.

2783    Battersby, J. (1997) 'Differentiation in teaching and learning geography' in Tilbury, D. and Williams, M. (eds) *Teaching and Learning Geography*. London: Routledge, pp. 69–79.

2784    Bennetts, T. (1981) 'Progression in the geography curriculum' in Walford, R. (ed) *Signposts for Geography Teaching*. Harlow: Longman, pp. 164–185.

2785    Bennetts, T. (1986) 'Structure and progression in geography' in Boardman, D. (ed) *Handbook for Geography Teachers*. Sheffield: Geographical Association, pp. 149–163.

2786  Bennetts, T. (1995) 'Continuity and progression', *Teaching Geography*, 20, 2, pp. 75–80.

2787  Bennetts, T. (1996) 'Progression and differentiation' in Bailey, P. and Fox, P. (eds) *Geography Teachers' Handbook.* Sheffield: Geographical Association, pp. 81–93.

2788  Bowles, R. (1995) 'Progression in practice' in Bowles, R. (ed) *Practical Guides: Geography.* Leamington Spa: Scholastic Publications, pp. 137–152.

2789  Carter, R. (1992) 'Planning for KS2 and 3: progression and continuity' in De Villiers, M. (ed) *Primary Geography Matters: Change in the Primary Curriculum.* Sheffield: Geographical Association, pp. 1–3.

2790  Daugherty, R. (1996) 'Defining and measuring progression in geography' in Rawling, E. and Daugherty, R. (eds) *Geography into the Twenty-first Century.* Chichester: John Wiley, pp. 195–215.

2791  Frew, J. (1980) 'Progression in fieldwork throughout a secondary school', *Teaching Geography*, 5, 4, pp. 147–155.

2792  Heaps, A. (1982) *An Investigation into Curriculum Continuity in Geography between Middle and High Schools in a London Borough*, unpublished MA dissertation. University of London Institute of Education.

2793  Kemp, R. (1986) 'Mixed ability groups' in Boardman, D. (ed) *Handbook for Geography Teachers.* Sheffield: Geographical Association, pp. 164–170.

2794  Marsden, W. E. (1997) 'Continuity after the National Curriculum', *Teaching Geography*, 22, 2, pp. 68–70.

2795  Martin, F. (1993) 'Planning for progression', *Teaching Geography*, 18, 1, pp. 31–32.

2796  Maton, J. C. (1975) *An Experimental Investigation of Two Methods of Teaching Geography in Mixed Ability Classes in a Comprehensive School*, unpublished MA dissertation. University of London Institute of Education.

2797  Milton, M. (1984) *A Case Study of Mixed Ability Teaching in Some Geography and Integrated Studies Classes at Two Comprehensive Schools'*, unpublished MA dissertation. University of London Institute of Education.

2798  Morton, C. A. (1997) *Continuity and Progression – an Elusive Goal?: A Study of How Effective Liaison Can Help to Achieve Continuity and Progression in Geographical Education across Key Stages 2 and 3*, unpublished MA (Ed) dissertation. University of Southampton.

2799  Piggott, B. (1995) 'Differentiation in geography', *Primary Geographer*, 21, pp. 30–32.

2800  Rawling, E. (1997) 'Issues of continuity and progression in post-16 geography' in Powell, A. (ed) *Handbook of Post-16 Geography.* Sheffield: Geographical Association, pp. 11–30.

2801  Rawling, E. and Westaway, J. (1994) 'Progression and assessment in geography at key stage 3', *Teaching Geography*, 21, 3, pp. 123–129.

2802  Rider, M. and Rider, C. (1995) 'Differentiation: geography', *Special Children*, 80, pp. 1–12.

2803  Slater, A. (1993) 'Planning for mixed ability groups', *Teaching Geography*, 18, 3, pp. 127–128.

2804  Slater, A. (1996) 'Differentiating mapwork', *Teaching Geography*, 21, 4, pp. 186–187.

2805  Smyth, T. (1993) 'Linking across the primary–secondary interface', *Teaching Geography*, 18, 3, pp. 175–176.

2806    Surrell, G. P. (1989) *Continuity in Education with Specific Reference to Liaison Procedures Throughout the Middle Years of Schooling in Southern Hampshire*, unpublished MSc (Ed) dissertation. University of Southampton.

2807    Szpakowski, B. (1985) 'Continuity in geography between primary and secondary schools' in Derricott, R. (ed) *Curriculum Continuity: Primary to Secondary*. Windsor: Schools Council/NFER-Nelson, pp. 50–67.

2808    Taylor, S. (1996) 'Progression and gender differences in mapwork', *Primary Geographer*, 24, pp. 24–25.

2809    Tomkinson, M. (1987) *An Investigation into the Way Geography Teachers Cope with the Range of Ability in Pupils*, unpublished MA dissertation. University of London Institute of Education.

2810    Warner, H. (1997) 'Planning for progression in IT activities', *Teaching Geography*, 22, 1, pp. 38–39.

2811    Waters, A. (1995) 'Differentiation and classroom practice', *Teaching Geography*, 20, 2, pp. 81–84.

2812    Williams, M. (1996) 'Curriculum coherence: geographical education in the transition from primary to secondary schools' in van der Schee, J., Schoenmaker, G., Trimp, H. and van Westrhenen, H. (eds) *Innovation in Geographical Education (Netherlands Geographical Studies, 208)*. Utrecht/Amsterdam: IGUCGE/Centrum voor Educatieve Geografie Vrije Universiteit Amsterdam, pp. 249–257.

2813    Williams, M. (1997) 'Progression and transition in a coherent geography curriculum' in Tilbury, D. and Williams, M. (eds) *Teaching and Learning Geography*. London: Routledge, pp. 59–68.

2814    Williams, M. and Howley, R. (1989) 'Curriculum discontinuity: a study of a secondary school and its feeder primary schools', *British Educational Research Journal*, 15, 1, pp. 61–76.

## (f) Special needs

2815    Andrews, S. K., Otis-Witborn, A. and Young, T. M. (1991) *Beyond Seeing and Hearing: Teaching Geography to Sensory Impaired Children*. Indiana, PA: National Council for Geographic Education.

2816    Boardman, D. (ed) (1982) *Geography with Slow Learners*. Sheffield: Geographical Association.

2817    Boardman, D. (1986) 'Slow learners' in Boardman, D. (ed) *Handbook for Geography Teachers*. Sheffield: Geographical Association, pp. 176–180.

2818    Boardman, D. (1988) 'Current thinking on low attainers and geography teaching' in Dilkes, J. L. and Nicholls, A. C. (eds) *Low Attainers and the Teaching of Geography*. Sheffield/Stafford: Geographical Association/National Association for Remedial Education, pp. 7–11.

2819    Booth, M. (1980) 'Teaching geography to lower ability children', *Teaching Geography*, 5, 3, pp. 99–105.

2820    Catling, S. (1984) 'Building less-able children's map skills', *Remedial Education*, 19, 1, pp. 21–27.

2821    Catling, S. (1988) 'Building less-able children's map skills' in Dilkes, J. L. and Nicholls, A. C. (eds) *Low Attainers and the Teaching of Geography*. Sheffield/Stafford: Geographical Association/National Association for Remedial Education, pp. 25–28.

2822    Ciesla, M. J. (1988) 'Geography for slow learners in the secondary school' in Dilkes, J. L. and Nicholls, A. C. (eds) *Low Attainers and the Teaching of Geography*. Sheffield/Stafford: Geographical Association/National Association for Remedial Education, pp. 40–43.

2823    Corney, G. and Rawling, E. (1982) *Teaching Geography to Less Able 11–14 Year Olds*. Sheffield: Geographical Association.

2824    Corney, G. and Rawling, E. (eds) (1985) *Teaching Slow Learners Through Geography*. Sheffield: Geographical Association.

2825    Detheridge, T. (1993) 'IT and special needs', *Teaching Geography*, 18, 2, pp. 84–85.

2826    Devon County Council (1993) *Meeting your Needs: National Curriculum History and Geography in Special Schools*. Exeter: Devon County Council.

2827    Dilkes, J. L. (1982) 'Teaching geography to remedial first- and second-year pupils in a comprehensive school', *Teaching Geography*, 7, 3, pp. 103–106.

2828    Dilkes, J. L. (1984) 'Geography across the curriculum', *Remedial Education*, 19, 1, pp. 29–33.

2829    Dilkes, J. L. (1986) 'They're yours: do what you like with them', *Teaching Geography*, 11, 4, pp. 148–151.

2830    Dilkes, J. L. (1989) 'Advice on teaching children with special needs' in Wiegand, P. (ed) *Managing the Geography Department*. Sheffield: Geographical Association, pp. 169–173.

2831    Dilkes, J. L. and Nicholls, A. C. (eds) (1988) *Low Attainers and the Teaching of Geography*. Sheffield/Stafford: Geographical Association/National Association for Remedial Education.

2832    Dodds, A, G. (1989) 'Tactile maps: a psychologist's perspective', *Cartographic Journal*, 26, 1, pp. 3–6.

2833    Fahy, G. (1984) 'Geography and the remedial pupil in the junior post-primary school', *Geographical Viewpoint*, 13, pp. 31–45.

2834    Fernando, B. N. A. B. (1989) *Strategies Designed to Encourage Bilingual Pupils to Overcome Learning Difficulties in Geography and Humanities Classes*, unpublished MA dissertation. University of London Institute of Education.

2835    Grenyer, N. (1983) *Geography for Gifted Pupils*. Harlow: Schools Council/Longman.

2836    Grenyer, N. (1986) 'Bright Pupils' in Boardman, D. (ed) *Handbook for Geography Teachers*. Sheffield: Geographical Association, pp. 171–175.

2837    Harwood, D. (1986) 'Introducing mapwork to children with moderate learning difficulties: developing and assessing road atlas skills', *Support for Learning*, 1, 3, pp. 25–31.

2838    Harwood, D. (1988) 'Introducing map-work to ESN(M) children' in Dilkes, J. L. and Nicholls, A. C. (eds) *Low Attainers and the Teaching of Geography*. Sheffield/Stafford: Geographical Association/National Association for Remedial Education, pp. 29–39.

2839    Hickey, M. and Bein, F. L. (1996). 'Students' learning difficulties in geography and teachers' interventions: teaching cases from K-12 classrooms', *Journal of Geography*, 95, 3, pp. 118–25.

2840    Hughes, J. and Thomas, D. (1994) 'Geography for special children' in Marsden, W. E. and Hughes, J. (eds) *Primary School Geography*. London: David Fulton, pp. 170–185.

2841    Humberside County Council (1992) *Access to Geography: Geography for Children with Special Educational Needs*. Hull: Humberside County Council.

2842    Jordan, J. (1984) 'Some teaching techniques for less able pupils', *Teaching Geography*, 9, 5, pp. 228–230.

2843    Kemp, R. (1980) 'Teaching strategies for the less able', *Teaching Geography*, 5, 2, pp. 52–56.

2844    Kemp, R. (1988) 'Teaching strategies for the less able' in Dilkes, J. L. and Nicholls, A. C. (eds) *Low Attainers and the Teaching of Geography*. Sheffield/Stafford: Geographical Association/National Association for Remedial Education, pp. 84–86.

2845    Lawless, J. V. (1983) 'Teaching geography to intermediate certificate with less able pupils', *Geographical Viewpoint*, 12, pp. 56–65.

2846    Laws, K. (1984) 'Teaching the gifted student in geography' in Fien, J., Gerber, R. and Wilson, P. (eds) *The Geography Teacher's Guide to the Classroom*. Melbourne: Macmillan, pp. 226–234.

2847    McMullen, K. (1984) 'Resources and teaching strategies for the less-able 16+ pupil' in Orrell, K. and Wiegand, P. (eds) *Evaluation and Assessment in Geography*. Sheffield: Geographical Association, pp. 17–19.

2848    Nicholls, A. C. (1988) 'Readability: aid or hindrance?' in Dilkes, J. L. and Nicholls, A. C. (eds) *Low Attainers and the Teaching of Geography*. Sheffield/Stafford: Geographical Association/National Association for Remedial Education, pp. 44–56.

2849    Pick, W. and Renwick, M. (1984) 'Teaching the less able student in geography' in Fien, J., Gerber, R. and Wilson, P. (eds) *The Geography Teacher's Guide to the Classroom*. Melbourne: Macmillan, pp. 208–225.

2850    Sebba, J. (1991) *Planning for Geography for Pupils with Learning Difficulties*. Sheffield: Geographical Association.

2851    Sebba, J. (1995) *Geography for All*. London: David Fulton.

2852    Sebba, J. and Clarke, J. (1993) 'Practical approaches to increasing access to geography', *Support for Learning*, 8, 2, pp. 70–76.

2853    Shaw, F. (1984) 'Teaching geography to children with moderate learning difficulties', *Teaching Geography*, 9, 4, pp. 162–163.

2854    Smith, S. (1988) 'Geography for children with special educational needs' in Mills, D. (ed) *Geographical Work in Primary and Middle Schools*. Sheffield: Geographical Association, pp. 61–69.

2855    Titman, W. (1994) *Special Places, Special People*. Godalming: World Wildlife Fund/Learning through Landscapes.

2856    Turnage, J. M. (1987) *Geography as a Medium of Education to Develop the Potential of Pupils with Special Educational Needs in the Comprehensive School*, unpublished MA dissertation. University of London Institute of Education.

2857    Westoby, G. (1996) 'Making reading "easier" in geography', *Teaching Geography*, 21, 3, pp. 113–117.

2858    Weston, B. and McCormick, V. (1981) 'Teaching geography in an EPA school', *Teaching Geography*, 7, 2, pp. 54–57.

2859    Wiegand, P. and Beveridge, S. (1997) 'Rights and independence in travel for young people with learning difficulties' in Naish, M. (ed) *Values in Geography Education: Proceedings*. London: IGUCGE/University of London Institute of Education, pp. 81–85.

## (g) Developing values and attitudes (see also Part C Sections 1–5)

2860    Ambrose, L. (1981) 'On teaching about values in the classroom: a lesson and a retrospect' in Walford, R. (ed) *Signposts for Geography Teaching*. Harlow: Longman, pp. 63–65.

2861    Bailey, P. (1983) 'Editorial: Values', *Teaching Geography*, 9, 1, p. 2.

2862    Banks, J. A. (1974) *Teaching Strategies for the Social Studies: Inquiry Valuing and Decision Making*. Reading, MA: Addison-Wesley.

2863    Blachford, K. R. (1972) 'Values and geographical education', *Geographical Education*, 1, 4, pp. 319–330.

2864    Blachford, K. R. (1979) 'Morals and values in geographical education: towards a metaphysics of the environment', *Geographical Education*, 3, 3, pp. 423–457.

2865    Butt, G. (1997) 'Instilling values into a centralised geography National Curriculum' in Naish, M. (ed) *Values in Geography Education: Proceedings*. London: IGUCGE/University of London Institute of Education, pp. 111–116.

2866    Carter, R. (1991) 'Industrial and economic understanding: a matter of values', *Teaching Geography*, 16, 1, p. 30.

2867    Catling, S. (1997) 'Values in English primary geography series: 1990–1996' in Naish, M. (ed) *Values in Geography Education: Proceedings*. London: IGUCGE/University of London Institute of Education, pp. 117–122.

2868    Chadwick, J. and Meux, M. (1971) 'Procedures for values analysis' in Metcalf, L. E. (ed) *Values Education (41st Yearbook of the National Council for the Social Studies)*. Washington, DC: National Council for the Social Studies.

2869    Cole, R. (1976) *A New Role for Geographic Education: Values and Environmental Concerns*. San Diego, CA: National Council for Geographic Education.

2870    Cowie, P. M. (1974) *Value Teaching and Geographical Education*, unpublished MA dissertation. University of London Institute of Education.

2871    Cowie, P. M. (1978) 'Geography: a value-laden subject in education', *Geographical Education*, 3, 2, pp. 133–146.

2872    Davies, P. (1993) 'Handling economic ideas and values in geography teaching', *Economic Awareness*, 6, 1, pp. 3–8.

2873    Denver, D. (1990) 'Does the content of the A level syllabus affect student attitudes?', *Teaching Geography*, 15, 2, pp. 50–51.

2874    Edynbry, D., Hellyer, M. J. and Turner, P. M. (1977) 'Attitudes and values in geography teaching', *Geography*, 62, 3, pp. 205–208.

2875    Farmer, G. (1988) 'Values and attitudes' in Mills, D. (ed) *Geographical Work in Primary and Middle Schools*. Sheffield: Geographical Association, pp. 29–30.

2876    Fien, J. (1981) 'Values probing: an integrated approach to values education', *Journal of Geography*, 80, 1, pp. 19–22.

2877    Fien, J. and Slater, F. (1985) 'Four strategies for values education in geography' in Boardman, D. (ed) *New Directions in Geographical Education*. London: Falmer Press, pp. 171–186.

2878    Hart, C. (1982) *Values Enquiry in Practice (Geography 16–19 Occasional Paper No. 3)*. London: University of London Institute of Education.

2879    Hartley, R. M. (1980) *Values and Values Education in Geography Teaching*, unpublished MA dissertation. University of London Institute of Education.

2880    Haubrich, H. (1996) 'Global ethics in geographical education' in Gerber, R. and Lidstone, J. (eds) *Developments and Directions in Geographical Education*. Clevedon: Channel View Publications, pp. 163–173.

2881    Hernando, A. (1997) 'Values in geography education and teacher training' in Naish, M. (ed) *Values in Geography Education: Proceedings*. London: IGUCGE/University of London Institute of Education, pp. 95–100.

2882    Huckle, J. (1977) 'Geography and values in higher education', *Journal of Geography in Higher Education*, 1, 2, pp. 1–16.

2883    Huckle, J. (1980) 'Values and the teaching of geography: towards a curriculum rationale', *Geographical Education*, 3, 4, pp. 533–544.

2884    Huckle, J. (1981) 'Geography and values education' in Walford, R. (ed) *Signposts for Geography Teaching*. Harlow: Longman, pp. 147–164.

2885    Huckle, J. (1985) 'Values education through geography: a radical critique' in Boardman, D. (ed) *New Directions in Geography Teaching*. London: Falmer Press, pp. 187–197.

2886    John, A. (1991) 'Assessing values in GCSE geography', *Teaching Geography*, 16, 3, p. 118.

2887    Kelly, P. A. (1978) *Values and Attitudes in Geographical Education with Special Reference to Environmental Problems*, unpublished MA dissertation. University of London Institute of Education.

2888    Lambert, D. (1992) 'Towards a geography of social concern' in Naish, M. (ed) *Geography and Education: National and International Perspectives*. London: University of London Institute of Education.

2889    Lee, M. C. E. (1982) *The Need for Values Education and its Application in Geography*, unpublished MA dissertation. University of London Institute of Education.

2890    Lewis, D. (1980) *Geography Teaching, Values Education and the Multicultural Curriculum*, unpublished MA dissertation. University of London Institute of Education.

2891    Marsden, W. E. (1995) 'The values and attitudes dimension: issues-based geography' in Marsden, W. E. *Geography 11–16: Rekindling Good Practice*. London: David Fulton, pp. 137–153.

2892    Martorella, P. H. (1977) 'Teaching geography through value strategies' in Manson, G. A. and Ridd, M. K. (eds) *New Perspectives on Geographical Education: Putting Theory into Practice*. New York: Kendall Hunt, pp. 139–161.

2893    Maye, B. (1984) 'Developing valuing and decision making skills in the geography classroom' in Fien, J., Gerber, R. and Wilson, P. (eds) *The Geography Teacher's Guide to the Classroom*. Melbourne: Macmillan, pp. 29–43.

2894    Naish, M. (ed) (1997) *Values in Geography Education: Proceedings*. London: IGUCGE/University of London Institute of Education.

2895    Norton, B. G. and **Hannon, B.** (1997) 'Environmental values: a place-based theory', *Environmental Ethics*, 19, 3, pp. 227–245.

2896    Owen-Jones, G. (1987) *Values Education through Fieldwork*, unpublished MA dissertation. University of London Institute of Education.

2897    Ranger, G. and **Bamber, C.** (1990) 'Values enquiry in practice: investigating a local controversial issue', *Teaching Geography*, 15, 2, pp. 60–61.

2898    Raw, M. (1989) 'Teaching of issues and values in GCSE geography', *Teaching Geography*, 14, 1, pp. 18–25.

2899    Reid, A. (1996) 'Exploring values in sustainable development', *Teaching Geography*, 21, 4, pp. 168–172.

2900    Robertson, M. (1996) 'New meanings in time and space: ethical dilemmas for teachers' in Gerber, R. and Lidstone, J. *Developments and Directions in Geographical Education*. Clevedon: Channel View Publications, pp. 225–236.

2901    Slater, F. (1980) 'Values clarification: some practical suggestions for the classroom' in Slater, F. and Spicer, B. (eds) *Perception and Preference Studies at the International Level*. Tokyo: IGUCGE/AIP, pp. 224–231.

2902    Slater, F. (1982) 'Interpreting and analysing attitudes and values' in Slater, F. *Learning through Geography*. London: Heinemann, pp. 81–105.

2903    Slater, F. (1989) 'Research in geography education in the areas of environmental education, values education, concept development and language' in Graves, N., Kent, A., Lambert, D., Naish, M. and Slater, F. *Research in Geographical Education: MA Dissertations 1968–1988*. London: University of London Institute of Education, pp. 44–79.

2904    Slater, F. (1992) '... to travel with a different view' in Naish, M. (ed) *Geography and Education: National and International Perspectives*. London: University of London Institute of Education, pp. 97–113.

2905    Slater, F. (1994) 'Education through geography: knowledge, understanding, values and culture', *Geography*, 79, 2, pp. 147–163.

2906    Slater, F. (1996) 'Values: towards mapping their locations in geography' in Kent, A., Lambert, D., Naish, M. and Slater, D. (eds) *Geography in Education: Viewpoints on Teaching and Learning*. Cambridge: Cambridge University Press, pp. 200–230.

2907    **Smith, D. M.** (1978) 'Values and the teaching of geography', *Geographical Education*, 3, 2, pp. 147–162.

2908    **Smith, D. M.** (1995) 'Moral teaching in geography', *Journal of Geography in Higher Education*, 19, 3, pp. 271–283.

2909    Waterman, S. and **Maitland, S.** (1984) 'Value positions in teaching about development', *Teaching Geography*, 9, 3, pp. 104–105.

2910    Watson, J. W. (1977) 'Values in the classroom', *Geography*, 62, 3, pp. 198–204.

2911    Wiegand, P. (1986) 'Values in geographical education' in Tomlinson, P. and Quinton, M. (eds) *Values across the Curriculum*. London: Falmer Press, pp. 51–76.

# 2. Curriculum Planning in Primary Geography

This section contains references to planning in general. References to specific aspects of planning (e.g. assessment, differentiation or resources) can be found elsewhere in this part. (See also Part A Section 6 on the National Curriculum.)

2912    Alen, J. (1974) 'Geography for children aged 5 to 13 years' in Long, M. (ed) *Handbook for Geography Teachers*. London: Methuen, pp. 13–35.

2913    Bale, J. (1987) *Geography in the Primary School*. London: Routledge and Kegan Paul.

2914    Benwell, J. F. N. (1995) *The 9–13 Geography Curriculum: A Comparative Study of Geography in State and Independent Schools*, unpublished MSc (Ed) dissertation. University of Southampton.

2915    Blyth, A. and Krause, J. (1996) *Primary Geography*. London: Hodder and Stoughton.

2916    Bowles, R. (1995) *Practical Guides: Geography*. Leamington Spa: Scholastic Publications.

2917    Bowles, R. (ed) (1997) *Geography Guidance for Key Stages 1 and 2*. Sheffield: Geographical Association.

2918    Carter, R. (1990) 'Planning the geography programme through topic work', *Primary Geographer*, 5, pp. 12–13.

2919    Catling, S. (1987) 'Approaches to course organisation in the schools: primary level' in Bailey, P. and Binns, T. (eds) *A Case for Geography*. Sheffield: Geographical Association, pp. 48–50.

2920    Catling, S. (1993) 'Initiating geography INSET', *Primary Geographer*, 13, pp. 14–15.

2921    Catling, S. (1993) 'Coordinating geography', *Primary Geographer*, 14, pp. 10–11.

2922    Conner, C. (1974) *An Investigation into the Place and Function of Geography in the Curriculum of Middle Schools (9–13 Years)*, unpublished MA dissertation. University of London Institute of Education.

2923    Curriculum Council for Wales (1993) *History and Geography: Planning the National Curriculum at KS1 and KS2: A Guide for Headteachers and Curriculum Leaders*. Cardiff: CCW.

2924    Department of Education and Science (1978) *The Teaching of Ideas in Geography: Some Suggestions for the Middle and Secondary Years of Schooling*. London: HMSO.

2925    Department of Education and Science (1986) *Geography from 5 to 16: Curriculum Matters 7*. London: HMSO.

2926    Department of Education and Science (1989) *Aspects of Primary Education: The Teaching and Learning of History and Geography*. London: HMSO.

2927    Department of Education and Science (1990) *Geography for Ages 5 to 16*. London: HMSO.

2928    Foley, M. and Janikoun, J. (1996) *The Really Practical Guide to Primary Geography*. London: Stanley Thornes.

2929    Gatward, Y. (1984) *The Place of Geography in the Middle School*, unpublished MA dissertation. University of London Institute of Education.

2930    Gwilliam, P. (1996) *In a Post-Dearing Era, What do we Mean by the 'Direct Experience' we Give Primary Aged Pupils in Geography?*, unpublished MA dissertation. University of London Institute of Education.

2931    Hughes, J. and Marsden, W. E. (1995) 'Revising courses at Key Stage 1', *Primary Geographer*, 21, pp. 15–17.

2932    Kent, A. (1994) 'Curriculum planning in action' in Marsden, W. E. and Hughes, J. (eds) *Primary School Geography*. London: David Fulton, pp. 62–76.

2933    Mackintosh, M. (1995) 'Revising courses at Key Stage 1', *Primary Geographer*, 21, pp. 12–14.

2934    Milner, A. (1994) *Geography Starts Here: Practical Approaches with Nursery and Reception Children*. Sheffield: Geographical Association.

2935    Milner, A. (1997) *Geography through Play*. Sheffield: Geographical Association.

2936    Morgan, W. (1991) *Planning for Key Stage 2*. Sheffield: Geographical Association.

2937    Morgan, W. (1993) *Geography in a Nutshell*. Sheffield: Geographical Association.

2938    Morgan, W. (1995) 'Planning your geography for KS1 and 2', *Primary Geographer*, 23, pp. 10–11.

2939    Morgan, W. (1995) *Plans for Primary Geography*. Sheffield: Geographical Association.

2940    Plumb, E. (1991) 'Planning a whole school programme', *Primary Geographer*, 7, pp. 3–6.

2941    Raikes, J. (1991) *Planning for Key Stage 1*. Sheffield: Geographical Association.

2942    Rainey, D. and Krause, J. (1994) 'The geography curriculum coordinator in the primary school' in Harrison, M. (ed) *Beyond the Core Curriculum: Coordinating the Other Foundation Subjects in Primary Schools*. Plymouth: Northcote House, pp. 74–91.

2943    Rawling, E. (1992) *Programmes of Study: Try this Approach*. Sheffield: Geographical Association.

2944    School Curriculum and Assessment Authority (1995) *Planning the Curriculum at Key Stages 1 and 2*. London: SCAA.

2945    School Curriculum and Assessment Authority (1997) *Geography at Key Stage 2: Curriculum Planning Guidance for Teachers*. London: SCAA.

2946    Waters, A. (1993) 'Writing a primary geography policy statement: structure and sources', *Primary Geographer*, 12, pp. 12–13.

2947    Weldon, M. and Richardson, R. (1995) *Planning Primary Geography for the Revised National Curriculum KS 1 and 2*. London: John Murray.

2948    Wiegand, P. (1993) *Children and Primary Geography*. London: Cassell.

## 3. Curriculum Planning in Secondary Geography

This section contains references to planning in general. References to specific aspects of planning (e.g. assessment, differentiation or resources) can be found elsewhere in this part. (See also Part A Section 6 on the National Curriculum.)

2949    Bailey, P. (1974) *Teaching Geography*. Newton Abbot: David and Charles.

2950    Bailey, P. (1989) 'Geography, new subject, new curricular conditions' in Wiegand, P. and Rayner, M. (eds) *Curriculum Progress 5–16: School Subjects and the National Curriculum Debate*. London: Falmer Press, pp. 175–189.

2951    Bailey, P. and Fox, P. (eds) (1996) *Geography Teachers' Handbook*. Sheffield: Geographical Association.

2952    Battersby, J. (1996) *Teaching Geography at Key Stage 3*. Cambridge: Chris Kington Publishing.

2953    Bennetts, T. (1986) 'Structure and progression in geography' in Boardman, D. (ed) *Handbook for Geography Teachers*. Sheffield: Geographical Association, pp. 149–163.

2954    Benwell, J. F. N. (1995) *The 9–13 Geography Curriculum: A Comparative Study of Geography in State and Independent Schools*, unpublished MSc (Ed) dissertation. University of Southampton.

2955    Boardman, D. (1986) 'Planning with objectives' in Boardman, D. (ed) *Handbook for Geography Teachers*. Sheffield: Geographical Association, pp. 27–40.

2956    Boden, P. (1976) *Developments in Geography Teaching*. London: Open Books.

2957    Brown, S. and Slater, F. (1993) 'Evaluating a curriculum document', *Geographical Education*, 7, 1, pp. 45–50.

2958    Bunce, V. (1984) *An Investigation into Whether Viewpoints and Images of Geography held by Curriculum Decision-makers Reflect its Potential as a Valuable Medium for Education*, unpublished MA dissertation. University of London Institute of Education.

2959    Butt, G. and Lambert, D. (1993) 'Key Stage 3: professional guidance?', *Teaching Geography*, 18, 2, pp. 82–83.

2960    Dalton, T. H. (1988) *The Challenge of Curriculum Innovation: A Study of Ideology and Practice*. London: Falmer Press.

2961    Daugherty, R. and Walford, R. (1980) 'A framework for the school curriculum', *Geography*, 65, 3, pp. 232–235.

2962    Department of Education and Science (1978) *The Teaching of Ideas in Geography: Some Suggestions for the Middle and Secondary Years of Schooling*. London: HMSO.

2963    Department of Education and Science (1986) *Geography from 5 to 16: Curriculum Matters 7*. London: HMSO.

2964    Department of Education and Science (1990) *Geography for Ages 5 to 16*. London: HMSO.

2965    Di Landro, C. (1995) *School Based Curriculum Development*, unpublished MA dissertation. University of London Institute of Education.

2966    Dowgill, P. and Lambert, D. (1992) 'Cultural literacy and school geography', *Geography*, 77, 1, pp. 143–151.

2967    Edwards, K. (1992) 'Planning a scheme of work: a case study for Key Stage 3', *Teaching Geography*, 17, 3, pp. 107–110.

2968    Fien, J. (1984) 'School-based curriculum development in geography' in Fien, J., Gerber, R. and Wilson, P. (eds) *The Geography Teacher's Guide to the Classroom*. Melbourne: Macmillan, pp. 235–247.

2969   Fien, J. (1984) 'Planning and teaching a geography curriculum unit' in Fien, J., Gerber, R. and Wilson, P. (eds) *The Geography Teacher's Guide to the Classroom*. Melbourne: Macmillan, pp. 248–257.

2970   Foskett, N. (1996) 'Policy-making in geographical and environmental education: the research context' in Williams, M. (ed) *Understanding Geographical and Environmental Education: The Role of Research*. London: Cassell, pp. 220–229.

2971   Fry, P. and Schofield, A. (1993) *Teachers' Experiences of National Curriculum Geography in Year 7*. Sheffield, Geographical Association.

2972   Graves, N. (1975) *Geography in Education*. London: Heinemann.

2973   Graves, N. (1979) *Curriculum Planning in Geography*. London: Heinemann.

2974   Graves, N. (1980) *Geographical Education in Secondary Schools*. Sheffield: Geographical Association.

2975   Graves, N. (1996) 'Curriculum development in geography: an ongoing process' in Kent, A., Lambert, D., Naish, M. and Slater, F. (eds) *Geography in Education: Viewpoints on Teaching and Learning*. Cambridge: Cambridge University Press, pp. 72–99.

2976   Grimwade, K. (1995) 'Revising courses', *Teaching Geography*, 20, 2, pp. 62–66.

2977   Hacking, E. (1992) *Geography into Practice*. Harlow: Longman.

2978   Hall, D. (1976) *Geography and the Geography Teacher*. London: George Allen and Unwin.

2979   Hewitt, M. (1991) 'Implementing National Curriculum geography at KS 3', *Teaching Geography*, 16, 3, pp. 99–102.

2980   Kent, A. (1996) 'Evaluating the geography curriculum' in Kent, A., Lambert, D., Naish, M. and Slater, F. (eds) *Geography in Education: Viewpoints on Teaching and Learning*. Cambridge: Cambridge University Press, pp. 133–195.

2981   Kent, A. (1996) *Process and Pattern of a Curriculum Innovation*, unpublished PhD thesis. University of London Institute of Education.

2982   McEwen, N. (1986) 'Phenomenology and the curriculum: the case of secondary school geography' in Taylor, P. H. (ed) *Recent Developments in Curriculum Studies*. London: NFER/Nelson, pp. 156–167.

2983   Marsden, W. E. (1976) *Evaluating the Geography Curriculum*. Edinburgh: Oliver and Boyd.

2984   Marsden, W. E. (1976) 'Principles, concepts and exemplars and the structuring of curriculum units in geography', *Geographical Education*, 2, 4, pp. 421–429.

2985   Marsden, W. E. (1995) *Geography 11–16: Rekindling Good Practice*. London: David Fulton.

2986   Molyneux, F. and Tolley, H. (1987) *Teaching Geography: A Teaching Skills Workbook*. London: Macmillan.

2987   Murray, L. (ed) (1994) *Lesson Planning in Geography*. Portsmouth: LDJ Educational.

2988   Naish, M. (1992) 'Geography in the secondary curriculum' in Naish, M. (ed) *Geography and Education: National and International Perspectives*. London: University of London Institute of Education, pp. 34–50.

2989     Naish, M. (1996) 'Developing understanding of the dynamics of change in the geography curriculum' in van der Schee, J., Schoenmaker, G., Trimp, H., and van Westrhenen, H. (eds) *Innovation in Geographical Education (Netherlands Geographical Studies, 208)*. Utrecht/Amsterdam: IGUCGE/Centrum voor Educatieve Geografie Vrije Universiteit Amsterdam, pp. 239–248.

2990     Naish, M. (1997) 'Geography and education: knowledge and control' in Convey, A. and Nolzen, H. (eds) *Geography and Education (Münchner Studien zur Didaktik der Geographie, Band 10)*. Munich: Lehrstuhl für Didaktik der Geographie der Universität München, pp. 199–208.

2991     Naish, M. (1997) 'The scope of school geography: a medium for education' in Tilbury, D. and Williams, M. (eds) *Teaching and Learning Geography*, London: Routledge, pp. 49–58.

2992     **Office for Standards in Education** (1993) *Geography Key Stages 1, 2 and 3: The First Year 1991–92*. London: HMSO.

2993     Rawling, E. (1992) *Programmes of Study: Try this Approach*. Sheffield: Geographical Association.

2994     Rawling, E. (1997) 'Challenges for geography in the 14–19 curriculum', *Geographical Education*, 10, pp. 6–14.

2995     Roberts, M. (1997) 'Curriculum planning and course development: a matter of professional judgement' in Tilbury, D. and Williams, M. (eds) *Teaching and Learning Geography*. London: Routledge, pp. 35–48.

2996     Royce, D. H. (1985) *A Developing Relationship between Planners and Schools with Implications for Geography Teachers*, unpublished MSc (Ed) dissertation. University of Southampton.

2997     St Peter, P. H. and Lenegran, D. A. (1993) 'The five fundamental themes of geography as advance organisers in instructional design', *IRGEE*, 2, 1, pp. 51–63.

2998     Sawicka, E. (1996) 'Planning your lessons' in Bailey, P. and Fox, P. (eds) *Geography Teachers' Handbook*. Sheffield: Geographical Association, pp. 65–79.

2999     Slater, F. (1977) 'The place of objectives in curriculum development in geography', *New Zealand Journal of Geography*, 63, pp. 20–27.

3000     Slater, F. (1981) 'A strategy for determining objectives in curriculum construction in geography', *Geography Viewpoint*, 8, pp. 5–16.

3001     Slater, F. (1982) *Learning Through Geography*. London: Heinemann.

3002     Slater, F. (1986) 'Steps in planning' in Boardman, D. (ed) *Handbook for Geography Teachers*. Sheffield: Geographical Association, pp. 41–55.

3003     Swift, D. and Serf, J. (1993) 'Geography in the 1990s: teenage popular culture', *Teaching Geography*, 18, 1, pp. 7–10.

3004     Walford, R. and Machon, P. (eds) (1994) *Challenging Times: Implementing the National Curriculum in Geography*. Cambridge: Cambridge Publishing Services.

3005     Warner, P. J. (1984) *Curriculum Planning in 11–14 Geography*, unpublished MA dissertation. University of London Institute of Education.

3006     Wiegand, P. (ed) (1989) *Managing the Geography Department*. Sheffield: Geographical Association.

3007     Williams, M. (1984) *Designing and Teaching Integrated Courses*. Sheffield: Geographical Association.

3008    Williams, M. (1997) 'Instructional design' in Tilbury, D. and Williams, M. (eds) *Teaching and Learning Geography*. London: Routledge, pp. 133–142.

## 4. Curriculum Planning in Further Education

This section contains references to planning in general. References to specific aspects of planning (e.g. assessment, differentiation or resources) can be found elsewhere in this part.

3009    Allchin, A. (1991) *Geography in Access: An Investigation into the Role of Geography in Access Courses*, unpublished MA dissertation. University of London Institute of Education.

3010    Allchin, A. (1997) 'Geography teaching on access courses' in Powell, A. (ed) *Handbook of Post-16 Geography*. Sheffield: Geographical Association, pp. 139–145.

3011    Astles, A. and Dawson, M. (1997) 'Travel, tourism and leisure courses' in Powell, A. (ed) *Handbook of Post-16 Geography*. Sheffield: Geographical Association, pp. 129–138.

3012    Bradford, M. (1995) 'The new A level and AS level geography syllabuses', *Teaching Geography*, 20, 3, pp. 145–149.

3013    Bradford, M. (1996) 'Geography at the secondary/higher education interface: change through diversity' in Rawling, E. and Daugherty, R. (eds) *Geography into the Twenty-first Century*. Chichester: John Wiley, pp. 277–288.

3014    Brown, R. H. (1970) *An Examination of Changes in the Place and Function of Geography in the Curriculum of Colleges of Commerce*, unpublished MEd thesis. University of Leeds.

3015    Burtenshaw, D. (1996) 'Assessment post-16' in Bailey, P. and Fox, P. (eds) *Geography Teachers' Handbook*. Sheffield: Geographical Association, pp. 225–232.

3016    Butt, G. (1993) 'The scenario post-16', *Teaching Geography*, 18, 1, pp. 36–37.

3017    Butt, G. (1996) 'Developments in geography 14–19: a changing system' in Rawling, E. and Daugherty, R. (eds) *Geography into the Twenty-first Century*. Chichester: John Wiley, pp. 173–193.

3018    Butt, G. (1997) 'Post-16 geography in schools' in Powell, A. (ed) (1997) *Handbook of Post-16 Geography*. Sheffield: Geographical Association, pp. 31–40.

3019    Butt, G. and Lambert, D. (1993) 'Modules, cores and the new A/AS levels', *Teaching Geography*, 18, 3, pp. 180–181.

3020    Carter, R. (1996) 'The future of geography in the 16–19 curriculum', *Teaching Geography*, 21, 4, pp. 191–192.

3021    Clark, J. (1997) 'National vocational qualifications and geography' in Powell, A. (ed) *Handbook of Post-16 Geography*. Sheffield: Geographical Association, pp. 125–128.

3022    Cook, A. (1985) *The Nature of the Interface between A-level and Undergraduate Courses in Geography*, unpublished MSc (Ed) dissertation. University of Southampton.

3023    Cook, A. (1987) 'The interface between A-level and university courses in geography', *Geography*, 72, 1, pp. 49–55.

3024    Convey, A. (1997) 'Geography and the International Baccalaureate' in Powell, A. (ed) *Handbook of Post-16 Geography*. Sheffield: Geographical Association, pp. 105–110.

3025    Denver, D. (1990) 'Does the content of A-level syllabuses affect student attitudes?', *Teaching Geography*, 15, 2, pp. 50–51.

3026    Dove, J. (1987) 'Attitudes towards A-level geography project work', *Geography*, 72, 4, pp. 317–322.

3027    Frampton, S. (1997) 'Geography in post-16 colleges' in Powell, A. (ed) *Handbook of Post-16 Geography*. Sheffield: Geographical Association, pp. 41–55.

3028    Frampton, S. (1997) 'Planning and managing effective teaching and learning in post-16 colleges' in Powell, A. (ed) *Handbook of Post-16 Geography*. Sheffield: Geographical Association, pp. 55–66.

3029    Geographical Association (1982) *Geography in the Curriculum 16–19*. Sheffield: Geographical Association.

3030    Graves, N. (ed) (1979) *Geographical Education: Curriculum Problems in Certain European Countries with Special Reference to the 16–19 Age Group*. London: IGUCGE/University of London Institute of Education.

3031    Hall, D. (1986) 'Advanced level examinations' in Boardman, D. (ed) *Handbook for Geography Teachers*. Sheffield: Geographical Association, pp. 257–268.

3032    Hall, D. (1996) 'Developments at A-level' in Rawling, E. and Daugherty, R. (eds) *Geography into the Twenty-first Century*. Chichester: John Wiley, pp. 145–172.

3033    Holroyd, D. (1985) *An Evaluation of the Contribution of Geography to BTEC Modules in Travel and Tourism*, unpublished MA dissertation. University of London Institute of Education.

3034    Jones, A. I. (1986) *Structuralism and Geographical Education: Some Inferences and Implications for A-level Teaching and Learning*, unpublished MA dissertation. University of London Institute of Education.

3035    Jowitt, R. G. (1979) *An Investigation into the Response by Sixth Form College Geography Departments, CSE Regional Examination Boards and the Geography 16–19 Curriculum Development Project Team to the Pressures for Curriculum Change Resulting from the Expansion of the New Sixth Group of Students*, unpublished MA dissertation. University of London Institute of Education.

3036    Lambert, D. (1978) 'Methodological issues for the sixth form', *Teaching Geography*, 3, 4, pp. 163–166.

3037    McDonald, A. (1988) 'Assessing decision-making in the 16–19 examination', *Teaching Geography*, 13, 4, pp. 149–151.

3038    McSorley, F. (1984) *A Case Study of Curriculum Development and Planning for One Year Geography Courses in the Sixth Form*, unpublished MA dissertation. University of London Institute of Education.

3039    Marriott, A. (1990) 'The status of geography in further education', *Geography*, 75, 3, pp. 222–227.

3040    Naish, M. (1985) 'Geography 16–19' in Boardman, D. (ed) *New Directions in Geographical Education*. London: Falmer Press, pp. 99–118.

3041    Naish, M. (1997) 'Curriculum development in A-level courses' in Powell, A. (ed) *Handbook of Post-16 Geography*. Sheffield: Geographical Association, pp. 79–93.

3042    Naish, M., Kent, A. and Rawling, E. (1980) 'The man-environment approach to geography: a focus for curriculum development at 16–19', *Journal of Geography in Higher Education*, 3, 1, pp. 77–79.

3043 Naish, M. and **Rawling, E.** (1990) 'Geography 16–19: some implications for higher education', *Journal of Geography in Higher Education*, 14, 1, pp. 55–75.

3044 Naish, M., **Rawling, E.** and **Hart, C.** (1987) *Geography 16–19: The Contribution of a Curriculum Development Project to 16–19 Education.* Harlow: Longman.

3045 **Nuttall, S. E.** (1981) *Geography in Further Education: Past, Present and Future*, unpublished MA dissertation. University of London Institute of Education.

3046 **Oettle, R. E.** (1984) *An Investigation into the Problems Associated with the Development and Design of Geography Courses for the 'New' Sixth Former*, unpublished MA dissertation. University of London Institute of Education.

3047 **Phillips, A.** (1997) 'Managing IT in post-16 geography' in Powell, A. (ed) *Handbook of Post-16 Geography.* Sheffield: Geographical Association, pp. 73–77.

3048 **Powell, A.** (1986) *Geography in the 16–19 Further Education Curriculum*, unpublished MA dissertation. University of London Institute of Education.

3049 **Powell, A.** (1996) 'Geography in post-16 colleges' in Bailey, P. and Fox, P. (eds) *Geography Teachers' Handbook.* Sheffield: Geographical Association, pp. 309–313.

3050 **Powell, A.** (ed) (1997) *Handbook of Post-16 Geography.* Sheffield: Geographical Association.

3051 **Rawling, E.** (1997) 'Challenges for geography in the 14–19 curriculum', *Geographical Education*, 10, pp. 6–14.

3052 **Rawling, E.** (1997) 'Issues of continuity and progression in post-16 geography' in Powell, A. (ed) *Handbook of Post-16 Geography.* Sheffield: Geographical Association, pp. 11–30.

3053 **Slater, F.** (1977) 'Geography, the trades descriptions act and the sixth former', *Journal of Geography in Higher Education*, 1, 1, pp. 87–88.

3054 **Smith, M.** (1996) *The Secondary–Tertiary Interface in Geography Education*, unpublished MA dissertation. University of London Institute of Education.

3055 **Turton, D.** (1997) 'Teaching A-level courses' in Powell, A. (ed) *Handbook of Post-16 Geography.* Sheffield: Geographical Association, pp. 93–104.

3056 **Warren, J.** (1981) *A Survey of One Year Geography Courses for 'New Sixth Formers' in Schools, with Special Reference to the Certificate of Extended Education*, unpublished MA dissertation. University of London Institute of Education.

3057 **Westwood, S.** (1987) *The Contribution of Geography to Pre-vocational Education*, unpublished MA dissertation. University of London Institute of Education.

## 5. Curriculum Planning in Higher Education

3058 **Abler, R., Adams, J. S., Brooker-Gross, S. R., Conkey, L., Fernald, E., Griffin, E., Mercier, J.** and **Moline, N.** (1994) 'Reconsidering faculty roles and rewards in geography', *Journal of Geography in Higher Education*, 18, 1, pp. 7–18.

3059 **Barff, R.** (1995) 'Small classes and research experience for new undergraduates', *Journal of Geography in Higher Education*, 19, 3, pp. 299–306.

3060 **Bondi, L.** (1996) 'Geography degrees and gender: interpreting the patterns', *Area*, 28, 2, pp. 221–224.

3061    Boots, B. (1996) 'Referees as gatekeepers: some evidence from geographical journals', *Area*, 28, 2, pp. 177–185.

3062    Bradbeer, J. (1996) 'Problem-based learning and fieldwork: a better method of preparation', *Journal of Geography in Higher Education*, 20, 1, pp. 11–18.

3063    Bradford, M. (1996) 'Geography at the secondary/higher education interface: change through diversity' in Rawling, E. and Daugherty, R. (eds) *Geography into the Twenty-first Century*. Chichester: John Wiley, pp. 277–288.

3064    Bramley, W. and Wood, P. (1982) 'Collaboration, consultation and conflict: the process of change in a teaching department', *Journal of Geography in Higher Education*, 5, pp. 45–54.

3065    Bromley, R. D. (1995) 'Contract and part-time academic staff in UK geography departments', *Area*, 27, 3, pp. 268–274.

3066    Brown, B. (1989) 'Management strategies for meeting increased enrolments in introductory college geography courses', *Journal of Geography in Higher Education*, 8, pp. 226–229.

3067    Brown, E. H. and Mead, W. R. (1992) 'Curriculum development in universities' in Naish, M. (ed) *Geography and Education: National and International Perspectives*. London: University of London Institute of Education, pp. 51–60.

3068    Bryson, J. (1997, 'Breaking through the A-level effect', *Journal of Geography in Higher Education*, 21, 2, pp. 163–170.

3069    Buckingham-Hatfield, S. (1995) 'Student–community partnerships: advocating community enterprise projects in geography', *Journal of Geography in Higher Education*, 19, 2, pp. 143–150.

3070    Chapman, K. (1993) 'Degree results in geography 1973–1990: students, teachers and standards', *Area*, 25, 2, pp. 117–126.

3071    Chapman, K. (1994) 'Variability of degree results in geography in the United Kingdom universities: preliminary results and policy implications', *Studies in Higher Education*, 19, 1, pp. 89–102.

3072    Chapman, K. (1995) 'Geography degrees and gender: patterns and possible explanations', *Area*, 27, 1, pp. 62–73.

3073    Chapman, K. (1996). 'An analysis of degree results in geography by gender', *Assessment and Evaluation in Higher Education*, 21, 4, pp. 293–311.

3074    Charman, D. J. and Fullerton, H. (1995) 'Interactive lectures: a case study in a geographical concepts course', *Journal of Geography in Higher Education*, 19, 1, pp. 57–68.

3075    Church, A. and Bull, P. (1995) 'Evaluating and assessing student oral presentations: a limited but effective role for employers in the geography curriculum', *Journal of Geography in Higher Education*, 19, 2, pp. 196–202.

3076    Corney, G. and Middleton, N. (1996) 'Teaching environmental issues in schools and higher education' in Rawling, E. and Daugherty, R. (eds) *Geography into the Twenty-first Century*. Chichester: John Wiley, pp. 323–338.

3077    Cowley, J. W. (1979) *An Evaluation of a Second Year Undergraduate Course Teaching Techniques in Physical Geography: A Case Study in Course Design, Development and Implementation*, unpublished MSc (Ed) dissertation. University of Southampton.

3078 Davidson, J. and Mottershead, D. (1996) 'The experience of physical geography in schools and higher education' in Rawling, E. and Daugherty, R. (eds) *Geography into the Twenty-first Century*. Chichester: John Wiley, pp. 307–322.

3079 Department of Education and Science (1992) *A Survey of Geography Fieldwork in Degree Courses*. Stanmore: DES.

3080 Fox, M. and Wilkinson, T. (1977) 'A self-paced instruction scheme in geography for a first year introductory course', *Journal of Geography in Higher Education*, 1, 2, pp. 61–70.

3081 Fox, M., Rowsome, W. S. and Wilkinson, T. (1987) 'A decade of mastery learning: evolution and evaluation', *Journal of Geography in Higher Education*, 11, 1, pp. 11–26.

3082 Gold, J. R., Jenkins, A., Lee, R., Monk, J., Riley, J., Shepherd, I. and Unwin, D. (1991) *Teaching Geography in Higher Education: A Manual of Good Practice*. Oxford: Basil Blackwell/Institute of British Geographers.

3083 Gould, P. (1973) 'The open geographic curriculum' in Chorley, R. J. (ed) *Directions in Geography*. London: Methuen, pp. 253–284.

3084 Haigh, M. J. (1986) 'The evaluation of an experiment in physical geography teaching', *Journal of Geography in Higher Education*, 10, 2, pp. 133–147.

3085 Haines-Young, R. H. (1983) 'Nutrient cycling and problem-solving: a simple teaching model', *Journal of Geography in Higher Education*, 7, 2, pp. 125–139.

3086 Harrison, M. E. (1995) 'Images of the Third World: teaching a geography of the Third World', *Journal of Geography in Higher Education*, 19, 3, pp. 285–299.

3087 Hay, I. (1994) 'Justifying and applying oral presentations in geographical education', *Journal of Geography in Higher Education*, 18, 1, pp. 43–55.

3088 Hay, I. and Delaney, E. J. (1994) 'Who teaches, learns: writing groups in geographical education', *Journal of Geography in Higher Education*, 18, 3, pp. 317–334.

3089 Healey, M. (1997) 'Geography and education: perspectives on quality in UK higher education', *Progress in Human Geography*, 21, 1, pp. 97–108.

3090 Healey, M., Matthews, H., Livingstone, I. and Foster, I. (1996) 'Learning in small groups in university geography courses: designing a core module', *Journal of Geography in Higher Education*, 20, 2, pp. 167–180.

3091 Healey, M. and Roberts, M. (1996) 'Human and regional geography in schools and higher education' in Rawling, E. and Daugherty, R. (eds) *Geography into the Twenty-first Century*. Chichester: John Wiley, pp. 289–306.

3092 Higher Education Funding Council for England (1995) *Quality Assessment for Geography 1994–5: Subject Overview Report*. Bristol: HEFCE.

3093 Hindle, B. P. (1993) 'The "Project": putting student small group work and transferable skills at the core of a geography course', *Journal of Geography in Higher Education*, 17, 1, pp. 11–20.

3094 Jenkins, A. (1990) 'Teaching geography in British higher education' in Walford, R. (ed) *Viewpoints on Geography Teaching*. Harlow: Longman, pp. 103–109.

3095 Jenkins, A. (1993) 'Teaching large classes in geography: some practical suggestions', *Journal of Geography in Higher Education*, 17, 2, pp. 149–162.

3096 Jenkins, A. (1994) 'Control and independence strategies for large geography classes', *Journal of Geography in Higher Education*, 18, 2, pp. 245–248.

3097    Jenkins, A. (1997) *Fieldwork with More Students*. Oxford: Oxford Centre for Staff Development.

3098    Jenkins, A. and Smith, P. (1993) 'Expansion, efficiency and teaching quality: the experience of British geography departments 1986–91', *Transactions of the Institute of British Geographers*, 18, 4, pp. 500–515.

3099    Jenkins, A. and Ward, A. (eds) (1995) *Developing Skill Based Curricula through the Disciplines: Case Studies of Good Practice in Geography*. Birmingham: Staff and Educational Development Association.

3100    Johnston, R. J. and Oliver, M. (1991) 'Urban poverty and social welfare policy in the United States: an undergraduate research/training programme', *Journal of Geography in Higher Education*, 15, 1, pp. 25–34.

3101    Kakela, P. (1979) 'Remembering teaching', *Journal of Geography in Higher Education*, 3, 1, pp. 5–12.

3102    Kneale, P. (1997) 'Maximising play time: time management for geography students', *Journal of Geography in Higher Education*, 21, 2, pp. 293–301.

3103    McDowell, L. (1992) 'Engendering change: curriculum transformation in human geography', *Journal of Geography in Higher Education*, 16, 2, pp. 185–198.

3104    Mellor, V. A. (1981) *Teaching and Learning in Higher Education with Particular Reference to Independent Study and to Geography Education*, unpublished MA dissertation. University of London Institute of Education.

3105    Millard, J. (1977) *A Discussion on the Relationship between Undergraduate Geographical Education and Employment*, unpublished MSc (Ed) dissertation. University of Southampton.

3106    Mohan, J. (1995) 'Thinking local: service learning, education for citizenship and geography', *Journal of Geography in Higher Education*, 19, 2, pp. 129–142.

3107    Mossa, J. (1995) 'Topic synthesis: a vehicle for improving oral communication skills, comprehension and retention in higher education', *Journal of Geography in Higher Education*, 19, 2, pp. 151–158.

3108    Naish, M. and Rawling, E. (1990) 'Geography 16–19: some implications for higher education', *Journal of Geography in Higher Education*, 14, 1, pp. 55–75.

3109    O'Riordan, T. (1981) 'Environmentalism and education', *Journal of Geography in Higher Education*, 5, 1, pp. 3–18.

3110    Pepper, D. (1987) 'Physical and human integration: an educational perspective from British higher education', *Progress in Human Geography*, 11, 3, pp. 379–404.

3111    Phillips, M. and Healey, M. (1996) 'Teaching the history and philosophy of geography', *Journal of Geography in Higher Education*, 20, 2, pp. 223–242.

3112    Sharp, N. (1989) 'How to teach oral and groupwork skills in geography', *Journal of Geography in Higher Education*, 13, 2, pp. 207–209.

3113    Shepherd, I. (1993) 'Teaching dilemmas', *Journal of Geography in Higher Education*, 17, 2, pp. 212–215.

3114    Shepherd, I. and Bleasdale, S. (1993) 'Student reading and course readers in geography', *Journal of Geography in Higher Education*, 17, 2, pp. 103–121.

3115    Smith, D. M. (1995) 'Moral teaching in geography', *Journal of Geography in Higher Education*, 19, 3, pp. 271–284.

3116    Smith, M. (1996) *The Secondary–Tertiary Interface in Geography Education*, unpublished MA dissertation. University of London Institute of Education.

3117    Unwin, T. (1992) *The Place of Geography*. Harlow: Longman.

3118    Unwin, T. (1997) 'Rotten to the core: against a core curriculum for geography in UK higher education', *Journal of Geography in Higher Education*, 21, 2, pp. 252–260.

3119    Walker, G. (1993) 'Mock job interviews and the teaching of oral skills', *Journal of Geography in Higher Education*, 17, 1, pp. 73–78.

3120    Watts, H. D. (1993) 'No-tutor groups in geography: the student experience', *Journal of Geography in Higher Education*, 17, 2, pp. 141–147.

# 6. Curriculum Projects in Geography

## (a) Geography for the young school leaver

3121    Ash, S. and Mobbs, D. (1987) 'The GYSL TRIST Project', *Teaching Geography*, 12, 5, pp. 222–223.

3122    Battersby, J., Webster, A. and Younger, M. (1995) *The Case Study in GCSE Geography: Experiences from the Avery Hill Project*. Cardiff: Welsh Joint Education Committee/Midland Examining Group.

3123    Beddis, R. (1973) 'Developing a curriculum: a reconsideration of content' in Walford, R. (ed) *New Directions in Geography Teaching*. London: Longman, pp. 175–180.

3124    Beddis, R. (1981) 'GYSL criticised', *Bulletin of Environmental Education*, 126, p. 23.

3125    Bilski, R. (1985) 'River management studies at O level: issue-based suggestions for class and fieldwork', *Teaching Geography*, 11, 1, pp. 34–38.

3126    Birkill, S. (1980) 'Some comparisons of project approaches: some aspects of the findings and discussions of workshop groups' in Rawling, E. (ed) *Geography into the 1980s*. Sheffield: Geographical Association, pp. 49–56.

3127    Boardman, D. (1976) 'Developing a curriculum unit: "Cities and People" in Birmingham', *Teaching Geography*, 2, 1, pp. 20–23.

3128    Boardman, D. (ed) (1981) *GYSL with the Disadvantaged*. Sheffield: Geographical Association.

3129    Boardman, D. (1985) 'Geography for the Young School Leaver' in Boardman, D. (ed) *New Directions in Geographical Education*. London: Falmer Press, pp. 65–83.

3130    Boardman, D. (ed) (1988) *The Impact of a Curriculum Project: Geography for the Young School Leaver (Educational Review Occasional Publications No. 14)*. Birmingham: University of Birmingham.

3131    Boardman, D. (1988) 'The shifting centres of a curriculum innovation' in Gerber, R. and Lidstone, J. (eds) *Skills in Geographical Education Symposium '88, Volume 1*. Brisbane: IGUCGE/Brisbane College of Advanced Education, pp. 229–240.

3132    Brenchley, S. and Moon, A. (1995) *Geography – Avery Hill Candidate Profiles: A Research Project*. Cardiff: Welsh Joint Education Committee/Midland Examining Group.

3133 Currie, S. and Whittall, R. (1994) *Geography – Avery Hill: Reducing Under-Achievement and Learning to Succeed*. Cardiff: Welsh Joint Education Committee/Midland Examining Group.

3134 Dalton, T. H. (1988) *The Challenge of Curriculum Innovation: A Study of Ideology and Practice*. London: Falmer Press.

3135 Davies, P. (1983) 'GYSL: how a curriculum project has influenced the examining of geography in Wales', *Quest*, 5, pp. 5–9.

3136 Davies, P. (1996) *Geography – Avery Hill: The 1996 Examination: How did you do?* Cardiff: Welsh Joint Education Committee/Midland Examining Group.

3137 Davies, P. and Davies, B. (1991) *Differentiation in Examinations: The Factors which Influence Differentiation in the Terminal Examinations of the WJEC Avery Hill and Mainstream Geography Examinations, Summer 1990*. Cardiff: Welsh Joint Education Committee/Midland Examining Group.

3138 Gill, D. (1981) 'GYSL: a critique', *Bulletin of Environmental Education*, 126, pp. 35–39.

3139 Gill, D. (1984) 'GYSL: education or indoctrination?', *Contemporary Issues in Geography and Education*, 1, 2, pp. 34–38.

3140 Greasley, B. (1978) *The Implementation of the Schools Council Curriculum Development Project 'Geography for the Young School Leaver' in Schools in East Anglia*, unpublished MA dissertation. University of London Institute of Education.

3141 Hacking, E. (1991) 'A school experience of GYSL' in Walford, R. (ed) *Viewpoints on Geography Teaching*. Harlow: Longman, pp. 41–45.

3142 Hebden, R., Jones, M., Parsons, C. and Walsh, B. E. (1977) 'Changing the geography syllabus: what do the pupils think?', *Teaching Geography*, 3, 1, pp. 30–33.

3143 Hebden, R., Jones, M. and Walsh, B. E. (1979) 'Case studies in small scale evaluation', *British Educational Research Journal*, 5, 1, pp. 69–73.

3144 Higginbottom, T. (1980) 'Geography for the Young School Leaver' in Rawling, E. (ed) *Geography into the 1980s*. Sheffield: Geographical Association, pp. 11–20.

3145 Higginbottom, T. (1980) 'Geography for the Young School Leaver: response' in Stenhouse, L. (ed) *Curriculum Research and Development in Action*. London: Heinemann, pp. 176–178.

3146 Jones, B. and Wales, R. (1983) 'Thoughts related to the pupil studies demanded by the Avery Hill O-level syllabus', *Teaching Geography*, 9, 1, pp. 31–34.

3147 MacDonald, B. and Walker, R. (1976) 'A project profile of GYSL' in MacDonald, B. and Walker, R. *Changing the Curriculum*. London: Open Books, pp. 51–75.

3148 Mansell, J. (1978) 'Using GYSL throughout the secondary school', *Teaching Geography*, 4, 1, pp. 10–11.

3149 Morris, J. S. (1986) 'Geography for the Young School Leaver: the case for reform', *Curriculum*, 7, 2, pp. 90–95.

3150 Moss, R. W. (1985) *The Practice and Impact of Teacher Based Assessment in the 14–16 Curriculum: A Study of the Coventry Mode III Geography Scheme at 16+*, unpublished MA dissertation. University of Warwick.

3151 Parsons, C. (1980) 'Geography for the Young School Leaver' in Stenhouse, L. (ed) *Curriculum Research and Development in Action*. London: Heinemann, pp. 163–175.

3152   Parsons, C. (1981) *The Schools Council Geography for the Young School Leaver Project: A Case Study in Curriculum Change*, unpublished PhD thesis. University of Leeds.

3153   Parsons, C. (1988) *The Curriculum Change Game: A Longitudinal Study of the Schools Council GYSL Project*. London: Falmer Press.

3154   Price, J. and Medd, A. (1981) 'Working up local materials for GYSL: an example from Morecambe', *Teaching Geography*, 6, 4, p. 163.

3155   Renwick, M. (1985) *The Essentials of GYSL*. Sheffield: GYSL National Centre.

3156   Smith, N. (1996) 'Oral assessment in geography', *Teaching Geography*, 21, 2, pp. 87–90.

3157   Sutherland, A. E. (1985) *From Avery Hill to Ulster: The Implementation of the Geography for the Young School Leaver Project in Northern Ireland*. Belfast: Northern Ireland Schools Examination Council/Queen's University.

3158   Tucker, B. (1992) 'Oral assessment in geography', *Teaching Geography*, 17, 1, pp. 11–14.

3159   Walker, J. M. (1979) *Changing the Curriculum: The GYSL experience*. Sheffield: Sheffield City Polytechnic.

3160   Wheatley, A. (1976) 'Implementing a resource-based project: Geography for the Young School Leaver' in Boden, P. (1976) *Developments in Geography Teaching*. London: Open Books, pp. 70–79.

## (b) Geography 14–18

3161   Georgas, S. (1982) 'Curriculum change in geography through involvement in a national curriculum project' in Wiegand, P. and Orrell, K. (eds) *New Leads in Geographical Education*. Sheffield: Geographical Association, pp. 33–37.

3162   Hickman, G., Reynolds, J. and Tolley, H. (1973) *A New Professionalism for a Changing Geography*. London: Schools Council.

3163   Jones, S. (1976) 'The challenge of change in geography teaching', *Geography*, 61, 4, pp. 195–205.

3164   Jones, S. and Reynolds, J. (1973) 'The development of a new O-level syllabus', *Geography*, 58, 3, pp. 263–268.

3165   Lane, J. A. (1980) *An Evaluation of Some Aspects of the Kent Consortium 14–18 Geography Project*, unpublished MA dissertation. University of London Institute of Education.

3166   Orrell, K. (1985) 'Geography 14–18' in Boardman, D. (ed) *New Directions in Geographical Education*. London: Falmer Press, pp. 85–98.

3167   Orrell, K. (1991) 'The Schools Council 14–18 project' in Walford, R. (ed) *Viewpoints on Geography Teaching*. Harlow: Longman, pp. 39–40.

3168   Reynolds, J. (1971) 'Schools Council curriculum development project: Geography 14–18 years', *Geography*, 56, 1, pp. 32–34.

3169   Reynolds, J. (1972) 'Curriculum change and the Schools Council Geography 14–18 project', *Area*, 4, 2, pp. 128–131.

3170   Reynolds, J. (1972) 'Geography 14–18: a framework for development' in Hoyle, E. and Bell, R. (eds) *Problems of Curriculum Innovation (E283, Unit 14)*. Milton Keynes: Open University Press, pp. 80–87.

3171    Reynolds, J. (1976) 'Portrait of a national project (Geography 14–18)' in Open University *Curriculum Design and Development (E203, Case Study 4 Pack)*. Milton Keynes: Open University Press.

3172    Stevens, G. (1975) 'On course for a new O-level', *Teaching Geography*, 1, 2, pp. 55–60.

3173    Tolley, H. (1973) 'Launching the Geography 14–18 project', *Education*, 23, pp. 540–542.

3174    Tolley, H. and Reynolds, J. (1977) *Geography 14–18: A Handbook for School-based Curriculum Development*. London: Macmillan Education.

## (c) Geography 16–19

3175    Abbett, J. and Kent, A. (1991) 'Geography 16–19/TVEI project', *Links*, 16, 3, pp. 7–12.

3176    Burden, J. (1982) 'Local employment study for 16–19-year-olds', *Bulletin of Environmental Education*, 126, pp. 17–19.

3177    Clark, M. (1979) 'The Geography 16–19 project: an initial evaluation', *Journal of Geography in Higher Education*, 3, 1, pp. 80–81.

3178    Cook, A. (1986) 'Using examination papers as the basis for teaching exercises', *Teaching Geography*, 11, 2, pp. 52–56.

3179    Corney, G. (1981) *Teacher Education and Geography 16–19 (Geography 16–19 Occasional Paper No. 1)*. London: University of London Institute of Education.

3180    Corney, G. (1982) 'Geography 16–19 and teacher education', *Bulletin of Environmental Education*, 126, pp. 20–21.

3181    Farms, J. and Smith, F. (1984) 'Changing approaches to A-level fieldwork', *Teaching Geography*, 10, 1, pp. 25–26.

3182    Hall, P. (1979) 'Geography 16–19: a response', *Journal of Geography in Higher Education*, 3, 1, pp. 82–83.

3183    Hart, C. (1981) *Geography and Pre-employment Courses in the Sixth Form*. London: Geography 16–19 Project/University of London Institute of Education.

3184    Hart, C. (ed) (1982) *The Geographical Component of 17+ Pre-Employment Courses*. London: Geography 16–19 Project/University of London Institute of Education.

3185    Hart, C. (1982) *Values Enquiry in Practice (Geography 16–19 Occasional Paper No. 3)*. London: University of London Institute of Education.

3186    Hart, C. (1983) *Fieldwork the 16–19 Way (Geography 16–19 Occasional Paper No. 4)*. London: University of London Institute of Education.

3187    Hart, C. (1984) 'Common core: no cause for concern', *Teaching Geography*, 9, 4, pp. 148–150.

3188    Hart, C. (1984) 'Geography 16–19: going to the country', *Review of Environmental Education and Development*, 12, 1, pp. 12–15.

3189    Hart, C. and Winter, C. (1983) 'Putting geography to work at 17+', *Teaching Geography*, 8, 3, pp. 112–113.

3190    Hilary, M. L. (1980) *An Analysis of the Forces Shaping the 16–19 Geography Project*, unpublished MA dissertation. University of London Institute of Education.

3191    Holloway, P. M. (1991) *An Investigation into Teachers' and Students' Perceptions of Teacher Assessment in the Geography 16–19 Project A Level*, unpublished MSc dissertation. University of Oxford.

3192    Hones, G. (1991) 'Geography 16–19' in Walford, R. (ed) *Viewpoints on Geography Teaching*. Harlow: Longman, pp. 46–47.

3193    Kent, A. (1982) 'Geography and environmental education', *Geographical Viewpoint*, 9, pp. 19–28.

3194    Jowitt, R. G. (1979) *An Investigation into the Response by Sixth Form College Geography Departments, CSE Regional Examination Boards and the Geography 16–19 Curriculum Development Project Team to the Pressures for Curriculum Change Resulting from the Expansion of the New Sixth Group of Students*, unpublished MA dissertation. University of London Institute of Education.

3195    McDonald, A. (1988) 'Assessing decision-making in the 16–19 examination', *Teaching Geography*, 13, 4, pp. 149–151.

3196    McElroy, B. I. (1980) *School Based Curriculum Development: An Investigation into Teachers' Perceptions of the Role, the Major Constraints and the In-service Implications in this Form of Curriculum Development*, unpublished MA dissertation. University of London Institute of Education.

3197    McSorley, F. (1984) *A Case Study of Curriculum Development and Planning for One Year Geography Courses in the Sixth Form*, unpublished MA dissertation. University of London Institute of Education.

3198    Naish, M. (1976) 'Geography 16–19: a new Schools Council curriculum development project', *Teaching Geography*, 1, 3, pp. 127–128.

3199    Naish, M. (1976) 'Tasks for a new Schools Council curriculum development project in England and Wales' in Graves, N. *Geography in Education: Abstracts and Papers*. Moscow: International Geographical Union.

3200    Naish, M. (1980) 'Geography for the 16–19-year-old' in Rawling, E. (ed) *Geography into the 1980s*. Sheffield: Geographical Association, pp. 25–27.

3201    Naish, M. (1985) 'Geography 16–19' in Boardman, D. (ed) *New Directions in Geographical Education*. London: Falmer Press, pp. 99–115.

3202    Naish, M. (1986) 'Geography and environmental education: meeting the challenge through the Geography 16–19 project', *Geographical Education*, 5, 2, pp. 26–30.

3203    Naish, M. (1986) 'Decisions, decisions: teaching and assessing environmental thinking', *Geographical Education*, 5, 2, pp. 31–34.

3204    Naish, M. (1988) 'The development of teaching materials for Geography 16–19' in Haubrich, H. (ed) *Perception of People and Places through Media, Volume 2*. Freiburg: IGUCGE/Pädagogische Hochschule Freiburg, pp. 534–549.

3205    Naish, M. (1991) 'Managing change in the geography curriculum: the case of Geography 16–19', *Asian Geographer*, 9, 2, pp. 123–129.

3206    Naish, M. (1996) 'Developing understanding of the dynamics of change in the geography curriculum' in van der Schee, J., Schoenmaker, G., Trimp, H., and van Westrhenen, H. (eds) *Innovation in Geographical Education (Netherlands Geographical Studies, 208)*. Utrecht/Amsterdam: IGUCGE/Centrum voor Educatieve Geografie Vrije Universiteit Amsterdam, pp. 239–248.

3207    Naish, M., Kent, A. and Rawling, E. (1979) 'Answering the challenge: a review of the work of the Schools Council curriculum development project: Geography 16–19' in Graves, N. (ed) *Geographical Education: Curriculum Problems in Certain European Countries with Special Reference to the 16–19 Age Group*. London: IGUCGE/University of London Institute of Education, pp. 188–207.

3208    Naish, M., Kent, A. and Rawling, E. (1980) 'The man-environment approach to geography: a focus for curriculum development at 16–19', *Journal of Geography in Higher Education*, 3, 1, pp. 77–79.

3209    Naish, M. and Rawling, E. (1990) 'Geography 16–19: some implications for higher education', *Journal of Geography in Higher Education*, 14, 1, pp. 55–75.

3210    Naish, M., Rawling, E. and Hart, C. (1987) *Geography 16–19: The Contribution of a Curriculum Development Project to 16–19 Education*. Harlow: Longman.

3211    Pitts, D. F. (1978) *The Geography 16–19 Project: A Case Study of Curriculum Development in its Formative Stages*, unpublished MA dissertation. University of London Institute of Education.

3212    Poole, D. (1993) *An Investigation into the 'Value Added' Contribution made by Geography 16–19 within Bushey Meads School*, unpublished MA dissertation. University of London Institute of Education.

3213    Rawling, E. (1981) 'Geography 16–19: new potential for environmental education', *Review of Environmental Education and Development*, 9, 2, pp. 14–17.

3214    Rawling, E. (1981) 'More shops for Abingdon: a decision-making exercise' in Walford, R. (ed) *Signposts for Geography Teaching*. Harlow: Longman, pp. 66–77.

3215    Rawling, E. (1981) 'New opportunities in environmental education' in Walford, R. (ed) *Signposts for Geography Teaching*. Harlow: Longman, pp. 203–212.

3216    Smith, B. (1985) 'Which way for Queen Victoria Road?', *Teaching Geography*, 10, 3, pp. 120–122.

3217    Stephens, P. (1988) *An Enquiry into the Extent to which the Geography 16–19 Project has Fulfilled its Objectives with Regard to its Enquiry Approach to Learning and its Distinctive Approach to Geographical Education*, unpublished MA dissertation. University of London Institute of Education.

3218    Tisdale, E. G. (1980) *Schools Council 16–19 Geography Project: An Assessment of its Applicability in Theory and Practice in Constructing a One Year Sixth Form CEE Course*, unpublished MA dissertation. University of London Institute of Education.

3219    Warren, J. (1981) *A Survey of One Year Geography Courses for 'New Sixth Formers' in Schools with Special Reference to the CEE*, unpublished MA dissertation. University of London Institute of Education.

3220    Welch, P., Weston, C., Foskett, N. and Hardwick, J. (1983) 'Geography 16–19: an appraisal of the first two years', *Teaching Geography*, 9, 2, pp. 53–57.

## (d) History, geography and social science 8–13

3221    Blyth, A. (1973) 'Discovering time, place and society', *Education 3–13*, 1, 2, pp. 69–74.

3222    Blyth, A. (1973) 'History, geography and social science 8–13: a second-generation project' in Taylor, P. H. and Walton, J. (eds) *The Curriculum: Research, Innovation and Change*. London: Ward Lock Educational, pp. 40–51.

3223  Blyth, A. (1973) 'One development project's awkward thinking about objectives', *Journal of Curriculum Studies*, 6, 2, pp. 99–111.

3224  Blyth, A. (1990) 'Place, time and society in the national primary curriculum', *Social Science Teacher*, 20, 1, pp. 11–12.

3225  Blyth, A., Cooper, K., Derricott, R., Elliott, G. G., Sumner, H. and Waplington, A. (1975) *Place, Time and Society 8–13: An Introduction*. Bristol: Collins/ESL.

3226  Blyth, A., Cooper, K., Derricott, R., Elliott, G. G., Sumner, H. and Waplington, A. (1976) *Place, Time and Society 8–13: Curriculum Planning in History, Geography and Social Science*. Bristol: Collins/ESL.

3227  Cooper, K. (1975) *Evaluation, Assessment and Record Keeping in History, Geography and Social Science*. Bristol: Collins/ESL.

3228  Derricott, R. (1975) *Themes in Outline*. Bristol: Collins/ESL.

3229  Derricott, R. (1984) 'Place, time and society 8–13: retrospect and prospect', *Social Science Teacher*, 13, 3, pp. 811–883.

3230  Derricott, R., Elliott, G. G., Sumner, H. and Waplington, A. (1977) *Themes in Outline*. Bristol: Collins/ESL.

3231  Elliott, G. G. (1974) 'Integrated studies: some problems and possibilities for the geographer' in Williams, M. (1976) *Geography and the Integrated Curriculum: A Reader*. London: Heinemann, pp. 160–165.

3232  Elliott, G. G. (1975) *Putting Place on the Map (Occasional Paper, Schools Council History, Geography and Social Science 8–13 Project)*. Bristol: Collins/ESL.

3233  Elliott, G. G. (1976) *Place, Time and Society 8–13: Teaching for Concepts*. Bristol: Collins/ESL.

3234  Elliott, G. G. and Saunders, M. (1976) 'Project and school working together' in Boden, P. *Developments in Geography Teaching*. London: Open Books, pp. 59–69.

3235  Wenham, P. D. (1976) 'Leeds and Liverpool: the development of a Schools Council project in one education authority', *Teaching History*, 4, pp. 339–346.

## (e) Geography, schools and industry (see also Part C Section 3)

3236  Corney, G. (ed) (1985) *Geography, Schools and Industry*. Sheffield: Geographical Association.

3237  Corney, G. (1986) 'The Geography, Schools and Industry Project (GSIP): teaching for economic understanding', *Teaching Geography*, 11, 3, pp. 106–110.

3238  Corney, G. (1986) *A Survey of Current Practice in Schools in Teaching about Industry (GSIP Project Paper No. 1)*. Oxford: University of Oxford Department of Educational Studies.

3239  Corney, G. (1987) 'Economic processes and policies and teaching geography: the example of the Geographical Association's Geography, Schools and Industry Project' in Bailey, P. and Binns, J. A. (eds) *A Case for Geography*. Sheffield: Geographical Association, pp. 45–47.

3240  Corney, G. (ed) (1987) *Teaching about the Sports Industry (GSIP Project Paper No. 4)*. Oxford: University of Oxford Department of Educational Studies.

3241 Corney, G. (ed) (1987) *A First Year Local Studies Project at Haggerston School (GSIP Project Paper No. 5)*. Oxford: University of Oxford Department of Educational Studies.

3242 Corney, G. (ed) (1987) *Understanding Industry through Active Learning (GSIP Project Paper No. 6)*. Oxford: University of Oxford Department of Educational Studies.

3243 Corney, G. (1988) 'What influences school-centred curriculum development?: the teachers' perspective' in Gerber, R. and Lidstone, J. G. (eds) *Skills in Geographical Education Symposium '88, Volume 1*. Brisbane: IGUCGE/Brisbane College of Advanced Education, pp. 168–182.

3244 Corney, G. (1991) *Geogmart: Teaching Geography for Economic Understanding in the National Curriculum*. London: Banking Information Service.

3245 Corney, G. (1991) 'The Geography, Schools and Industry Project' in Walford, R. (ed) *Viewpoints on Geography Teaching*. Harlow: Longman, pp. 48–51.

3246 Corney, G. (1991) *Teaching Economic Understanding through Geography*. Sheffield: Geographical Association.

3247 Corney, G. (1992) *Teaching Economic Understanding through Geography: The Experience of the Geography, Schools and Industry Project*. Sheffield: Geographical Association.

3248 Crowley, S. and Parker, E. (1991) 'Shopping around', *Child Education*, 68, 10, pp. 50–51.

3249 Hawkes, D. S. (1986) *Geography, Schools and Industry: An Investigation of Employers' Perceptions*, unpublished MA dissertation. University of London Institute of Education.

3250 Kelly, J. (1986) 'GSIP: action and involvement', *Teaching Geography*, 11, 3, pp. 115–117.

3251 Nisbet, J. (1986) *The Role of a Co-ordinator Working with a Group of Project Schools (GSIP Project Paper No. 3)*. Oxford: University of Oxford Department of Educational Studies.

3252 Rawling, E. (1990) 'Geography: working with the community to study a local issue', *Economic Awareness*, 2, 3, pp. 9–14.

## (f) Other projects

3253 Fuchs, F. (1978) 'The teaching unit of the regional RCFP group in Frankfurt in relation to the aims of the RCFP and the new 16–19 curriculum' in Graves, N. (ed) *Geographical Education: Curriculum Problems in Certain European Countries with Special Reference to the 16–19 Age Group*. London: IGUCGE/University of London Institute of Education, pp. 90–103.

3254 Geipel, R. (1978) 'The aims and organisation of the RCFP of the Federal German Republic' in Graves, N. (ed) *Geographical Education: Curriculum Problems in Certain European Countries with Special Reference to the 16–19 Age Group*. London: IGUCGE/University of London Institute of Education, pp. 74–89.

3255 Geipel, R. (1979) 'Curriculum development and society: West German geographers respond to the American High School Geography Project', *Journal of Geography in Higher Education*, 3, 1, pp. 84–85.

3256 Gunn, A. M. (1971) 'Geography in an urban age', *Journal of Curriculum Studies*, 3, 1, pp. 65–76.

3257 Halfyard, C. H. R. (1975) *Geology in the Primary School: A Comparison of Some Aspects of an Experimental Project in Geology with those in the Schools Council Environmental Studies Project and Science 5–13*, unpublished MA dissertation. University of London Institute of Education.

3258 Helburn, N. (1983) 'Reflections on the High School Geography Project' in Huckle, J. (ed) *Geographical Education: Reflection and Action.* Oxford: Oxford University Press, pp. 20–28.

3259 Marsden, W. E. (1979) 'The German geography curriculum project (RCFP)', *Teaching Geography*, 9, 3, pp. 128–30.

3260 Marsden, W. E. (1980) 'The West German geography curriculum project: a comparative view', *Journal of Curriculum Studies*, 12, 1, pp. 13–27.

3261 Natoli, S. J. and Ritter, F. A. (1979) 'The revision of the High School Geography Project', *Journal of Geography in Higher Education*, 3, 2, pp. 102–105.

3262 Nolzen, H. (1979) 'The integration of the natural sciences into geography education: the example of the RCF Project of the Central Association of German Geographers', *European Journal of Science Education*, 1, 2, pp. 147–155.

3263 RBP (1972) 'High School Geography Project: geography in an urban age', *Social Education*, 36, 7, pp. 750–752.

3264 Rolfe, J. (1971) 'The completion of the American High School Geography project', *Geography*, 56, 3, pp. 216–220.

3265 Schools Council (1973) *Teachers' Guide: Starting from Rocks; Starting from Maps; Case Studies (Environmental Studies 5–13 Project).* London: Hart-Davies Educational.

3266 Slater, F. and Renner, J. M. (1974) '"Geography in an urban age": trials of High School Geography Project materials in New Zealand Schools', *Geographical Education*, 2, 2, pp. 195–220.

3267 Stoltman, J. (1976) 'Student perception of teacher style: the effects of the High School Geography Project' in Stoltman, J. (ed) *International Research in Geographical Education.* Kalamazoo, MI: IGUCGE/Western Michigan University, pp. 89–114.

3268 Stoltman, J. (1980) 'Round one for HSGP: a report on acceptance and diffusion', *Professional Geographer*, 32, 2, pp. 209–215.

## (g) General

3269 Bailey, P. (1976) 'Changing the curriculum: after the major projects', *Teaching Geography*, 2, 1, p. 2.

3270 Beddis, R. (1983) 'Geographical education since 1960: a personal view' in Huckle, J. (ed) *Geographical Education: Reflection and Action.* Oxford: Oxford University Press, pp. 10–19.

3271 Boardman, D. (1980) 'Dissemination strategies in four geography curriculum projects', *Journal of Curriculum Studies*, 12, 2, pp. 109–121.

3272 Boardman, D. and McPartland, M. (1993) 'Innovation and change 1970–1982', *Teaching Geography*, 18, 3, pp. 117–120.

3273 Graham, I. M. (1980) *The Dissemination of Schools Council Geography Projects in England and Wales*, unpublished MSc (Ed) dissertation. University of Southampton.

3274    Graves, N. (ed) (1978) *Geographical Education: Curriculum Problems in Certain European Countries with Special Reference to the 16–19 Age Group.* London: IGUCGE/University of London Institute of Education.

3275    Graves, N. (1996) 'Curriculum development in geography: an ongoing process' in Kent, A., Lambert, D., Naish, M. and Slater, F. (eds) *Geography in Education: Viewpoints on Teaching and Learning.* Cambridge: Cambridge University Press, pp. 72–99.

3276    Hall, D. (1976) 'Prescriptions for change: national curriculum projects' in Hall, D. *Geography and the Geography Teacher.* London: George Allen and Unwin, pp. 152–191.

3277    Heng, M. L. C. (1988) *Dissemination Agencies and Strategies in Geography Curriculum Projects in England and Wales*, unpublished MSc (Ed) dissertation. University of Southampton.

3278    MacDonald, B. and Walker, R. (1976) *Changing the Curriculum.* London: Open Books.

3279    Maund, D. and Wyatt, H. (1980) 'Managing curriculum change in an LEA', *Teaching Geography*, 5, 4, pp. 176–178.

3280    Parsons, C. (1977) 'Strategies behind curriculum change', *British Journal of In-Service Education*, 4, 1/2, pp. 45–49.

3281    Rawling, E. (ed) (1980) *Geography into the 1980s: The Proceedings of a Conference 'From 14–19': The Contribution of Three Schools Council Projects to Geography in Secondary Education.* Sheffield: Geographical Association.

3282    Rawling, E. (1991) 'Innovations in the geography curriculum 1970–1990: a personal view' in Walford, R. (ed) *Viewpoints on Geography Teaching.* Harlow: Longman, pp. 33–38.

3283    Steadman, S. D., Parsons, C. and Salter, B. G. (1980) *Impact and Take-up Project: A Second Interim Report to the Schools Council.* London: Schools Council.

3284    Steadman, S. D., Parsons, C., Lillis, K. and Salter, B. G. (1981) *The Schools Council: Its Take-up in Schools and General Impact: A Final Report.* London: The Schools Council.

3285    Walker, M. J. (1976) 'Changing the curriculum', *Teaching Geography*, 1, 4, pp. 163–166.

# 7. Fieldwork and Outdoor Education

## (a) General

3286    Bailey, P. (1974) 'Field work' in Bailey, P. *Teaching Geography.* Newton Abbot: David and Charles, pp. 184–206.

3287    Bailey, P. (1976) 'Is anyone doing local fieldwork?', *Teaching Geography*, 2, 1, pp. 4–6.

3288    Barber, L. (1993) *An Investigation to Establish Whether a Short Period of Outdoor Activities in a Residential Setting would Promote Personal and Social Development in an Individual*, unpublished MA (Ed) dissertation. University of Southampton.

3289    Bentley, J., Gowing, D. and Roberson, B. S. (1974) 'Outdoor education' in Long, M. (ed) *Handbook for Geography Teachers.* London: Methuen, pp. 137–170.

3290    Berry, D. (1993) *The Preferred Classroom: A Study of Outdoor Adventurous Pursuits*, unpublished MA (Ed) dissertation. University of Southampton.

3291   Bilham-Boult, A. (1988) *Using Computers in Fieldwork*. Coventry: Microelectronics Education Support Unit.

3292   Bland, K., Chambers, B., Donert, K. and Thomas, T. (1996) 'Fieldwork' in Bailey, P. and Fox, P. (eds) *Geography Teachers' Handbook*. Sheffield: Geographical Association, pp. 165–175.

3293   Boardman, D. (1974) 'Objectives and constraints on geographical fieldwork', *Journal of Curriculum Studies*, 6, 2, pp. 158–166.

3294   Bolton, T. and Newbury, P. A. (1970) *Geography through Fieldwork*. London: Blandford Press.

3295   Bowles, R. (1997) 'Teaching about the local community: using first hand experience' in Tilbury, D. and Williams, M. (eds) *Teaching and Learning Geography*. London: Routledge, pp. 218–230.

3296   Briggs, K. (1970) *Fieldwork in Urban Geography*. Edinburgh: Oliver and Boyd.

3297   Brunsden, D. (1987) 'The science of the unknown', *Geography*, 72, 2, pp. 193–208.

3298   Bull, G. B. G. (1972) *A Rural Studies Companion*. London: Hulton.

3299   Cooper, G. (1991) 'The role of outdoor and field study centres in educating for the environment', *Journal of Adventure Education and Outdoor Leadership*, 8, 2, pp. 78–83.

3300   Cox, D. J. (1977) *The Place of Fieldwork in Geographical Education: An Examination of Current Problems and their Implications*, unpublished MSc (Ed) dissertation. University of Southampton.

3301   Department of Education and Science (1989) *Safety in Outdoor Education*. London: HMSO.

3302   Department of Education and Science (1992) *A Survey of Geography Fieldwork in Degree Courses*. Stanmore: DES.

3303   Driscoll, K. J. (1971) *Town Study: A Sample Urban Geography*. London: George Philip and Son.

3304   Everson, J. (1973) 'Fieldwork in school geography' in Walford, R. (ed) *New Directions in Geography Teaching*. London: Longman, pp. 107–114.

3305   Everson, J. (1973) 'Some aspects of teaching geography through fieldwork' in Bale, J., Graves, N. and Walford, R. (eds) *Perspectives on Geographical Education*. Edinburgh: Oliver and Boyd, pp. 197–210.

3306   Ewert, A. (1983) 'The perceived importance of outdoor adventure activities', *Recreational Review*, 10, 2, pp. 28–34.

3307   Falk, J. H. (1983) 'Field trips: a look at environmental effects on learning', *Journal of Biological Education*, 17, 2, pp. 137–142.

3308   Falk, J. H. and Balling, J. D. (1982) 'The field trip milieu: learning and behaviour as functions of contextual events', *Journal of Educational Research*, 76, 1, pp. 22–28.

3309   Fitzgerald, B. P. (1973) 'A model hypothetical approach to urban fieldwork' in Walford, R. (ed) *New Directions in Geography Teaching*. London: Longman, pp. 58–66.

3310   Ford, P. (1981) *Principles and Practices of Outdoor Environmental Education*. New York: John Wiley.

3311   Foskett, N. (1997) 'Teaching and learning through fieldwork' in Tilbury, D. and Williams, M. (eds) *Teaching and Learning Geography*. London: Routledge, pp. 189–201.

3312   Frew, J. (1986) *Geography Fieldwork*. London: Macmillan.

3313   Gass, M. and **Priest, S.** (1993) 'Using metaphors and isomorphs to transfer learning in adventure education', *Journal of Adventure and Outdoor Education Leadership*, 10, 4, pp. 18–23.

3314   **Geographical Association** (1984) 'The enduring purpose of fieldwork', *Teaching Geography*, 9, 5, pp. 209–211.

3315   **Geographical Association** (1990) *Geography Outside the Classroom*. Sheffield: Geographical Association.

3316   **Greasley, B.** (1984) *Project Fieldwork*. London: Bell and Hyman.

3317   **Haddon, J.** (1971) *Local Geography in Towns*. London: George Philip and Son.

3318   **Hawkins, G.** (1987) 'From awareness to participation: new directions in the outdoor experience', *Geography*, 72, 2, pp. 217–221.

3319   **Her Majesty's Inspectorate** (1985) *Learning out of doors: An HMI Survey*. London: HMSO.

3320   **Humphreys, T. J.** (1987) 'The evaluation of fieldwork: concept elucidation by transects', *Journal of Biological Education*, 21, 1, pp. 28–34.

3321   **Job, D.** (1996) 'Geography and environmental education: an exploration of perspectives and strategies' in Kent, A., Lambert, D., Naish, M., Slater, F. (eds) *Geography in Education: Viewpoints on Teaching and Learning*. Cambridge: Cambridge University Press, pp. 22–49.

3322   **Keighley, P. W. S.** (1997) 'The impact of experiences out-of-doors on personal development and environmental attitudes', *Horizons*, 2, pp. 27–28.

3323   **Kent, A.** (1996) 'A strategy for geography fieldwork' in van der Schee, J., Schoenmaker, G., Trimp, H., and van Westrhenen, H. (eds) *Innovation in Geographical Education (Netherlands Geographical Studies, 208)*. Utrecht/Amsterdam: IGUCGE/Centrum voor Educatieve Geografie Vrije Universiteit Amsterdam, pp. 167–177.

3324   **Kern, E. L.** and **Carpenter, J. R.** (1986) 'The effect of field activities on student learning', *Journal of Geological Education*, 34, pp. 180–183.

3325   **Lawler, C. D.** (1986) *CAL and Physical-based Fieldwork in Geography*, unpublished MA dissertation. University of London Institute of Education.

3326   **Laws, K.** (1984) 'Learning geography through fieldwork' in Fien, J., Gerber, R. and Wilson, P. (eds) *The Geography Teacher's Guide to the Classroom*. Melbourne: Macmillan, pp. 134–145.

3327   **Lenon, B.** and **Cleves, P.** (1984) *Techniques and Fieldwork in Geography*. London: University Tutorial Press.

3328   **Lidstone, J.** (1988) 'Teaching and learning geography through fieldwork' in Gerber, R. and Lidstone, J. (eds) *Developing Skills in Geographical Education*. Brisbane: IGUCGE/Jacaranda Press, pp. 53–59.

3329   **Lucas, R.** (1993) 'IT and fieldwork', *Teaching Geography*, 18, 1, pp. 38–39.

3330   **McElroy, B.** (1984) 'Models and reality: integrating practical work and fieldwork in geography' in Fien, J., Gerber, R. and Wilson, P. (eds) *The Geography Teacher's Guide to the Classroom*. Melbourne: Macmillan, pp. 123–133.

3331   **Mackenzie, A. A.** and **White, R. T.** (1982) 'Fieldwork in geography and long-term memory structures', *American Education Research Journal*, 19, 4, pp. 623–632.

3332    McKenzie, G. D., Utgard, R. O. and Lisowski, M. (1986) 'The importance of field trips', *Journal of College Science Teaching*, 16, pp. 17–20.

3333    McPartland, M. and Harvey, P. (1987) 'A question of fieldwork', *Teaching Geography*, 12, 4, pp. 162–164.

3334    Mansell, J. E. (1976) *Fieldwork in English Schools: A Critical Appraisal of its Development 1900–1975*, unpublished MA dissertation. University of London Institute of Education.

3335    Martinez, M. and Paterson, A. (1988) 'Going back to "look and see"', *Teaching Geography*, 13, 3, pp. 130–131.

3336    May, S. and Cook, J. (1993) *An Enquiry Approach (Fieldwork in Action 2)*. Sheffield: Geographical Association.

3337    May, S., Richardson, P. and Banks, V. (1993) *Planning Fieldwork (Fieldwork in Action)*. Sheffield: Geographical Association.

3338    Nichols, G. (1994) 'Major issues in the evaluation of the impact of outdoor-based experiences', *Journal of Adventure Education and Outdoor Leadership*, 11, 1, pp. 11–14.

3339    Noble, P. (1987) 'Why residential? – because it's there', *Journal of Adventure Education and Outdoor Leadership*, 4, 3, pp. 24–26.

3340    Orion, N. and Hofstein, A. (1994) 'Factors that influence learning during a scientific field trip in a natural environment', *Journal of Research in Science Teaching*, 31, 10, pp. 1097–1119.

3341    Orion, N., Hofstein, A., Tamir, P. and Giddings, G. J. (1997) 'Development and validation of an instrument for assessing the learning environment of outdoor science activities', *Science Education*, 81, 2, pp. 161–171.

3342    Owen-Jones, G. (1987) *Values Education through Fieldwork*, unpublished MA dissertation. University of London Institute of Education.

3343    Pearce, T. (1987) 'Teaching and learning through direct experience' in Bailey, P. and Binns, T. *A Case for Geography*. Sheffield: Geographical Association, pp. 34–37.

3344    Pocock, D. C. D. (1982) 'Geographical fieldwork: an experiential perspective', *Geography*, 68, 4, pp. 319–325.

3345    Robinson, R. (1991) 'Illuminative evaluation for an outdoor education centre', *Journal of Adventure Education and Outdoor Leadership*, 7, 4, pp. 10–12.

3346    Sadler, I. (1997) 'The role of exchanges in geography fieldwork', *Teaching Geography*, 22, 1, pp. 30–32.

3347    Sharma, N. P. (1989) *Teaching and Learning School Geography through Fieldwork in Britain: The Implications for Geographical Education in Nepal*, unpublished MSc (Ed) dissertation. University of Southampton.

3348    Smith, G. (1997) *An Examination of the Changes to Fieldwork between 1974 and 1996*, unpublished MA (Ed) dissertation. University of Southampton.

3349    Smith, P. L. (1992) *Geography Fieldwork Planning in a Period of Change 1985–1990*, unpublished PhD thesis. University of London Institute of Education.

3350    Smith, P. R. (1987) 'Outdoor education and its educational objectives', *Geography*, 72, 2, pp. 209–216.

3351    Steer, D. and Jenness, R. (1988) 'Issue-based geography and local planning', *Teaching Geography*, 13, 4, pp. 157–161.

3352    Taylor, J. (1980) *Fieldwork Techniques in Schools (Bibliographic Notes No. 7)*. Sheffield: Geographical Association.

3353    Thomas, T. and May, S. (1994) *Managing Out-of-Classroom Activities (Fieldwork in Action 3)*. Sheffield: Geographical Association.

3354    Ward, H. (1987) 'Fieldwork at what cost?', *Teaching Geography*, 12, 2, p. 79.

3355    Wheeler, K. S. (1970) *Geography in the Field*. London: Blond Educational.

3356    Wurdinger, S. (1994) 'Examining the learning process used in adventure education', *Journal of Adventure Education and Outdoor Leadership*, 11, 3, pp. 25–27.

## (b) Primary level

3357    Bale, J. (1987) 'Using the locality' in Bale, J. *Geography in the Primary School*. London: Routledge and Kegan Paul, pp. 57–89.

3358    Bloomfield, P. (1997) '"Europe in context": fieldwork or holiday?', *Primary Geographer*, 29, pp. 24–25.

3359    Bowden, D. (1994) 'Fieldwork and IT: choosing the right tool for the task', *Primary Geographer*, 17, pp. 22–23.

3360    Bowles, R. (1995) 'Fieldwork' in Bowles, R. (ed) *Practical Guides: Geography*. Leamington Spa: Scholastic Publications, pp. 21–52.

3361    Catling, S. (1994) 'Planning geographical activities involving fieldwork', *Primary Geographer*, 18, pp. 11–12.

3362    Chapman, J. (1997) 'A little local differentiation', *Primary Geographer*, 28, pp. 31–33.

3363    Clare, R. (1988) 'Fieldwork in urban and rural areas' in Mills, D. (ed) *Geographical Work in Primary and Middle Schools*. Sheffield: Geographical Association, pp. 108–134.

3364    Cook, J. and May, S. (1993) 'An enquiry approach to local fieldwork', *Primary Geographer*, 15, pp. 12–13.

3365    Firth, F. M. (1972) *Field Studies in the Primary School*, unpublished MA dissertation. University of London Institute of Education.

3366    Foley, M. and Janikoun, J. (1996) 'Geographical fieldwork' in Foley, M. and Janikoun, J. *The Really Practical Guide to Primary Geography*. London: Stanley Thornes, pp. 100–117.

3367    Gwilliam, P. (1984) 'Experiential learning: a role for geography in the primary school', *Teaching Geography*, 10, 1, pp. 16–18.

3368    Lewis, E. (1994) 'Photo-fit geography: using colour photographs to enhance field enquiry', *Primary Geographer*, 18, pp. 4–5.

3369    May, S. (ed) (1996) *Primary Fieldwork Projects (Fieldwork in Action 4)*. Sheffield: Geographical Association.

3370    Morron, M. (1996) 'Land use – UK: an exciting curriculum opportunity', *Primary Geographer*, 24, pp. 10–12.

3371    Pearce, T. (1995) 'Local geography from first-hand experience' in De Villiers, M. (ed) *Developments in Primary Geography: Theory and Practice*. Sheffield: Geographical Association, pp. 1–10.

3372   Pickford, T. (1993) 'Exploring a contrasting UK locality through fieldwork', *Primary Geographer*, 14, pp. 16–20.

3373   Platten, L. (1992) 'Resourcing local studies', *Primary Geographer*, 11, pp. 12–13.

3374   Rowbotham, D. (1982) 'Can we do fieldwork in primary school?', *Teaching Geography*, 8, 2, pp. 75–77.

3375   Rowbotham, D. (1988) 'School journeys: out of classroom residential experiences' in Mills, D. (ed) *Geographical Work in Primary and Middle Schools*. Sheffield: Geographical Association, pp. 135–141.

3376   Scoffham, S. (1980) *Using the School's Surroundings*. London: Ward Lock.

3377   Scoffham, S. (1995) 'Local investigations', *Primary Geographer*, 21, pp. 42–43.

3378   Scoffham, S. (1996) 'Street detectives', *Primary Geographer*, 26, pp. 22–23.

3379   Thomas, T. (1996) 'Fieldwork: regulations and implications', *Primary Geographer*, 27, pp. 20–21.

3380   Walford, R. (1997) 'The magnificent seven: land-use survey and key skills', *Primary Geographer*, 30, pp. 4–5.

3381   Wass, S. (1990) *Explorations: A Guide to Field Study in the Primary School*. London: Hodder and Stoughton.

## (c) Secondary and tertiary levels

3382   Adams, K. and Croft, R. (1985) 'Fieldwork in regional disparity', *Teaching Geography*, 10, 2, pp. 78–80.

3383   Arnold, R. and Foskett, N. (1979) 'Physical geography in an urban environment: two examples', *Teaching Geography*, 5, 2, pp. 60–63.

3384   Bamber, C. and Ranger, G. (1990) 'Values enquiry in practice: investigating a local controversial issue', *Teaching Geography*, 15, 2, pp. 60–62.

3385   Barratt, R., Burgess, H. and Cass, D. (1997) 'An enquiry approach to geography fieldwork', *Teaching Geography*, 22, 2, pp. 77–81.

3386   Chell, K. and Hare, R. T. (1990) 'The great geographical egg race', *Teaching Geography*, 15, 1, pp. 22–26.

3387   Cooper, C. and Latham, J. (1988) 'Visits out of school', *Teaching Geography*, 13, 2, pp. 72–73.

3388   Farms, J. and Smith, F. (1984) 'Changing approaches to A-level fieldwork', *Teaching Geography*, 10, 1, pp. 25–26.

3389   Fenoughty, T. (1992) 'Organising an overseas fieldwork expedition', *Teaching Geography*, 17, 3, pp. 132–134.

3390   George, B. (1992) 'A school exchange: fieldwork in an Indian village', *Teaching Geography*, 17, 2, pp. 61–65.

3391   Hamill, A. (1985) *A Survey of the Status and Role of Geographical Fieldwork in the Curriculum of Secondary Schools in a Selected Area*, unpublished MA dissertation. University of London Institute of Education.

3392   Hart, C. (1983) *Fieldwork the 16–19 Way (Geography 16–19 Occasional Paper No. 4)*. London: University of London Institute of Education.

3393    Hart, C. and Thomas, T. (1986) 'Framework fieldwork' in Boardman, D. (ed) *Handbook for Geography Teachers*. Sheffield: Geographical Association, pp. 205–218.

3394    Harvey, P. K. (1991) *The Role and Value of A-level Geography Fieldwork: A Case Study*, unpublished PhD thesis. University of Durham.

3395    Henry, E. A. (1983) *A Survey of the Factors which Influence and Inhibit the Amount of Fieldwork Undertaken by Secondary Schools in a Selected Region*, unpublished MA dissertation. University of London Institute of Education.

3396    Jenkins, A. (1997) *Fieldwork with More Students*. Oxford: Oxford Centre for Staff Development.

3397    Lancastle, T. (1984) *Fieldwork in the English Secondary School: An Appraisal of its Value to the Geography Curriculum with Particular Reference to Secondary Schools within the London Borough of Bromley*, unpublished MA dissertation. University of London Institute of Education.

3398    McPartland, M. and Harvey, P. (1987) 'A question of fieldwork', *Teaching Geography*, 12, 4, pp. 162–165.

3399    Raw, M. (1989) 'Organising an A-level residential fieldcourse' in Wiegand, P. (ed) *Managing the Geography Department*. Sheffield: Geographical Association, pp. 160–168.

3400    Richardson, D. (1987) 'Field study exchanges abroad', *Teaching Geography*, 12, 5, pp. 225–227.

3401    Rouncefield, J. A. (1977) *An Appraisal of the Position of Fieldwork in the A-level Syllabus and the Way in which it is Examined*, unpublished MA dissertation. University of London Institute of Education.

3402    Rudd, G. (1983) *Curriculum Approaches in Residential Field Centres for Environmental Studies with 11–14 Year Olds*, unpublished MA dissertation. University of London Institute of Education.

3403    Sadler, I. (1997) 'The role of exchanges in geography fieldwork', *Teaching Geography*, 22, 1, pp. 30–31.

3404    St John, P. and Richardson, D. (1989) *Methods of Presenting Fieldwork Data*. Sheffield: Geographical Association.

3405    St John, P. and Richardson, D. (1990) *Methods of Statistical Analysis of Fieldwork Data*. Sheffield: Geographical Association.

3406    Schools Council Geography Committee (1980) *Outdoor Education in Secondary Schools*. London: Schools Council.

3407    Thomas, G. and Grimwade, K. (1996) 'Geography in the secondary school: a survey', *Teaching Geography*, 21, 1, pp. 37–39.

3408    Walford, R. (1995) 'Fieldwork on parade', *Teaching Geography*, 20, 3, pp. 112–117.

3409    Wilby, P. (1984) 'Evaluating the role of fieldwork' in Orrell, K. and Wiegand, P. (eds) *Evaluation and Assessment in Geography*. Sheffield: Geographical Association, pp. 12–13.

# (d) Orienteering and geographical education

3410    Barrell, G. V. and Cooper, P. J. (1986) 'Cognitive processes in orienteering: the interpretation of contours and responses to the map as a whole', *Scientific Journal of Orienteering*, 2, 1, pp. 25–46.

3411    Blades, M. and Spencer, C. (1989) 'Children's wayfinding and map using abilities', *Scientific Journal of Orienteering*, 5, 1, pp. 48–60.

3412    Cornell, E. H. and Hay, D. H. (1984) 'Children's acquisition of a route via different media', *Environment and Behaviour*, 16, pp. 627–641.

3413    Lawes, B. (1995) 'Orienteering for beginners!', *Teaching Geography*, 20, 3, pp. 122–124.

3414    McNeill, C., Martland, J. R. and Palmer, P. (1992) *Orienteering in the National Curriculum*. Doune: Harveys.

3415    Martland, J. R. (1983) 'An empirical study of the application of psychological principles in the teaching of orienteering', *Journal of Education for Teaching*, 9, 1, pp. 77–96.

3416    Martland, J. R. (1986) *Monitoring Technical Skills and Strategies in Young Orienteers*. London: British Orienteering Federation.

3417    Martland, J. R. (1988) 'Which direction first?: a pilot study of the teaching and learning of thumb compass and mapguide compasses with children aged ten years', *Scientific Journal of Orienteering*, 4, 2, pp. 78–96.

3418    Martland, J. R. (1995) 'Developing navigational skills', *Coaching News*, 45, pp. 6–7.

3419    Martland, J. R. and Palmer, P. (1989) *The Coaching Collection: A Resource Book for Teachers and Coaches in Orienteering*. London: British Orienteering Federation.

3420    Martland, J. R., Stewart, R. R. and Walsh, S. E. (1991) 'How do we teach our young orienteers to use the compass more effectively?', *Scientific Journal of Orienteering*, 7, 2, pp. 104–114.

3421    Martland, J. R. and Walsh, S. E. (1991) 'Performance improvement in orienteering', *Compass Sport/The Orienteer*, 12, 7, pp. 16–18.

3422    Martland, J. R. and Walsh, S. E. (1993) *Developing Navigational Skills: Using the Silva Model 7DNS Compass*. Leeds/London: Coachwise Ltd/National Coaching Foundation/Sports Council.

3423    Spencer, C. and Blades, M. (1985) 'How children navigate', *Journal of Navigation*, 38, pp. 445–453.

3424    Spencer, C. and Darvizeh, Z. (1984) 'The importance of landmarks in the child's wayfinding through the large-scale environment', *Environmental Education and Information*, 3, 2, pp. 97–105.

3425    Stewart, R. R., Martland, J. R. and Walsh, S. E. (1991) 'Personal and social dimensions of developing orienteering and self-navigation in primary schools: a turn for the better?', *Social Science Teacher*, 20, 3, pp. 95–96.

3426    Walsh, S. E. and Martland, J. R. (1993) 'The orientation and navigational skills of young children: an application of two intervention strategies', *Journal of Navigation*, 46, 1, pp. 63–68.

3427    Walsh, S. E. and Martland, J. R. (1995) 'Maintaining orientation within route following tasks', *Cartographica*, 32, 2, pp. 30–36.

3428 Walsh, S. E. and Martland, J. R. (1996) 'Orientation and the young orienteer', *Journal of Navigation*, 49, 1, pp. 72–76.

3429 Walsh, S. E., Martland, J. R. and Stewart, R. R. (1991) 'The map orientation skills of young children: a preliminary investigation', *Scientific Journal of Orienteering*, 7, 2, pp. 90–103.

# 8. Teaching Resources at Primary Level

## (a) Textbooks

3430 Catling, S. (1997) 'Values in English primary geography series: 1990–1996' in Naish, M. (ed) *Values in Geography Education: Proceedings*. London: IGUCGE/University of London Institute of Education, pp. 117–122.

3431 Grubb, A. (1984) *A Readability Study of Selected Middle School Textbooks*, unpublished MA dissertation. University of London Institute of Education.

3432 Hawkins, M. L. (1977) 'Map and globe skills in elementary school textbooks', *Journal of Geography*, 76, 7, pp. 261–265.

3433 Howlett, C. (1986) *An Investigation into the Conceptual Basis of Lower School Geography Texts*, unpublished MA dissertation. University of London Institute of Education.

3434 Shaw, F. L. (1982) *Recent Primary Geography Series Evaluated against Published Guidelines and Recommendations*, unpublished MA dissertation. University of London Institute of Education.

3435 Turner, A. and Catling, S. (1982) 'A new consensus in primary geography?', *Teaching Geography*, 8, 1, pp. 24–26.

## (b) Video and audio-visual resources

3436 Bayliss, D. G. and Renwick, M. (1973) 'Photograph study in a junior school' in Bale, J., Graves, N. and Walford, R. (eds) *Perspectives on Geographical Education*. Edinburgh: Oliver and Boyd, pp. 119–130.

3437 Chambers, B., Nelder, G., Paterson, K. and Wareing, H. (1989) 'Viewing the earth from space', *Primary Geographer*, 1, pp. 7–10.

3438 Dillon, L. and Mackintosh, M. (1996) 'From the rooftops', *Primary Geographer*, 26, pp. 14–15.

3439 Glendinning, H. and Pearson, M. (1983) 'Using air photographs with young children', *Teaching Geography*, 9, 1, pp. 3–4.

3440 Harris, G. (1988) 'Pictures and slides' in Mills, D. (ed) *Geographical Work in Primary and Middle Schools*. Sheffield: Geographical Association, pp. 147–149.

3441 Lewis, E. (1994) 'Photo-fit geography: using colour photographs to enhance field enquiry', *Primary Geographer*, 18, pp. 4–6.

3442 Scoffham, S. and Jewson, T. (1995) 'Aerial photographs and satellite images', *Primary Geographer*, 20, pp. 18–19.

3443    Till, E. (1997) 'What's in a picture?', *Primary Geographer*, 28, pp. 18–19.

3444    Walker, A. (1988) 'Radio and television' in Mills, D. (ed) *Geographical Work in Primary and Middle Schools*. Sheffield: Geographical Association, pp. 150–151.

3445    Walker, G. (1994) 'Using vertical aerial photographs in Key Stage 2', *Primary Geographer*, 18, pp. 8–10.

3446    Wetton, S. (1994) 'Using aerial photographs to study a distant locality', *Primary Geographer*, 17, pp. 4–6.

## (c) Maps and atlases (see also Sub-section 1a on graphicacy)

3447    Anderson, J. (1985) 'Teaching map skills: an inductive approach' (parts 1–4), *Journal of Geography*, 84, 1, pp. 25–32; 84, 2, pp. 72–78; 84, 3, pp. 117–122; 84, 4, pp. 169–176.

3448    Balchin, W. (1996) 'Graphicacy and the primary geographer', *Primary Geographer*, 24, pp. 4–6.

3449    Bentley, J., Charlton, W. A., Goodenough, R. A., Price, R. R. and Rawcliffe, J. M. (1975) *The Use of Maps in School*. Oxford: Blackwell.

3450    Bloomfield, P. (1992) 'The map: top juniors', *Education 3–13*, 20, 2, pp. 24–29.

3451    Boardman, D. (1983) *On the Map: An Illustrated Exploration into the World of Maps*. London: British Broadcasting Corporation.

3452    Bowles, R. (1993) 'Maps and map-making' in Bowles, R. *Practical Guides: Geography*. Leamington Spa: Scholastic Publications, pp. 53–76.

3453    Catling, S. (1978) 'Cognitive mapping exercises as primary geographical experience', *Teaching Geography*, 3, 3, pp. 120–123.

3454    Catling, S. (1981) *Mapwork in Primary and Middle Schools (Bibliographic Notes No. 9)*. Sheffield: Geographical Association.

3455    Catling, S. (1984) *Resources for Mapwork in Primary and Middle Schools (Bibliographic Notes No. 27)*. Sheffield: Geographical Association.

3456    Catling, S. (1985) 'Mapwork' in Corney, G. and Rawling, E. (eds) *Teaching Slow Learners through Geography*. Sheffield: Geographical Association, pp. 54–66.

3457    Catling, S. (1988) 'Building less able children's map skills' in Dilkes, J. L. and Nicholls, A. C. (eds) *Low Attainers and the Teaching of Geography*. Sheffield/Stafford: Geographical Association/National Association for Remedial Education, pp. 25–28.

3458    Catling, S. (1988) 'Using maps and aerial photographs' in Mills, D. (ed) *Geographical Work in Primary and Middle Schools*. Sheffield: Geographical Association, pp. 168–188.

3459    Catling, S. (1990) 'Early mapwork: mapwork with five to eight year olds' in De Villiers, M. (ed) *Primary Geography Matters*. Sheffield: Geographical Association, pp. 52–58.

3460    Catling, S. (1990) 'Resourcing mapwork', *Primary Geographer*, 5, p. 14.

3461    Catling, S. (1995) 'Mapping the environment with children' in De Villiers, M. (ed) *Developments in Primary Geography: Theory and Practice*. Sheffield: Geographical Association, pp. 11–17.

3462    Catling, S. (1995) 'Going for the globe: introducing the world to 4–7 year olds', *Primary Geographer*, 23, pp. 4–6.

3463  Catling, S. (1996) 'Beginning to map the world', *Primary Geographer*, 24, pp. 13–15.

3464  David, D. W. (1990) 'Big maps – little people', *Journal of Geography*, 89, 2, pp. 58–62.

3465  Foley, M. and **Janikoun, J.** (1996) 'Mapwork' in Foley, M. and Janikoun, J. *The Really Practical Guide to Primary Geography*. London: Stanley Thornes, pp. 75–99.

3466  Harris, M. (1972) *Starting from Maps*. London: Rupert Hart-Davis.

3467  Harrison, P. and **Harrison, S.** (1988) *Discover Maps with Ordnance Survey*. London/Southampton: Holmes McDougall/Ordnance Survey.

3468  Harrison, P. and **Harrison, S.** (1988) *Master Maps with Ordnance Survey*. London/Southampton: Holmes McDougall/Ordnance Survey.

3469  Harwood, D. (1988) 'Introducing map-work to ESN(M) children' in Dilkes, J. L. and Nicholls, A. C. (eds) *Low Attainers and the Teaching of Geography*. Sheffield/Stafford: Geographical Association/National Association for Remedial Education, pp. 29–39.

3470  Keates, J. S. (1982) *Understanding Maps*. London: Longman.

3471  Mackle, A. (1980) *The Use of the Atlas in the Primary School*, unpublished MA dissertation. University of London Institute of Education.

3472  Sandford, H. A. (1974) 'Atlases' in Long, M. (ed) *Handbook for Geography Teachers*. London: Methuen, pp. 184–187.

3473  Sandford, H. A. (1988) 'Atlases and globes' in Mills, D. (ed) *Geographical Work in Primary and Middle Schools*. Sheffield: Geographical Association, pp. 189–197.

3474  Sandford, H. A. (1988) 'Guide to the selection of an atlas for young children' in Mills, D. (ed) *Geographical Work in Primary and Middle Schools*. Sheffield: Geographical Association, pp. 298–303.

3475  Satterly, D. J. (1973) 'Skills and concepts involved in map drawing and map interpretation' in Bale, J., Graves, N. and Walford, R. *Perspectives on Geographical Education*. Edinburgh: Oliver and Boyd, pp. 162–169.

3476  Schools Council (1979) *Understanding Maps: A Guide to Initial Learning*. London: Schools Council.

3477  Seabourne, M. (1995) 'Steps to mapwork: large-scale practical mapwork at KS1 and 2', *Primary Geographer*, 23, pp. 12–13.

3478  Taylor, S. (1996) 'Progression and gender differences in mapwork', *Primary Geographer*, 24, pp. 24–25.

3479  Wiegand, P. (1993) 'Geographical skills' in Wiegand, P. *Children and Primary Geography*. London: Cassell, pp. 15–64.

3480  Wiegand, P. and **Dickinson, J.** (1996) 'Draw me a map of the British Isles!', *Primary Geographer*, 25, pp. 20–21.

3481  Wright, D. (1994) 'Understanding the world map', *Child Education*, 71, 5, pp. 37–38.

## (d) Games and simulations

3482  Bloomfield, P. (1996) 'Graphicacy through games', *Primary Geographer*, 24, pp. 26–27.

3483  Bloomfield, P. (1996) 'River games', *Primary Geographer*, 25, pp. 17–19.

3484  Bloomfield, P. (1996) 'Settlement games', *Primary Geographer*, 26, pp. 31–33.

3485    Bloomfield, P. (1996) 'Environmental *jeux sans frontières*', *Primary Geographer*, 27, pp. 16–17.

3486    Bloomfield, P. (1997) 'Differentiation: a game plan', *Primary Geographer*, 28, pp. 16–17.

3487    Catling, S. (1996) *Placing Places*. Sheffield: Geographical Association.

3488    Cole, J. P. (1973) 'Fresh primary themes' in Bale, J., Graves, N. and Walford, R. (eds) *Perspectives on Geographical Education*. Edinburgh: Oliver and Boyd, pp. 131–136.

3489    Kemp, R. (1985) 'Role play and simulation' in Corney, G. and Rawling, E. (eds) *Teaching Slow Learners through Geography*. Sheffield: Geographical Association, pp. 67–71.

3490    Walford, R. (1988) 'Games and simulations' in Mills, D. (ed) *Geographical Work in Primary and Middle Schools*. Sheffield; Geographical Association, pp. 142–146.

## (e) Information technology

3491    Bowden, D. (1992) 'Geography software: the state of the game', *Primary Geographer*, 11, pp. 18–19.

3492    Bowles, R. (1993) 'Information technology' in Bowles, R. (1993) *Practical Guides: Geography*. Leamington Spa: Scholastic Publications, pp. 95–110.

3493    Chambers, B. and Donert, K. (1996) 'The role of information technology in geography at Key Stage 2' in Chambers, B. and Donert, K. *Teaching Geography at Key Stage 2*. Cambridge: Chris Kington Publishing, pp. 44–56.

3494    Curson, C. (1991) 'Geography and information technology in a reception class', *Primary Geographer*, 8, pp. 10–11.

3495    Kent, A. and Phillips, A. (1994) 'Geography through information technology: supporting geographical enquiry' in Marsden, W. E. and Hughes, J. (eds) *Primary School Geography*. London: David Fulton, pp. 93–106.

3496    Martin, F. (1995) 'The role of information technology in early years geography' in Martin, F. *Teaching Early Years Geography*. Cambridge: Chris Kington Publishing, pp. 39–49.

3497    Rawling, E. (1995) 'Geography and information technology: a minimum entitlement for pupils aged 5–16' in De Villiers, M. (ed) *Developments in Primary Geography: Theory and Practice*. Sheffield: Geographical Association, pp. 23–28.

3498    Russell, K. (1995) 'IT and geography in the revised National Curriculum', *Primary Geographer*, 21, pp. 39–41.

3499    Tapsfield, A. (1988) 'The use of microcomputers' in Mills, D. (ed) *Geographical Work in Primary and Middle Schools*. Sheffield: Geographical Association, pp. 162–166.

## (f) Literature

3500    Catling, S. (1993) 'There's a tale in place' in De Villiers, M. (ed) *Primary Geography Matters: Children's Worlds*. Sheffield: Geographical Association, pp. 1–9.

3501    Gadsden, A. (1991) *Geography and History through Stories*. Chester/Sheffield: Cheshire County Council/Geographical Association.

3502    Krause, J. (1994) '"Read all about it": using children's literature in support of primary geography' in Marsden, W. E. and Hughes, J. *Primary School Geography*. London: David Fulton, pp. 136–155.

3503    Lewis, E. and Watts, S. (1995) 'Story and language for primary geography' in De Villiers, M. (ed) *Developments in Primary Geography: Theory and Practice*. Sheffield: Geographical Association, pp. 51–53.

3504    Nicholson, H. N. (1992) 'Stories are everywhere: geographical understanding and children's fiction at Key Stages 1 and 2', *Reading*, 26, 1, pp. 18–20.

3505    Nicholson, H. N. (1996) *Place in Story Time: Geography through Stories at Key Stages 1 and 2*. Sheffield: Geographical Association.

3506    Scoffham, S. (1993) 'Stories, rhymes and geographical language' in De Villiers, M. (ed) *Primary Geography Matters: Children's Worlds*. Sheffield: Geographical Association, pp. 10–18.

3507    Scoffham, S. and Jewson, T. (1992) 'Geography through nursery rhymes', *Primary Geographer*, 11, p. 2.

3508    Scoffham, S. and Jewson, T. (1993) 'Geography through fairy tales', *Primary Geographer*, 12, p. 2.

3509    Wright, D. (1991) 'Geographical concepts in "Thomas the Tank Engine" stories', *Primary Geographer*, 6, pp. 4–5.

## (g) School links

3510    Beddis, R. and Mares, C. (1988) *School Links International: A New Approach to Primary School Linking around the World*. Bristol: Avon County Council Education Department/Tidy Britain Schools Research Project.

3511    Bell, G. H. (1991) *Developing a European Dimension in Primary Schools*. London: David Fulton.

3512    Bull, R. (1994) 'The Central Bureau: opportunities for international links, projects and exchanges', *Primary Geographer*, 19, pp. 15–16.

3513    Camino, E. (1996) '"I have a friend on the other side of the earth": twinning classes from different cultures to introduce environmental and development education', *Environmental Education Research*, 2, 3, pp. 331–344.

3514    Council of Europe (1989) *Using the New Technologies to Create Links between Schools Throughout the World*. Strasbourg: Council of Europe.

3515    Marsden, W. E. (1988) 'Geography in the primary curriculum: using the world's schools to promote empathy' in Gerber, R. and Lidstone, J. (eds) *Developing Skills in Geographical Education*. Brisbane: IGUCGE/Jacaranda Press.

3516    Riches, M. (1997) 'Building links: the playground equipment project', *Primary Geographer*, 29, pp. 18–19.

3517    Salahie, R. (1987) 'Kenya–UK school twins', *Green Teacher*, 4, pp. 20–21.

3518    Warren, M., Cambier, A. and Ranger, G. (1997) 'Geography meets French in the classroom: a contrasting locality study at Key Stage 2', *Primary Geographer*, 29, pp. 20–21.

## (h) Managing resources

3519    Blyth, A. and **Krause, J.** (1995) 'Choosing and using resources: the teaching and learning of primary geography' in Blyth, A. and Krause, J. *Primary Geography: A Developmental Approach*. London: Hodder and Stoughton, pp. 107–120.

3520    **Bowles, R.** (1993) 'Resources for Key Stages 1, 2 and 3' in Smeaton, M. (ed) *Geography National Curriculum Key Stages 1, 2 and 3 Support Material*. Sheffield: Geographical Association.

3521    **Foley, M. and Janikoun, J.** (1996) 'Resources' in Foley, M. and Janikoun, J. *The Really Practical Guide to Primary Geography*. London: Stanley Thornes, pp. 169–193.

3522    **Hughes, J.** (1992) 'The cost of resourcing the primary curriculum', *Primary Geographer*, 11, p. 9.

3523    **Hughes, J. and Marsden, W. E.** (1994) 'Resourcing primary geography: bringing the world into the classroom' in Marsden, W. E. and Hughes, J. (eds) *Primary School Geography*. London: David Fulton, pp. 50–61.

3524    **Platten, L.** (1992) 'Resourcing local studies', *Primary Geographer*, 11, pp. 12–13.

3525    **Storm, M.** (1995) 'Resources for the study of distant places' in De Villiers, M. (ed) *Developments in Primary Geography: Theory and Practice*. Sheffield: Geographical Association, pp. 18–22.

# 9. Teaching Resources at Secondary and Tertiary Levels

## (a) Textbooks

3526    **Acheson, D. A.** (1994) 'An analysis of how changing viewpoints in geography at university level have influenced school textbooks at GCSE and A level' in Slater, F. (ed) *Reporting Research in Geographical Education: Monograph No. 1*. London: University of London Institute of Education, pp. 9–25.

3527    **Ahier, J.** (1988) *Industry, Children and the Nation: An Analysis of National Identity in School Textbooks*. London: Falmer Press.

3528    **Atkinson, J.** (1992) 'How are women in the Third World portrayed in textbooks?' *Teaching Geography*, 17, 3, pp. 179–181.

3529    **Bennett, S.** (1996) 'Discourse analysis: a method for deconstruction' in Williams, M. (ed) *Understanding Geographical and Environmental Education*. London: Cassell, pp. 150–161.

3530    **Boden, P.** (1977) *Promoting International Understanding through School Textbooks: A Case Study*. Brunswick: Georg Eckert Institute for International Textbook Research.

3531    **Boden, P.** (1984) 'United Kingdom geography textbook structures: a sample study' in Haubrich, H. (ed) *Perception of People and Places through Media, Volume 2*. Freiburg: IGUCGE/Pädagogische Hochschule Freiburg, pp. 565–578.

3532    **Bohn, D.** (1997) 'International education through international textbook cooperation' in Convey, A. and Nolzen, H. (eds) *Geography and Education (Münchner Studien zur Didaktik der Geographie, Band 10)*. Munich: Lehrstuhl für Didaktik der Geographie der Universität München, pp. 33–42.

3533    Bowen, P. (1983) 'Geography and development education: a publisher's view' in Bale, J. (ed) *The Third World: Issues and Approaches*. Sheffield: Geographical Association, pp. 70–73.

3534    Butt, G. and Lambert, D. (1997) 'Geography assessment and Key Stage 3 textbooks', *Teaching Geography*, 22, 3, pp. 146–147.

3535    Clare, R. (1982) 'Writing a textbook for slow learners', *Teaching Geography*, 8, 2, pp. 52–55.

3536    Cox, B. (1973) 'Textbooks for secondary school geography' in Biddle, D. S. and Deer, C. E. (eds) *Readings in Geographical Education: Selections from Australian and New Zealand Sources, Volume 2: 1966–1972*. Sydney: Whitcombe and Tombs/Australian Geography Teachers' Association, pp. 206–211.

3537    Davies, F. (1988) 'Analysing and using textbooks in geography' in Dilkes, J. L. and Nicholls, A. C. (eds) *Low Attainers and the Teaching of Geography*. Sheffield/Stafford: Geographical Association/National Association for Remedial Education, pp. 68–82.

3538    Gilbert, R. (1984) 'Environment, space and technology: images in geography' in Gilbert, R. *The Impotent Image: Reflections of Ideology in the Secondary School Curriculum*. London: Falmer Press, pp. 65–99.

3539    Gilbert, R. (1988) 'Critical skills in geography teaching' in Gerber, R. and Lidstone, J. (eds) *Developing Skills in Geographical Education*. Brisbane: IGUCGE/Jacaranda Press, pp. 169–171.

3540    Graves, N. (1997) 'Networks of authors and the nature of geography textbooks, 1875–1925', *Paradigm*, 22, pp. 10–14.

3541    Graves, N. (ed) (1997) 'Textbooks and textbook research in geographical education', *IRGEE*, 6, 1, pp. 60–105.

3542    Hanson, J. (1982) 'Textbooks of the past: what can we learn from them?', *Teaching Geography*, 7, 3, pp. 124–127.

3543    Hicks, D. (1979) *Bias in Geography Textbooks: Images of the Third World and Multi-ethnic Britain (Geography Working Paper No. 1)*. London: University of London Institute of Education.

3544    Hicks, D. (1980) 'Bias in books', *World Studies Journal*, 1, 3, pp. 14–22.

3545    Hicks, D. (1981) 'Teaching about other peoples: how biased are textbooks?', *Education 3–13*, 9, 2, pp. 14–19.

3546    Hoepper, B. (1985) 'Teasing the text: an approach to getting more out of geography textbooks', *Geographical Education*, 5, 1, pp. 18–20.

3547    Howlett, C. (1986) *An Investigation into the Conceptual Basis of Lower School Geography Texts as a Pre-requisite to Planning an Inter-disciplinary Humanities Curriculum*, unpublished MA dissertation. University of London Institute of Education

3548    Jackson, R. H. (1976) 'The persistence of outmoded ideas in high school geography texts', *Journal of Geography*, 75, 7, pp. 199–208.

3549    Johnson, J. P. (1977) *School Geography Textbooks 1803–1970: A Study of Textbook Development with Particular Reference to those Produced for English Secondary Schools*, unpublished MSc (Ed) dissertation. University of Southampton.

3550    Kent, A. (1996) 'Evaluating the geography curriculum' in Kent, A., Lambert, D., Naish, M. and Slater, F. (eds) *Geography in Education: Viewpoints on Teaching and Learning*. Cambridge: Cambridge University Press, pp. 173–182.

3551 Kington, C. (1991) 'Resourcing the classroom: text and reference books' in Walford, R. (ed) *Viewpoints on Geography Teaching.* Harlow: Longman, pp. 63–66.

3552 Kington, C. (1994) 'Resourcing the National Curriculum' in Walford, R. and Machon, P. (eds) *Challenging Times: Implementing the National Curriculum in Geography.* Cambridge: Cambridge Publishing Services, pp. 71–78.

3553 Lambert, D. (1996) 'The choice of textbooks for use in secondary school geography departments: some answers and some further questions', *Paradigm*, 21, pp. 21–31.

3554 Lambert, D. and Butt, G. (1996) 'The role of textbooks: an assessment issue?', *Teaching Geography*, 21, 4, pp. 202–203.

3555 Larimore, A. E. (1978) 'Humanising the writing in cultural geography textbooks', *Journal of Geography*, 77, 5, pp. 183–185.

3556 Lester, A. J. (1995) *Conceptualising Social Formation: A Textbook on South Africa*, unpublished PhD thesis. University of London Institute of Education.

3557 Lidstone, J. (1990) 'Researching the use of textbooks in geography classrooms', *Internationale Schulbuchforschung*, 12, pp. 427–444.

3558 Lidstone, J. (1992) 'In defence of textbooks' in Naish, M. (ed) *Geography and Education: National and International Perspectives.* London: University of London Institute of Education, pp. 177–193.

3559 Lidstone, J. (1994) 'Using a conventional geography textbook' in Murray, L. (ed) *Lesson Planning in Geography.* Southsea: LDJ Educational, pp. 54–70.

3560 Lidstone, J. (1985) 'Introduction: textbooks in geography teaching', *Geographical Education*, 5, 1, p. 2.

3561 Long, M. (ed) (1974) *Handbook for Geography Teachers.* London: Methuen.

3562 Marsden, W. E. (1979) 'The language of the geography textbook: an historical appraisal', *Westminster Studies in Education*, 2, pp. 53–65.

3563 Marsden, W. E. (1988) 'Continuity and change in geography textbooks: perspectives from the 1930s to the 1960s', *Geography*, 74, 4, pp. 327–343.

3564 Massey, D. (1986) 'Inside a textbook', *Journal of Geography*, 85, 3, pp. 116–119.

3565 Meijer, H. and Wiegand, P. (1990) *Dutch–British Conference on the Revision of Geography Textbooks.* Utrecht: Information and Documentation Centre for the Geography of the Netherlands.

3566 Millar, J. B. (1980) *The Nature and Role of Textbooks in Current Use for Teaching the Regional Geography of Tropical Africa*, unpublished MSc (Ed) dissertation. University of Southampton.

3567 Rider, M. D. (1986) *Perspectives on the Use of Graphics in Geography Textbooks Designed for 11–16 Year Old Pupils*, unpublished MA dissertation. University of London Institute of Education.

3568 School Curriculum and Assessment Authority (1997) *Analysis of Educational Resources 1996/7: Key Stage 3 Geography Textbooks.* London: SCAA.

3569 Spooner, D. (1993) 'How good were my textbooks?', *Geography*, 78, 2, p. 207.

3570 Warwick, P. J. (1979) *The Evaluation of Curriculum Materials: An Enquiry into the Use of Schemes for the Analysis of Geography Textbooks*, unpublished MA dissertation. University of London Institute of Education.

3571    Williams, M. (1978) 'School textbooks: their language, presentation and use', *Teaching Geography*, 4, 2, pp. 84–85.

3572    Williams, M. (1981) 'Textbooks and other published materials' in Williams, M. (ed) *Language Teaching and Learning: Geography*. London: Ward Lock Educational, pp. 23–38.

3573    Winter, C. (1996) 'Challenging the dominant paradigm in the geography National Curriculum: reconstructing place knowledge', *Curriculum Studies*, 4, 3, pp. 367–384.

3574    Winter, C. (1997) 'Ethnocentric bias in geography textbooks: a framework for reconstruction' in Tilbury, D. and Williams, M. (eds) *Teaching and Learning Geography*. London: Routledge, pp. 180–188.

3575    Wright, D. (1983) 'International textbook research: facts and issues', *Internationale Schulbuchforschung*, 5, pp. 310–314.

3576    Wright, D. (1983) 'International textbook research: past stagnation and future potential', *Curriculum*, 4, 2, pp. 14–18.

3577    Wright, D. (1986) 'Evaluating textbooks' in Boardman, D. (ed) *Handbook for Geography Teachers*. Sheffield: Geographical Association, pp. 92–95.

3578    Wright, D. (1986) 'Whose outline of American geography?: an exercise in textbook research', *Social Studies*, 77, 1, pp. 44–46.

3579    Wright, D. (1987) 'A pupil's perspective on textbooks', *Internationale Schulbuchforschung*, 9, pp. 137–142.

3580    Wright, D. (1988) 'Applied textbook research in geography' in Gerber, R. and Lidstone, J. (eds) *Developing Skills in Geographical Education*. Brisbane: IGUCGE/Jacaranda Press, pp. 327–332.

3581    Wright, D. (1990) 'The role of pupils in textbook evaluation', *Internationale Schulbuchforschung*, 12, pp. 445–454.

3582    Wright, D. (1996) 'A curriculum palimpsest: continuity and change in UK geography textbooks, 1820–1970', *Paradigm*, 21, pp. 32–39.

3583    Wright, D. (1996) 'Ten approaches to textbook research in geographical and environmental education', *Internationale Schulbuchforschung*, 18, 2, pp. 3–14.

3584    Wright, D. (1996) 'Textbook research in geographical and environmental education' in Williams, M. (ed) *Understanding Geographical and Environmental Education*. London: Cassell, pp. 172–182.

3585    Wright, D. and Young, E. W. (1977) 'Authors and their books: "a walking stick and not a crutch"', *Teaching Geography*, 2, 4, pp. 173–175.

3586    Zhang, H. (1996) *A Study of Changes in the Curriculum Context in Geography through Textbook Analysis*, unpublished PhD thesis. University of Southampton.

## (b) Video and audio-visual resources

3587    Benneworth, L. (1995) 'Using video discussion in issue-based learning', *Teaching Geography*, 20, 4, pp. 179–182.

3588    Butt, G. (1991) 'Have we got a video today?', *Teaching Geography*, 16, 2, pp. 51–55.

3589    Carter, D. (1986) 'Satellite imagery' in Boardman, D. (ed) *Handbook for Geography Teachers*. Sheffield: Geographical Association, pp. 145–148.

3590 Dove, J. and Owen, D. (1991) 'Teaching geography through music and sound', *Teaching Geography*, 16, 1, pp. 3–6.

3591 Durbin, C. (1995) 'Using televisual resources in geography', *Teaching Geography*, 20, 3, pp. 118–121.

3592 Durbin, C. (1996) 'Teaching geography with televisual resources' in Bailey, P. and Fox, P. (eds) *Geography Teachers' Handbook*. Sheffield: Geographical Association, pp. 261–270.

3593 Edwards, R. (1995) 'From the "box" to the classroom', *Teaching Geography*, 20, 4, pp. 176–178.

3594 Goldschneider, L. (1981) *The Value of Air Satellite Photography to the Teaching of Climatology, Meteorology and Weather Studies*, unpublished MA dissertation. University of London Institute of Education.

3595 Hilton, K. (1991) 'Earth observation satellites', *Teaching Geography*, 16, 4, pp. 159–162.

3596 Hilton, K. (1992) 'Remote sensing' in Naish, M. (ed) *Geography and Education: National and International Perspectives*. London: University of London Institute of Education, pp. 212–229.

3597 Homewood, T. (1987) *An Evaluation of the Use of Near Natural and False Colour Landsat Imagery as a Means of Communication in the Geography Curriculum of Secondary Schools*, unpublished MA dissertation. University of London Institute of Education.

3598 Lambert, D. (1988) 'Using video film', *Teaching Geography*, 13, 1, pp. 22–23.

3599 Lewis, S. (1991) 'Teaching geography using aerial photographs', *Teaching Geography*, 16, 3, pp. 113–115.

3600 Macdonald, A. (1991) 'Aerial photography: a record of the changing landscape', *Teaching Geography*, 16, 3, pp. 107–112.

3601 McMorrow, J. (1992) 'Explaining false colours: why is the grass orange?', *Teaching Geography*, 17, 4, pp. 158–162.

3602 Malindine, D. (1987) *An Investigation and Evaluation of the Contribution to Geographical Education of Independently Produced Video Material*, unpublished MA dissertation. University of London Institute of Education.

3603 Newman, R. J. (1975) *The Development of the Use of Geographical (Still) Pictures in British Secondary Schools 1900–1975*, unpublished MA dissertation. University of London Institute of Education.

3604 Newsham, P. A. (1986) *Cognitive and Affective Dimensions of Mainstream Television*, unpublished MA dissertation. University of London Institute of Education.

3605 Perry, A. (1987) 'The celluloid landscape', *Teaching Geography*, 12, 3, pp. 131–132.

3606 Pettitt, D. L. (1980) *An Investigation into Young Secondary School Children's Interpretation of Landsat False Colour Imagery*, unpublished MA dissertation. University of London Institute of Education.

3607 Ritchie, A. B. (1987) *A Small Scale Investigation into the Use of False Colour Landsat Images of Land Use as a Means of Teaching Suggested by Geographical Skills and Concepts*, unpublished MA dissertation. University of London Institute of Education.

3608 Roberts, M. (1987) 'Using videocassettes', *Teaching Geography*, 12, 3, pp. 114–117.

3609    Robinson, R. (1986) 'Discussing photographs' in Boardman, D. (ed) *Handbook for Geography Teachers*. Sheffield: Geographical Association, pp. 103–107.

3610    Selmes, I. (1991) 'Using satellite images in teaching geography', *Teaching Geography*, 16, 4, pp. 163–168.

3611    Senior, D. (1992) *Video: Entertainment or Tool? A Study of the Ways in which the Video Recorder is Used in the Classroom*, unpublished MA dissertation. University of London Institute of Education.

3612    Serf, J. (1986) 'Using videotapes' in Boardman, D. (ed) *Handbook for Geography Teachers*. Sheffield: Geographical Association, pp. 108–111.

3613    Smith, R. M. (1978) *Landsat Photography as a Resource in Secondary School Geography*, unpublished MA dissertation. University of London Institute of Education.

3614    Smyth, A. (1985) *An Experimental Investigation into Children's Interpretation of Landsat Imagery*, unpublished MA dissertation. University of London Institute of Education.

3615    Standen, J. and Hilton, K. (1993) 'Low cost earth imaging and meteorological data', *Teaching Geography*, 18, 4, pp. 150–154.

3616    Trebble, D. W. (1987) 'Geography on the box', *Teaching Geography*, 12, 3, pp. 118–119.

3617    Warwick, P. (1987) 'How do children see geographical pictures?', *Teaching Geography*, 12, 3, pp. 132–133.

3618    Whiteman, P. H. G. (1982) *The Relative Influence of False Colour and Monochrome Landsat Imagery in Classroom Geography*, unpublished MA dissertation. University of London Institute of Education.

3619    Williams, G. B. (1980) *Geography and Visual Media: An Evaluation of Learning Strategies and their Influence on the Effectiveness of Using Maps and Photographs in the Teaching of Geography*, unpublished MA dissertation. University of London Institute of Education.

## (c) Maps and atlases (see also Sub-section 1a on graphicacy)

3620    Bailey, P. and Fox, P. (1996) 'Teaching and learning with maps' in Bailey, P. and Fox, P. (eds) *Geography Teachers' Handbook*. Sheffield: Geographical Association.

3621    Bartz, B. S. (1970) 'Maps in the classroom', *Journal of Geography*, 69, 1, pp. 18–24.

3622    Boardman, D. (1986) 'Map reading skills' in Boardman, D. (ed) *Handbook for Geography Teachers*. Sheffield: Geographical Association, pp. 123–129.

3623    Boardman, D. (1986) 'Relief interpretation' in Boardman, D. (ed) *Handbook for Geography Teachers*. Sheffield: Geographical Association, pp. 130–138.

3624    Boardman, D. (1991) 'Developing map skills in the National Curriculum', *Teaching Geography*, 16, 4, pp. 155–158.

3625    Boardman, D. (1996) 'Learning with Ordnance Survey maps' in Bailey, P. and Fox, P. (eds) *Geography Teachers' Handbook*. Sheffield: Geographical Association, pp. 117–123.

3626    Burton, M. St J. W. (1992) 'Teaching drawing skills: straight-jackets, [*sic*] squiggles and strokes', *Teaching Geography*, 17, 3, pp. 125–127.

3627    Castner, H. W. and Wheate, R. (1979) 'Re-assessing the role played by shaded relief in topographic scale maps', *Cartographic Journal*, 16, 2, pp. 77–85.

3628   Gerber, R. and Wilson, P. (1984) 'Maps in the geography classroom' in Fien, J., Gerber, R. and Wilson, P. (eds) *The Geography Teacher's Guide to the Classroom*. Melbourne: Macmillan, pp. 185–196.

3629   Lacey, P. J. (1978) *Maps and Education with Particular Reference to Topographical Maps in Geographical Education*, unpublished MSc (Ed) dissertation. University of Southampton.

3630   Sandford, H. A. (1978) 'Taking a fresh look at atlases', *Teaching Geography*, 4, 2, pp. 62–65.

3631   Sandford, H. A. (1979) 'Things maps don't tell us', *Geography*, 64, 4, pp. 297–302.

3632   Sandford, H. A. (1983) 'Criteria for selecting a school atlas', *Teaching Geography*, 8, 2, pp. 107–109.

3633   Sandford, H. A. (1985) 'Atlases and atlas map work' in Boardman, D. (ed) *Handbook for Geography Teachers*. Sheffield: Geographical Association, pp. 139–144.

3634   Sandford, H. A. (1986) 'Objectives of school mapwork', *Teaching Geography*, 11, 1, pp. 22–26.

3635   Sandford, H. A. (1987) 'Why bother with an atlas?', *Teaching Geography*, 11, 3, pp. 166–167.

3636   Weeden, P. (1997) 'Learning through maps' in Tilbury, D. and Williams, M. (eds) *Teaching and Learning Geography*. London: Routledge, pp. 168–179.

3637   Wiegand, P. (1991) 'A model for the realisation of a school atlas', *Geography*, 76, 1, pp. 50–58.

## (d) Games and simulations

3638   Cranfield, J. (1978) *Games in Secondary School Geographical Education (with Small Scale Research)*, unpublished MA dissertation. University of London Institute of Education.

3639   Crookes, C. (1992) 'Issue-based teaching using role play drama', *Teaching Geography*, 18, 2, pp. 71–77.

3640   Dalton, T. H., Minshull, R., Robinson, A. and Garlic, J. (1972) *Simulation Games in Geography*. London: Macmillan.

3641   Fien, J., Hodgkinson, J. and Herschel, R. (1984) 'Using games and simulations in the geography classroom' in Fien, J., Gerber, R. and Wilson, P. (eds) *The Geography Teacher's Guide to the Classroom*. Melbourne: Macmillan, pp. 111–122.

3642   Hart, C. (1977) *The Application of the Simulation Method to the Teaching of Physical Geography in Schools*, unpublished MSc (Ed) dissertation. University of Southampton.

3643   Taylor, J. and Walford, R. (1972) *Simulation in the Classroom*. London: Penguin.

3644   Walford, R. (1981) 'Geographical games and simulations: learning through experience', *Journal of Geography in Higher Education*, 5, 2, pp. 113–119.

3645   Walford, R. (1986) 'Games and simulations' in Boardman, D. (ed) *Handbook for Geography Teachers*. Sheffield: Geographical Association, pp. 79–84.

3646   Walford, R. (1991) *Role-play and the Environment*. London: English Nature.

3647   Walford, R. (1996) 'The simplicity of simulation' in Bailey, P. and Fox, P. (eds) *Geography Teachers' Handbook*. Sheffield: Geographical Association, pp. 139–145.

3648    Wilkie, M. (1974) *Games and Simulations in Education with Particular Reference to Geography Teaching*, unpublished MA dissertation. University of London Institute of Education.

## (e) Information technology

3649    Barber, J. A. H. (1993) *The National Curriculum and IT in Geography in Secondary Schools*, unpublished MA dissertation. University of London Institute of Education.

3650    Barnett, M., Kent, A. and Milton, M. (1995) *Images of Earth: A Teacher's Guide to Remote Sensing in Geography at Key Stage 2*. Sheffield: Geographical Association.

3651    Barnett, M., Kent, A. and Milton, M. (1995) *Images of Earth: A Teacher's Guide to Remote Sensing in Geography at Key Stage 3 and GCSE*. Sheffield: Geographical Association.

3652    Barnett, M. and Milton, M. (1995) 'Satellite images and IT capability', *Teaching Geography*, 20, 3, pp. 142–144.

3653    Bilham-Boult, A. (1988) *Using Computers in Fieldwork*. Coventry: Microelectronics Education Support Unit.

3654    Brown, S. (1991) 'Geography fieldwork using spreadsheets', *Teaching Geography*, 16, 2, pp. 59–63.

3655    Burkill, S. (1996) 'Trends in school geography and information technology' in Rawling, E. and Daugherty, R. (eds) *Geography into the Twenty-first Century*. Chichester: John Wiley, pp. 217–234.

3656    Carr, R. D. (1985) *Computer Assisted Learning in Geography Teaching: Current Trends and Future Prospects*, unpublished MSc (Ed) dissertation. University of Southampton.

3657    Cracknell, J. R. (1985) *The Setting Up and Evaluation of an In-service Course for Computer-assisted Learning in Geography*, unpublished MA dissertation. University of London Institute of Education.

3658    Cummings, R. (1984) *Pupil Talk in Groups during a CAL Simulation Game*, unpublished MA dissertation. University of London Institute of Education.

3659    Davidson, J. (ed) (1990) 'Information technology, geography and the National Curriculum', *Teaching Geography*, 15, 4, pp. 184–185.

3660    Davidson, J. (1991) 'Geography and information technology: reflection and progression', *Teaching Geography*, 16, 3, pp. 134–135.

3661    Davidson, J. (1996) 'Information technology and the geography department' in Bailey, P. and Fox, P. (eds) *Geography Teachers' Handbook*. Sheffield: Geographical Association, pp. 249–259.

3662    Davidson, J. and Krause, J. (eds) (1992) *Geography, IT and the National Curriculum*. Sheffield: Geographical Association.

3663    Detheridge, T. (1993) 'IT and special needs', *Teaching Geography*, 18, 2, pp. 84–85.

3664    Dove, M. J. (1987) *Opportunities and Obstacles: The Adoption of Computer Assisted Learning by Geography Teachers in Victoria, Australia*, unpublished MA dissertation. University of London Institute of Education.

3665    Duncan, C. (1990) 'Meteorology, teaching and technology', *Geography*, 75, 1, pp. 27–35.

3666 English, A. S. (1988) *The Potential of PRESTEL as a Resource for Geography Teachers*, unpublished MA dissertation. University of London Institute of Education.

3667 Forer, P. (1984) 'Computers in the geography classroom' in Fien, J., Gerber, R. and Wilson, P. (eds) *The Geography Teacher's Guide to the Classroom*. Melbourne: Macmillan, pp. 172–184.

3668 Foskett, R. (1988) 'Support for the teacher: an introduction to the services provided by NERIS', *Teaching Geography*, 13, 4, pp. 162–163.

3669 Fox, P. and Tapsfield, A. (eds) (1986) *The Role and Value of New Technology in Geography*. Sheffield/Coventry: Geographical Association/Council for Educational Technology.

3670 Freeman, D. (1981) *Computer-assisted Learning in Geography: A Case Study of Hertfordshire Secondary Schools*, unpublished MA dissertation. University of London Institute of Education.

3671 Freeman, D. (1997) 'Using information technology and new technologies in geography' in Tilbury, D. and Williams, M. (eds) *Teaching and Learning Geography*. London: Routledge, pp. 202–217.

3672 Freeman, D. (1997) 'A review of software for geographers', *Teaching Geography*, 22, 4, pp. 196–197.

3673 Freeman, D., Green, D. and Hassell, D. (1994) 'A guide to geographical information systems', *Teaching Geography*, 19, 1, pp. 36–37.

3674 Freeman, D., Green, D., Hassell, D. and Paterson, K. (1993) 'Getting started with GIS', *Teaching Geography*, 18, 2, pp. 57–60.

3675 Gardner, D. (1997) 'Integrating IT into schemes of work', *Teaching Geography*, 22, 2, pp. 90–91.

3676 Gerber, R. (1992) 'Technology education: an emerging component in geographical education' in Hill, A. D. (ed) *International Perspectives on Geographical Education*. Boulder, CO/Skokie, IL: IGUCGE/Rand, McNally and Co., pp. 283–298.

3677 Goble, T. (1994) *The Development of a Computer Based Modelling Environment for Upper Secondary Schools Geography Classes*, unpublished PhD thesis. University of London Institute of Education.

3678 Grummit, S. (1978) *The Computer in the Classroom: Computer-assisted Learning in Geography at the Secondary School Level*, unpublished MA dissertation. University of London Institute of Education.

3679 Hall, D., Kent, A. and Wiegand, P. (1985) 'Computer-assisted learning in geography: the state of the art', *Teaching Geography*, 10, 2, pp. 73–76.

3680 Hassell, D. (1982) *Teacher Style and Computer-assisted Learning in Geography*, unpublished MA dissertation. University of London Institute of Education.

3681 Hassell, D. and Warner, H. (1995) *Using IT to Enhance Geography: Case Studies at Key Stages 3 and 4*. Sheffield/Coventry: Geographical Association/NCET.

3682 Jefferys, S. A. (1987) *Children Learning in the CAL Classroom*, unpublished MA dissertation. University of London Institute of Education.

3683 Kent, A. (1982) 'The challenge of the microcomputer' in Graves, N., Naish, M., Slater, F., Kent, A. and Hilton, K. *Geography in Education Now: Bedford Way Papers 13*. London: University of London Institute of Education, pp. 28–43.

3684 Kent, A. (ed) (1983) *Geography Teaching and the Micro*. Harlow: Longman.

3685    Kent, A. (ed) (1987) *Computers in Action in the Geography Classroom.* Sheffield: Geographical Association.

3686    Kent, A. (1988) 'The process of software development for geography in the UK' in Haubrich, H. (ed) *Perception of People and Places through Media, Volume 2.* Freiburg: IGUCGE/Pädagogische Hochschule Freiburg, pp. 725–737.

3687    Kent, A. (1992) 'The new technology and geographical education' in Naish, M. (ed) *Geography in Education: National and International Perspectives.* London: University of London Institute of Education, pp. 163–176.

3688    Kent, A. and Riley, D. (eds) (1988) *New Technology in Geography: Some Practical Suggestions.* Sheffield: Geographical Association.

3689    Kerr, R. A. (1988) *An Investigation into the Use of Real Time Satellite Meteorological Imagery in Secondary Education,* unpublished MA dissertation. University of London Institute of Education.

3690    Lawler, C. D. (1986) *CAL and Physical-based Fieldwork in Geography,* unpublished MA dissertation. University of London Institute of Education.

3691    Leonard, P. (1984) *The Process of Learning with a Micro: A Game Simulation Observed,* unpublished MA dissertation. University of London Institute of Education.

3692    Lucas, I. (1993) 'IT and fieldwork', *Teaching Geography,* 18, 2, pp. 38–39.

3693    Martin, F. and Smith, C. (1996) 'What can CD-ROMs do for us?', *Teaching Geography,* 21, 1, pp. 21–23.

3694    Midgely, H. and Fox, P. (1986) 'Microcomputers in the classroom' in Boardman, D. (ed) *Handbook for Geography Teachers.* Sheffield: Geographical Association.

3695    National Council for Educational Technology (1989) *Using New Technologies in Geography.* Coventry: NCET.

3696    National Council for Educational Technology (1991) *IT's Geography: The role of IT in PGCE Geography Courses (NCET Occasional Paper 3).* Coventry: NCET.

3697    Phillips, A. (1991) 'Project HIT: a curriculum development project for the future', *Teaching Geography,* 16, 1, pp. 86–87.

3698    Phillips, A. (1997) 'Managing IT in post-16 geography' in Powell, A. (ed) *Handbook of Post-16 Geography.* Sheffield: Geographical Association, pp. 73–78.

3699    Rawling, E. (1993) 'IT and geography: is there a minimum entitlement?', *Teaching Geography,* 18, 4, pp. 182–183.

3700    Robinson, A. (1996) 'Interactive computer-assisted learning in geography in Scottish schools' in van der Zijpp, T., van der Schee, J. and Trimp, H. (eds) *Innovation in Geographical Education: Proceedings of the 28th International Geographical Congress Commission on Geographical Education.* Amsterdam: IGUCGE/Centrum voor Educatieve Geografie Vrije Universiteit Amsterdam, pp. 223–227.

3701    Robinson, C. (1982) *An Evaluation of Pupil Attitudes towards Computer Assisted Learning in Geography,* unpublished MA dissertation. University of London Institute of Education.

3702    Rogers, S. (1987) *The Constraining and Enabling Influences on the Take-up of CAL in Geography in Essex Secondary Schools,* unpublished MA dissertation. University of London Institute of Education.

3703    Rogers, S. (1996) 'Geography and IT: preparing new teachers', *Teaching Geography,* 21, 4, pp. 200–201.

3704 Rudd, M. (1994) 'IT in geography: present and future', *Teaching Geography*, 19, 3, pp. 138–140.

3705 Russell, K. (1994) 'Using CD-ROM technology in geography', *Teaching Geography*, 19, 2, pp. 92–93.

3706 Tapsfield, A. (1991) 'From computer-assisted learning to information technology' in Walford, R. (ed) *Viewpoints on Geography Teaching*. Harlow: Longman, pp. 57–62.

3707 Thomas, K. M. (1985) *CAL in Geography: Pupil–Teacher Perspectives on the Problem of Software Evaluation*, unpublished MA dissertation. University of London Institute of Education.

3708 Twells, P. P. (1996) *Information Highways: The Present and Possible Future Implications for the Teaching and Learning of Geography in Schools*, unpublished MA dissertation. University of London Institute of Education.

3709 Walker, D. (1981) 'Educational computing and geography' in Walford, R. (ed) *Signposts for Geography Teaching*. Harlow: Longman, pp. 185–191.

3710 Warner, H. (1993) 'Equal opportunities: IT and gender', *Teaching Geography*, 18, 3, pp. 134–135.

3711 Warner, H. (1994) 'CD-ROM technology in geography: potential and issues', *Teaching Geography*, 19, 4, pp. 184–185.

3712 Warner, H. (1997) 'Planning for progression in IT activities', *Teaching Geography*, 22, 1, pp. 38–39.

3713 Watson, D. (ed) (1989) *Learning Geography with Computers*. Coventry: NCET.

3714 Whiddon, K. (1996) 'Virtual geography!', *Teaching Geography*, 21, 3, pp. 146–148.

3715 Wiegand, P. (1987) 'Teaching geography with spreadsheets', *Teaching Geography*, 12, 5, pp. 195–197.

3716 Williamson, D. (1997) *Looking for a Place: Information Technology in Secondary Geography*, unpublished MA (Ed) dissertation. University of Southampton.

## (f) Managing resources

3717 Bailey, P. (1986) 'Managing resources' in Boardman, D. (ed) *Handbook for Geography Teachers*. Sheffield: Geographical Association, pp. 85–91.

3718 Foskett, R. (1988) 'Support for the teacher: an introduction to services provided by NERIS', *Teaching Geography*, 13, 4, pp. 162–163.

3719 Hindson, J. (1989) 'Managing resources' in Wiegand, P. (ed) *Managing the Geography Department*. Sheffield: Geographical Association, pp. 174–183.

3720 Hordern, B. (1989) 'The management of stock and plant' in Wiegand, P. (ed) *Managing the Geography Department*. Sheffield: Geographical Association, pp. 202–209.

3721 Luker, K. (1996) 'Managing resources' in Bailey, P. and Fox, P. (eds) *Geography Teachers' Handbook*. Sheffield: Geographical Association, pp. 287–290.

3722 Martin, F. and Bailey, P. (1996) 'Evaluating and using resources' in Bailey, P. and Fox, P. (eds) *Geography Teachers' Handbook*. Sheffield: Geographical Association, pp. 235–247.

3723 Watson, M. (1984) 'Resources for geography teaching' in Orrell, K. and Wiegand, P. (eds) *Evaluation and Assessment in Geography*. Sheffield: Geographical Association, pp. 9–11.

3724 Wiegand, P. (ed) (1989) *Managing the Geography Department*. Sheffield: Geographical Association.

# 10. Assessment and Evaluation in Geography

## (a) Formative and summative assessment and evaluation

3725 Bainbridge, K. (1989) 'Descriptive assessment is transparent assessment', *Geographical Education*, 6, 1, pp. 17–18.

3726 Balderstone, D. and Lambert, D. (eds) (1992) *Assessment Matters*. Sheffield: Geographical Association.

3727 Ballantyne, R. and Sparks, R. (1991) 'Assessment training in geography education', *Journal of Geography in Higher Education*, 15, 2, pp. 151–160.

3728 Bassnett, J. (1995) *Developing Teacher Assessment in Geography*, unpublished MA dissertation. University of London Institute of Education.

3729 Biddle, D. S. (1973) 'The quest for reliability in marking responses to essay questions in geography' in Biddle, D. S. and Deer, C. E. (eds) *Readings in Geographical Education: Selections from Australian and New Zealand Sources, Volume 2: 1966–1972*. Melbourne: Whitcombe and Tombs/Australian Geography Teachers' Association, pp. 418–431.

3730 Black, H. D. and Dockrell, W. B. (1980) *Diagnostic Assessment in Geography*. Edinburgh: Scottish Council for Research in Education.

3731 Butt, G. (1992) 'The assessment maze', *Teaching Geography*, 17, 4, pp. 182–183.

3732 Butt, G., Lambert, D. and Telfer, S. (eds) (1995) *Assessment Works: Approaches to Assessment in Geography at Key Stages 1, 2 and 3*. Sheffield: Geographical Association.

3733 Catford, R. A. G. (1990) 'Effective prompts for profiling', *Teaching Geography*, 15, 4, pp. 163–165.

3734 Chalkley, B. (1997) 'Using optical mark readers for student assessment and course evaluation', *Journal of Geography in Higher Education*, 21, 1, pp. 99–106.

3735 Daniel, P. A. (1991) 'Assessing student-led seminars through a process of negotiation', *Journal of Geography in Higher Education*, 15, 1, pp. 57–62.

3736 Daugherty, R. (1990) 'Assessment in the geography curriculum', *Geography*, 75, 4, pp. 289–301.

3737 Daugherty, R. (1992) 'The role of assessment in geographical education: a framework for comparative analysis' in Hill, A. D. (ed) *International Perspectives on Geographical Education*. Boulder, CO/Skokie IL: IGUCGE/Rand, McNally and Co., pp. 111–118.

3738 Daugherty, R. (1995) 'Assessment in geographical education: a review of research' in Williams, M. (ed) *Understanding Geographical and Environmental Education: The Role of Research*. London: Cassell, pp. 242–250.

3739 Daugherty, R. and Lambert, D. (1994) 'Teacher assessment and geography in the National Curriculum', *Geography*, 79, 4, pp. 339–349.

3740 Davies, P. (1995) 'An inductive approach to levels of attainment', *IRGEE*, 4, 1, pp. 47–65.

3741 Digby, B. (1984) 'Monitoring pupil attitudes' in Orrell, K. and Wiegand, P. (eds) *Evaluation and Assessment in Geography*. Sheffield: Geographical Association, pp. 20–22.

3742 Dowgill, P. (1994) 'A tall order!', *Teaching Geography*, 19, 3, pp. 136–7.

3743 Drew, B. (1988) 'Assessment by criteria', *Teaching Geography*, 13, 3, pp. 104–107.

3744 Fitzgerald, B. (1988) 'See me: or Darren, I think you might have left the nomads to later', *Teaching Geography*, 13, 3, pp. 100–103.

3745 Frances, L. (1989) 'Assessment in geography: an overview of important questions and concepts', *Geographical Education*, 6, 1, pp. 6–8.

3746 Grant, A. T. (1988) *A Critical Review of the Development of Profiles, Profiling and Records of Achievement with Particular Reference to Geography*, unpublished MA dissertation. University of London Institute of Education.

3747 Graves, N. (1972) 'School examinations' in Graves, N. (ed) *New Movements in the Study and Teaching of Geography*. London: Temple Smith, pp. 171–187.

3748 Graves, N. (1980) 'Evaluation in geographical education' in Graves, N. *Geographical Education in Secondary Schools*. Sheffield: Geographical Association, pp. 69–78.

3749 Graves, N. (1980) 'Evaluation in geographical education' in Graves, N. *Geography in Education*. London: Heinemann, pp. 191–207.

3750 Graves, N. (1980) 'The evaluation of geographical education' in Graves, N. (ed) *New UNESCO Source Book for Geography Teaching*. Harlow: Longman, pp. 313–363.

3751 Graves, N. (1988) 'Graded tests in geography: an initial examination of the problems of their construction' in Haubrich, H. (ed) *Perception of People and Places through Media, Volume 2*. Freiburg: IGUCGE/Pädagogische Hochschule Freiburg, pp. 500–521.

3752 Graves, N. and Naish, M. (eds) (1986) *Profiling in Geography*. Sheffield: Geographical Association.

3753 Grimwade, K. (1996) 'Practical approaches to assessment, record keeping and reporting' in Bailey, P. and Fox, P. (eds) *Geography Teachers' Handbook*. Sheffield: Geographical Association, pp. 203–209.

3754 Halloway, W. (1984) 'Planning a school based assessment program' in Fien, J., Gerber, R. and Wilson, P. (eds) *The Geography Teacher's Guide to the Classroom*. Melbourne: Macmillan, pp. 278–293.

3755 Hogg, J. (1997) 'Geography students assess their learning using computer marked tests', *Journal of Geography in Higher Education*, 21, 1, pp. 121–125.

3756 Hones, G. (1973) 'Assessment and examinations' in Walford, R. (ed) *New Directions in Geography Teaching*. Harlow: Longman, pp. 115–131.

3757 Hones, G. (1973) 'Objective testing in geography', *Geography*, 58, 1, pp. 29–37.

3758 Hones, G. (1981) 'Evaluation in the 1980s' in Walford, R. (ed) *Signposts for Geography Teaching*. Harlow: Longman, pp. 213–215.

3759 Hopkin, J. (1995) 'Developing an assessment policy', *Teaching Geography*, 20, 4, pp. 192–193.

3760    Jones, A. (1997) 'Setting objective tests', *Journal of Geography in Higher Education*, 21, 1, pp. 106–114.

3761    Jones, M. (1986) 'Evaluation and assessment 11–16' in Boardman, D. (ed) *Handbook for Geography Teachers*. Sheffield: Geographical Association, pp. 234–249.

3762    Joseph, C. (1981) 'Examinations in the 1970s' in Walford, R. (ed) *Signposts for Geography Teaching*. Harlow: Longman, pp. 97–106.

3763    King, R. L. (1976) 'Assessment in geography: approaches to the formulation of objectives', *Studies in Higher Education*, 1, pp. 223–232.

3764    King, R. L. (1976) 'Student views on assessment in geography', *Assessment in Higher Education*, 1, 2, pp. 4–15.

3765    King, R. L. (1979) 'More on assessment', *Journal of Geography in Higher Education*, 3, 1, pp. 102–106.

3766    King, R. L. (1981) 'How shall they be judged?: notes and sources on assessment', *Journal of Geography in Higher Education*, 5, 1, pp. 61–72.

3767    Kurfman, D. G. (1970) *Evaluation in Geographic Education*. Belmont, CA: Fearon Publishers.

3768    Lambert, D. (1989) 'National assessment in the UK: implications of government plans for a National Curriculum', *Geographical Education*, 6, 1, pp. 24–6.

3769    Lambert, D. (1989) 'Some thoughts on National Curriculum assessment', *Teaching Geography*, 14, 3, pp. 108–110.

3770    Lambert, D. (1990) *Geography Assessment: A Guide and Resource for Teachers*. Cambridge: Cambridge University Press.

3771    Lambert, D. (1996) 'Assessing pupils' attainment and supporting learning' in Kent, A., Lambert, D., Naish, M. and Slater, F. (eds) *Geography in Education: Viewpoints on Teaching and Learning*. Cambridge: Cambridge University Press, pp. 260–287.

3772    Lambert, D. (1996) 'Issues in assessment' in Bailey, P. and Fox, P. (eds) *Geography Teachers' Handbook*. Sheffield: Geographical Association, pp. 187–202.

3773    Lambert, D. (1997) 'Principles of pupil assessment' in Tilbury, D. and Williams, M. (eds) *Teaching and Learning Geography*. London: Routledge, pp. 255–265.

3774    Lambert, D. (1997) 'Teacher assessment in the National Curriculum' in Tilbury, D. and Williams, M. (eds) *Teaching and Learning Geography*. London: Routledge, pp. 275–286.

3775    Lambert, D. and Butt, G. (1996) 'The role of textbooks: an assessment issue?', *Teaching Geography*, 21, 4, pp. 202–203.

3776    Lambert, D. and Purnell, K. (1994) 'International testing in geography: comparing students' achievements within and between countries', *Assessment in Education*, 1, 2, pp. 167–179.

3777    McElroy, B. (1984) 'Evaluating your geography courses' in Fien, J., Gerber, R. and Wilson, P. (eds) *The Geography Teacher's Guide to the Classroom*. Melbourne: Macmillan, pp. 294–305.

3778    Marsden, W. E. (1974) 'Analysing classroom tests in geography', *Geography*, 59, 1, pp. 55–64.

3779    Marsden, W. E. (1976) 'Assessment' in Marsden, W. E. *Evaluating the Geography Curriculum*. Edinburgh: Oliver and Boyd, pp. 165–254.

3780    Marsden, W. E. (1991) 'Attainment targets in context: some historical perspectives', *Studies in Educational Evaluation*, 17, 3, pp. 199–214.

3781    Marsden, W. E. (1995) 'Assessment, testing and examinations' in Marsden, W. E. *Geography 11–16: Rekindling Good Practice.* London: David Fulton Publishers, pp. 99–118.

3782    Murray, K. P. (1996) *A Case Study of Pupils' Perceptions of Coursework*, unpublished MA dissertation. University of London Institute of Education.

3783    Orrell, K. and Wiegand, P. (eds) (1984) *Evaluation and Assessment in Geography.* Sheffield: Geographical Association.

3784    Penn, H. (1985) *Coursework in Geography Examinations: A Study of the Attitudes and Opinions of Examination Candidates to Coursework Assessment*, unpublished MSc (Ed) dissertation. University of Southampton.

3785    Pope, A. (1989) 'Assessment: making the right choice', *Geographical Education*, 6, 1, pp. 10–11.

3786    Price, B. (1989) 'Assessment: it can make a world of difference', *Geographical Education*, 6, 1, pp. 12–16.

3787    Rawling, E. (1988) 'Assessment', *Teaching Geography*, 13, 3, p. 98.

3788    Salmon, R. B. and Masterton, T. H. (1974) *The Principles of Objective Testing in Geography.* London: Heinemann.

3789    Senathirajah, N. and Weiss, J. (1971) *Evaluation in Geography: A Resource Book for Teachers.* Toronto: Ontario Institute for Studies in Education.

3790    Stainer, L. (1997) 'Peer assessment and groupwork as a vehicle for student empowerment: a module evaluation', *Journal of Geography in Higher Education*, 21, 1, pp. 95–98.

3791    Stimpson, P. (1996) 'Reconceptualising assessment in geography' in Gerber, R. and Lidstone, J. (eds) *Developments and Directions in Geographical Education.* Clevedon: Channel View Publications, pp. 117–128.

3792    Swann, A. (1984) 'Assessing pupils' progress' in Orrell, K. and Wiegand, P. (eds) *Evaluation and Assessment in Geography.* Sheffield: Geographical Association, pp. 14–16.

3793    Taylor, E. G. and Nuttall, D. (1974) 'Question choice in examinations: an experiment in geography and science', *Educational Research*, 16, 2, pp. 143–150.

3794    Tucker, B. (1992) 'Oral assessment in geography', *Teaching Geography*, 17, 1, pp. 11–14.

3795    Walford, R. (1987) 'Marking', *Teaching Geography*, 9, 3, pp. 118–120.

3796    Weaver, R. and Chalkley, B. (1997) 'Introducing objective tests and OMR based student assessment: a case study', *Journal of Geography in Higher Education*, 21, 1, pp. 114–121.

## (b) Assessment at Key Stages 1 and 2

3797    Bentley, J. (1988) 'Evaluation and assessment in geography' in Mills, D. (ed) *Geographical Work in Primary and Middle Schools.* Sheffield: Geographical Association, pp. 267–281.

3798    Blyth, A. (1990) *Making the Grade for Primary Humanities*. Milton Keynes: Open University Press.

3799    Blyth, A. and Krause, J. (1995) 'Assessment in primary geography' in Blyth, A. and Krause, J. *Primary Geography: A Developmental Approach*. London: Hodder and Stoughton, pp. 81–92.

3800    Bowles, R. (1993) 'Recording and assessing' in Bowles, R. *Practical Guides: Geography*. Leamington Spa: Scholastic Publications, pp. 121–136.

3801    Chambers, B. and Donert, K. (1996) 'Assessment' in Chambers, B. and Donert, K. *Teaching Geography at Key Stage 2*. Cambridge: Chris Kington Publishing, pp. 32–35.

3802    Foley, M. and Janikoun, J. (1996) 'Assessment: not the bolt-on extra' in Foley, M. and Janikoun, J. *The Really Practical Guide to Primary Geography*. London: Stanley Thornes, pp. 57–68.

3803    Janikoun, J. (1995) 'Working with level descriptions', *Primary Geographer*, 21, pp. 18–19.

3804    Marsden, W. E. (1994) 'Beyond locational knowledge: good assessment practice in primary geography' in Marsden, W. E. and Hughes, J. (eds) *Primary School Geography*. London: David Fulton, pp. 77–91.

3805    Martin, F. (1995) 'Assessment and Key Stage 1 geography' in Martin, F. *Teaching Early Years Geography*. Cambridge: Chris Kington Publishing, pp. 25–28.

3806    Mee, K. (1996) 'Assessment: new opportunities', *Primary Geographer*, 24, pp. 16–17.

3807    Office for Standards in Education (1996) 'Geography' in OFSTED *Subjects and Standards: Issues for School Development Arising from OFSTED Inspection Findings 1994–5, Key Stages 1 and 2*. London: HMSO, pp. 12–13.

3808    School Curriculum and Assessment Authority (1993) *Standard Assessment Tasks: Geography Key Stage 1 Teacher's Pack*. London: HMSO.

3809    School Curriculum and Assessment Authority (1997) *Expectations in Geography at Key Stages 1 and 2*. London: SCAA.

3810    School Examinations and Assessment Council (1992) *Geography Standard Assessment Tasks: Key Stage 1*. London: SEAC.

3811    School Examinations and Assessment Council (1993) *Children's Work Assessed: Geography and History: Key Stage 1*. London: SEAC.

3812    Scoffham, S. (1997) 'Different achievements', *Primary Geographer*, 28, pp. 28–30.

3813    Smith, P. (1997) 'Differentiation: some definitions and examples', *Primary Geographer*, 28, pp. 4–6.

3814    Wiegand, P. (1997) 'Assessment in the primary school' in Tilbury, D. and Williams, M. (eds) *Teaching and Learning Geography*. London: Routledge, pp. 266–274.

## (c) Assessment at Key Stage 3

3815    Butt, G. (1995) 'Working with level descriptions', *Teaching Geography*, 20, 2, pp. 88–89.

3816    Butt, G. (1997) 'First attempts at Key Stage 3 levelling: how did it go?', *Teaching Geography*, 22, 4, pp. 198–199.

3817    Butt, G., Flinders, K., Hopkin, J., Lambert, D. and Telfer, S. (1997) 'Statutory teacher assessment at Key Stage 3: beyond testing?', *Teaching Geography*, 22, 2, pp. 92–93.

3818    Butt, G. and Lambert, D. (1993) 'Key Stage 3: professional guidance?', *Teaching Geography*, 18, 2, pp. 82–83.

3819    Butt, G. and Lambert, D. (1997) 'Geography assessment and Key Stage 3 textbooks', *Teaching Geography*, 22, 3, pp. 146–147.

3820    Curriculum and Assessment Authority for Wales (1996) *Consistency in Teacher Assessment: Exemplification of Standards Key Stage 3 Geography*. Cardiff: ACAC.

3821    Curriculum and Assessment Authority for Wales (1996) *Consistency in Teacher Assessment: Key Stage 3 Geography Optional Tests and Tasks*. Cardiff: ACAC.

3822    Daugherty, R. (1990) 'Assessment in the geography curriculum', *Geography*, 75, 4, pp. 289–301.

3823    Daugherty, R. (1992) 'Teacher assessment at Key Stage 3: a ten point guide', *Teaching Geography*, 17, 3, pp. 112–115.

3824    Digby, B. (1994) 'Stranded!: reflections upon assessment at Key Stage 3' in Walford, R. and Machon, P. (eds) *Challenging Times: Implementing the National Curriculum in Geography*. Cambridge: Cambridge Publishing Services, pp. 80–83.

3825    Digby, B. and Lambert, D. (1996) 'Using level descriptions at Key Stage 3', *Teaching Geography*, 21, 1, pp. 40–43.

3826    Edwards, H. M. (1989) *Assessment in Geography for Years 1 to 3: An Investigation into the Implementation of a New Syllabus and Related Assessment Scheme for Lower School Geography at Fairwater School*, unpublished MA dissertation. University of London Institute of Education.

3827    Grimwade, K. (1996) 'Assessment at Key Stage 3' in Bailey, P. and Fox, P. (eds) *Geography Teachers' Handbook*. Sheffield: Geographical Association, pp. 211–215.

3828    Howes, N. (1996) 'The portfolio as a Key Stage 3 assessment tool', *Teaching Geography*, 21, 3, pp. 143–145.

3829    Jones, B. (1997) 'Developing a scheme of assessment for Key Stage 3 geography', *Teaching Geography*, 22, 1, pp. 17–21.

3830    Lambert, D. and Daugherty, R. (1993) 'Teacher assessment in Key Stage 3: a snapshot of practice', *Teaching Geography*, 18, 3, pp. 113–115.

3831    Nash, P. (1993) 'Teacher assessment in Key Stage 3: planning for differentiation', *Teaching Geography*, 18, 3, pp. 108–112.

3832    Pierce, L. (1992) 'An approach to assessment at Key Stage 3', *Teaching Geography*, 17, 3, pp. 116–120.

3833    Rawling, E. and Westaway, J. (1996) 'Progression and assessment in geography at Key Stage 3', *Teaching Geography*, 21, 3, pp. 123–129.

3834    School Curriculum and Assessment Authority (1993) *CFAS Evaluation: Key Stage 3 Geography Pilot Tests*. London: SCAA

3835    School Curriculum and Assessment Authority (1996) *Consistency in Teacher Assessment: Exemplification of Standards: Key Stage 3 Geography*. London: SCAA.

3836    School Curriculum and Assessment Authority (1996) *Optional Tests and Tasks: Key Stage 3 Geography*. London: SCAA.

3837    School Examinations and Assessment Council (1991) *Teacher Assessment at Key Stage 3 (Geography)*. London: SEAC.

3838    School Examinations and Assessment Council (1993) *Pupils' Work Assessed: Geography*. London: SEAC.

3839    Tidmarsh, C. and Weeden, P. (1997) 'Using optional tests and tasks', *Teaching Geography*, 22, 2, pp. 71–76.

3840    Westaway, J. and Rawling, E. (1997) 'Preparing for statutory teacher assessments at Key Stage 3', *Teaching Geography*, 22, 1, pp. 40–41.

## (d) Assessment in 14–16 examinations

3841    Bailey, P. (1985) 'GCSE and the geography department', *Teaching Geography*, 10, 4, pp. 146–147.

3842    Butt, G. (1996) 'Developments in geography 14–19: a changing system' in Rawling, E. and Daugherty, R. (eds) *Geography into the Twenty-first Century*. Chichester: John Wiley, pp. 173–193.

3843    Carhart, J. (1986) 'GCSE: a matter of criteria', *Teaching Geography*, 11, 2, pp. 87–88.

3844    Crouch, N. (1991) *An Evaluation of Fieldwork Based GCSE Geography Coursework in Some Essex Schools*, unpublished MA dissertation. University of London Institute of Education.

3845    Daugherty, R. (1987) *Countdown to GCSE: Geography*. London: Macmillan.

3846    Daugherty, R. (1987) 'GCSE: the choice is yours', *Teaching Geography*, 12, 2, pp. 53–55.

3847    Dowgill, P. (1989) *GCSE Geography: A Case Study of Classroom Experience*, unpublished MA dissertation. University of London Institute of Education.

3848    Etherington, S. (1987) *The GCSE: Its Development and Implications for Geography Teachers*, unpublished MSc (Ed) dissertation. University of Southampton.

3849    Graves, N. (ed) (1982) *Report on Criteria for a 16+ Examination in Geography*. Sheffield: Geographical Association.

3850    Hall, D. (1976) 'The examination system at 16' in Hall, D. *Geography and the Geography Teacher*. London: Unwin, pp. 53–84.

3851    Holdsworth, M. A. (1980) *An Examination of the Relationship between the Results of the AH4 Group Test of Intelligence at 13+ and the Results of Public Examinations in Geography for a Group of Children in the London Borough of Merton*, unpublished MA dissertation. University of London Institute of Education.

3852    John, A. (1991) 'Assessing values in GCSE geography', *Teaching Geography*, 16, 3, pp. 118–119.

3853    Jones, B. and Wales, R. (1983) 'GYSL studies: thoughts related to the pupil studies demanded by the "Avery Hill" O level syllabus', *Teaching Geography*, 9, 1, pp. 31–34.

3854    Jones, M. (1986) 'Evaluation and assessment 11–16' in Boardman, D. (ed) *Handbook for Geography Teachers*. Sheffield: Geographical Association, pp. 234–249.

3855    Jones, S. (1986) 'Coursework assessment 14–16' in Boardman, D. (ed) *Handbook for Geography Teachers*. Sheffield: Geographical Association, pp. 250–256.

3856    Jones, S. and **Reynolds, J.** (1973) 'The development of a new O level syllabus', *Geography*, 58, 3, pp. 263–268.

3857    Joseph, C. (1981) 'Examinations in the 1970s' in Walford, R. (ed) *Signposts for Geography Teaching*. Harlow: Longman, pp. 97–106.

3858    Kemp, R. (1981) 'The common examination at 16+', *Teaching Geography*, 6, 4, p. 158.

3859    King, S. (1997) 'Geography and the GCSE' in Tilbury, D. and Williams, M. (eds) *Teaching and Learning Geography*. London: Routledge, pp. 287–297.

3860    Lambert, D. and **Milton, M.** (1987) 'Managing GCSE coursework', *Teaching Geography*, 12, 5, pp. 199–202.

3861    Larsen, B. (1989) 'Gender bias and the GCSE', *Contemporary Issues in Geography and Education*, 3, 1, pp. 80–84.

3862    Martin, F. (1980) 'Continuous assessment for the CSE: some immediate concerns', *Teaching Geography*, 5, 4, pp. 178–181.

3863    Morten, A. (1984) 'The responsibilities of the chief examiner' in Orrell, K. and Wiegand, P. (eds) *Evaluation and Assessment in Geography*. Sheffield: Geographical Association, pp. 41–42.

3864    Orrell, K. (1984) 'Designing coursework assessment units' in Orrell, K. and Wiegand, P. (eds) *Evaluation and Assessment in Geography*. Sheffield: Geographical Association, pp. 32–34.

3865    Orrell, K. (1987) 'Geography' in Horton, T. (ed) *GCSE: Examining the New System*. London: Harper Row, pp. 85–96.

3866    Orrell, K. (1994) 'Assessment at Key Stage 4: emerging issues' in Walford, R. and Machon, P. (eds) *Challenging Times: Implementing the National Curriculum in Geography*. Cambridge: Cambridge Publishing Services, pp. 84–86.

3867    Orrell, K. (1995) 'GCSE geography: what happens next?', *Teaching Geography*, 20, 3, pp. 137–138.

3868    Orrell, K. and **Wilson, P.** (1994) 'GCSE geography and the post-Dearing era', *Teaching Geography*, 19, 2, pp. 90–91.

3869    Orrell, K. and **Wilson, P.** (1996) 'GCSE syllabuses' in Bailey, P. and Fox, P. (eds) *Geography Teachers' Handbook*. Sheffield: Geographical Association, pp. 217–223.

3870    Pearson, M. (1981) *The Extent and Purpose of Objective Testing in Geography for the 16 Age Group in the Public Examination Set in England and Wales in 1980*, unpublished MA dissertation. University of London Institute of Education.

3871    Rawling, E. (1986) 'Being positive about GCSE', *Teaching Geography*, 12, 1, pp. 2–3.

3872    Roberson, B. S. (1971) 'Geography examinations at O and A level', *Geography*, 56, 2, pp. 96–104.

3873    Roberson, B. S. (1974) 'Geography for GCE O level' in Long, M. (ed) *Handbook for Geography Teachers*. London: Methuen, pp. 36–50.

3874    Roe, P. E. (1971) 'Examining CSE geography', *Geography*, 56, 2, pp. 105–111.

3875    **School Curriculum and Assessment Authority** (1994) *Examining GCSE Geography: A Synopsis of Findings of SEAC's/SCAA's Scrutiny*. London: HMSO.

3876    Stevens, G. (1975) 'On course for a new O level', *Teaching Geography*, 1, 2, pp. 55–60.

3877    Stoner, F. (1974) 'Geography for CSE' in Long, M. (ed) *Handbook for Geography Teachers*. London: Methuen, pp. 51–65.

3878  Thomas, B. (1975) 'Educational objectives and O level geography', *Teaching Geography*, 1, 3, pp. 130–134.

3879  Tidswell, V. (1982) '16+: the way ahead', *Teaching Geography*, 8, 2, pp. 88–89.

3880  Tidswell, V. (1984) 'Examinations: the 16+ question' in Orrell, K. and Wiegand, P. (eds) *Evaluation and Assessment in Geography*. Sheffield: Geographical Association, pp. 46–48.

3881  Tolley, H. (1984) 'A fresh look at the contribution of school-based assessment to examinations' in Orrell, K. and Wiegand, P. (eds) *Evaluation and Assessment in Geography*. Sheffield: Geographical Association, pp. 23–29.

3882  Walford, R. (1986) 'Geography – back to basics?: the new AEB test', *Teaching Geography*, 11, 3, pp. 128–129.

3883  Warn, C. (1984) 'The moderation of school-based assessment' in Orrell, K. and Wiegand, P. (eds) *Evaluation and Assessment in Geography*. Sheffield: Geographical Association, pp. 30–31.

3884  Warn, S. (1984) 'Some guidelines for devising examination questions' in Orrell, K. and Wiegand, P. (eds) *Evaluation and Assessment in Geography*. Sheffield: Geographical Association, pp. 43–45.

3885  Warn, S. (1989) 'Dealing with examination boards' in Wiegand, P. (ed) *Managing the Geography Department*. Sheffield: Geographical Association, pp. 152–159.

3886  Watkins, G. F. (1977) *Fieldwork and Local Studies in the CSE Examination in Geography: The Problem of Evaluation*, unpublished MA dissertation. University of London Institute of Education.

3887  White, M. (1988) 'Developing assessment in years 4 and 5', *Teaching Geography*, 13, 3, pp. 108–113.

3888  Wiegand, P. (1980) *An Investigation into the Feasibility of Using Objective Testing as Part of a Common Examination in Geography at 16+*, unpublished MA dissertation. University of London Institute of Education.

3889  Wiegand, P. (1981) 'The 16+ examination in geography: background to the debate', *Teaching Geography*, 7, 2, pp. 85–87.

3890  Wilson, P. (1985) 'GCSE geography: an update', *Teaching Geography*, 11, 1, pp. 24–25.

3891  Winter, A. (1985) *A Consideration of the Content Validity and Educational Objectives of the Syllabi and Question Papers Set for Examination at Ordinary Level for Geography in Summer 1984*, unpublished MA dissertation. University of London Institute of Education.

3892  Wynn, M. (1987) 'Modes 2 and 3 in GCSE geography', *Teaching Geography*, 12, 4, pp. 173–174.

3893  Younger, M. (1988) 'Oral assessment in GCSE geography', *Teaching Geography*, 13, 3, pp. 117–119.

## (e) Assessment at 16–19

3894  Bateman, D. (1991) 'Linking geography and German at A level', *Teaching Geography*, 16, 3, pp. 120–121.

3895    Bellamy, M. P. (1977) *An Investigation into the Development and Assessment of Affective Objectives in Geographic Education with Special Reference to 16–19 Year Old Pupils in South East London*, unpublished MA dissertation. University of London Institute of Education.

3896    Boardman, D. (1978) 'The N and F proposals: implications of a modular curriculum', *Teaching Geography*, 3, 4, pp. 174–176.

3897    Bowler, I. (1978) 'Quantitative methods in A level geography syllabuses', *Teaching Geography*, 3, 3, pp. 113–115.

3898    Bradford, M. (1995) 'The new A level and AS geography syllabuses', *Teaching Geography*, 20, 3, pp. 145–148.

3899    Burtenshaw, D. (1996) 'Assessment post-16' in Bailey, P. and Fox, P. (eds) *Geography Teachers' Handbook*. Sheffield: Geographical Association, pp. 225–232.

3900    Burtenshaw, D. (1997) 'Examining A- and AS-level geography' in Powell, A. (ed) *Handbook of Post-16 Geography*. Sheffield: Geographical Association, pp. 111–124.

3901    Butt, G. (1993) 'Modules, cores and the new A/AS levels', *Teaching Geography*, 18, 4, pp. 180–181.

3902    Butt, G. (1993) 'The scenario post-16', *Teaching Geography*, 18, 1, pp. 36–37.

3903    Butt, G. (1994) 'Geography, vocational education and assessment', *Teaching Geography*, 19, 4, pp. 182–183.

3904    Butt, G. (1996) 'Developments in geography 14–19: a changing system' in Rawling, E. and Daugherty, R. (eds) *Geography into the Twenty-first Century*. Chichester: John Wiley, pp. 173–193.

3905    Butt, G. (1997) 'Student assessment in geography post-16' in Tilbury, D. and Williams, M. (eds) *Teaching and Learning Geography*. London: Routledge, pp. 298–309.

3906    Clark, J. (1997) 'National Vocational Qualifications and geography: a brief summary' in Powell, A. (ed) *Handbook of Post-16 Geography*. Sheffield: Geographical Association, pp. 125–128.

3907    Convey, A. (1997) 'Geography and the International Baccalaureate' in Powell, A. (ed) *Handbook of Post-16 Geography*. Sheffield: Geographical Association, pp. 105–111.

3908    Daugherty, R. (1982) 'A common core for A level?', *Teaching Geography*, 8, 2, pp. 77–79.

3909    Daugherty, R. (1985) *Examining Geography at 16+: A Study of Decision Making in Two Geography Examinations*. London: Secondary Examinations Council.

3910    Dove, J. (1987) 'Attitudes to A level geography project work', *Geography*, 72, 4, pp. 317–322.

3911    Dutton, R. H. (1977) *An Evaluation of the New University of London Syllabus in Geography at Advanced Level for Examination in and after June 1978*, unpublished MA dissertation. University of London Institute of Education.

3912    Edwards, B. J. (1984) 'A level projects: practicalities and problems', *Teaching Geography*, 9, 4, pp. 159–161.

3913    Frey, A. (1978) 'The N and F proposals: geography in the next decade?', *Teaching Geography*, 3, 3, p. 124.

3914    Frey, A. (1978) 'The N and F debate', *Teaching Geography*, 4, 1, pp. 26–27.

3915 Fyfe, E., Hornby, B. and Jones, M. (1977) 'Constructing a teaching syllabus for the new JMB A level', *Teaching Geography*, 2, 4, pp. 157–161.

3916 Geographical Association (1979) 'Comments on the N and F proposals presented to the Schools Council by the Geographical Association', *Geography*, 64, 3, pp. 224–229.

3917 Geographical Association Sixth Form and University Working Group (1979) 'Skills and techniques for sixth form geography', *Geography*, 64, 1, pp. 37–45.

3918 Graves, N. (1976) 'Geography and the N and F examination proposals', *Teaching Geography*, 2, 3, pp. 131–132.

3919 Graves, N. (1982) 'The examinations jungle: CEE and after', *Teaching Geography*, 7, 3, pp. 133–135.

3920 Grenyer, N. (1978) 'A common syllabus for N and F level?', *Teaching Geography*, 3, 3, pp. 125–127.

3921 Hall, D. (1976) 'The 16–18 question' in Hall, D. (ed) *Geography and the Geography Teacher*. London: Unwin, pp. 192–224.

3922 Hall, D. (1986) 'Advanced level examinations' in Boardman, D. (ed) *Handbook for Geography Teachers*. Sheffield: Geographical Association, pp. 257–268.

3923 Hall, D. (1996) 'Developments at A level' in Rawling, E. and Daugherty, R. (eds) *Geography into the Twenty-first Century*. Chichester: John Wiley, pp. 145–172.

3924 Hart, C. (1984) 'Common core: no cause for concern', *Teaching Geography*, 9, 4, pp. 148–150.

3925 Johnston, R. J. and Gregory, S. (1979) 'Comments on "Skills and techniques for sixth form geography: a report"', *Geography*, 64, 3, pp. 230–231.

3926 Jones, P. F. (1974) 'O level geology and A level geography', *Geography*, 59, 2, pp. 155–157.

3927 Jones, P. F. (1978) 'The new geography at A level: syllabuses and questions', *Teaching Geography*, 3, 4, pp. 161–163.

3928 Jones, P. F. (1984) 'New directions in human geography and their impact on A level syllabuses', *Teaching Geography*, 9, 4, pp. 171–173.

3929 Lee, R. (1984) 'Process and region in the A level syllabus', *Geography*, 69, 2, pp. 97–107.

3930 Lewis, D. (1978) 'N and F: a cause for scepticism?', *Teaching Geography*, 4, 1, pp. 26–27.

3931 McDonald, A. (1988) 'Assessing decision-making in the 16–19 examination', *Teaching Geography*, 13, 4, pp. 149–151.

3932 Megarry, A. (1985) *A Review of Examinations 16–19 with Special Reference to Geography*, unpublished MSc (Ed) dissertation. University of Southampton.

3933 Milton, M. (1986) 'Geography at Advanced Supplementary (AS) level', *Teaching Geography*, 11, 2, p. 86.

3934 Naish, M. (1987) 'Remember AS levels?', *Teaching Geography*, 12, 5, pp. 221–222.

3935 Pilbeam, A. (1980) *Local Projects in A-level Geography*. London: Allen and Unwin.

3936 Price, D. (1979) 'N and F: is school based assessment such a good idea?', *Teaching Geography*, 4, 4, pp. 182–183.

3937    Roberson, B. S. (1971) 'Geography examinations at O and A level', *Geography*, 56, 2, pp. 96–104.

3938    Rynne, E. (1995) *To Understand the Process by which A-level Geography Students Undertake Personal Investigative Work as Part of their Assessment*, unpublished MA dissertation. University of London Institute of Education.

3939    School Curriculum and Assessment Authority (1993) *GCE A and AS Subject Core for Geography*. London: SCAA.

3940    Silson, A. L. (1978) 'Teaching and learning Syllabus B, A level JMB', *Teaching Geography*, 4, 1, pp. 20–22.

3941    Smith, C. (1979) 'Learning A level geography', *Teaching Geography*, 4, 3, pp. 132–133.

3942    Swain, J. R. (1975) 'The JMB Advanced level geography syllabus', *Teaching Geography*, 1, 2, pp. 89–90.

3943    Taylor, J. (1977) 'Examining A level fieldwork', *Teaching Geography*, 3, 1, pp. 12–13.

3944    Tolley, H. (1984) 'New directions for project work in A-level geography' in Orrell, K. and Wiegand, P. (eds) *Evaluation and Assessment in Geography*. Sheffield: Geographical Association, pp. 35–40.

3945    Underwood, B. L. (1983) *An Analysis and Interpretation of the Changing Structure, Content and Cognitive Demand of Selected Geography Examinations at Sixteen and Eighteen Plus*, unpublished PhD thesis. University of London Institute of Education.

3946    Weaver, R. and Chalkley, B. (1997) 'Introducing objective tests and OMR based student assessment: a case study', *Journal of Geography in Higher Education*, 21, 1, pp. 114–121.

3947    Webb, G. (1986) 'Factors affecting achievement in the University of Cambridge GCE A level geography examination', *Educational Research*, 28, 2, pp. 123–138.

3948    Wiegand, P. (1982) 'Objective testing in geography at 16+', *Geography*, 67, 4, pp. 332–336.

## 11. Geography as a Linking Subject

### (a) Arts/humanities/social subjects

3949    Adams, A. (1976) *The Humanities Jungle*. London: Ward Lock Educational.

3950    Andain, I. and Johnson, S. (1973) 'History and geography: an experiment in integration', *Teaching History*, 3, 10, pp. 121–125.

3951    Bailey, P. (1980) 'Relating subjects in the school curriculum: geography and religious education', *Teaching Geography*, 6, 1, pp. 27–29.

3952    Bailey, P. (1982) 'School geography: a decade of change' in Dufour, B. (ed) *New Movements in the Social Sciences and Humanities*. London: Temple Smith, pp. 164–177.

3953    Bailey, P. (1988) 'Combined courses and the geographer: some questions for course planners', *Teaching Geography*, 13, 2, pp. 74–75.

3954    Ball, J., Steinbrink, J. and Stoltman, J. (1971) *The Social Sciences and Geographic Education: A Reader*. New York: John Wiley and Sons.

3955    Banks, V. and Hackman, S. (1993) 'English and geography liaison', *Teaching Geography*, 18, 3, pp. 105–107.

3956    Barnett, S. (1989) 'The arts in environmental education', *Caribbean Journal of Education*, 16, 1/2, pp. 117–130.

3957    Bateman, D. (1991) 'Linking geography and German at A level', *Teaching Geography*, 16, 3, pp. 120–122.

3958    Blyth, A. (1990) *Making the Grade for Primary Humanities*. Milton Keynes: Open University Press.

3959    Blyth, A. (1994) 'History and geography in the primary curriculum' in Bourne, J. (ed) *Thinking through Primary Practice*. London/Milton Keynes: Routledge/Open University Press, pp. 148–156.

3960    Blyth, A., Cooper, K., Derricott, R., Elliott, G. G., Sumner, H. and Waplington, A. (1976) *Place, Time and Society 8–13: Curriculum Planning in History, Geography and Social Science*. Glasgow/Bristol: Collins/ESL for the Schools Council.

3961    Bolam, D. W. (1970/71) 'Integrating the curriculum: a case study in the humanities', *Paedagogica Europaea*, 6, pp. 157–171.

3962    Brough, E. (1983) 'Geography through art' in Huckle, J. (ed) *Geographical Education: Reflection and Action*. Oxford: Oxford University Press, pp. 56–63.

3963    Brown, M. (1986) 'Humanities in practice' in Boardman, D. (ed) *Handbook for Geography Teachers*. Sheffield: Geographical Association, pp. 227–233.

3964    Bunce, V. (1991) 'Geography and the humanities' in Gordon, P. (ed) *Teaching the Humanities*. London: Woburn Press, pp. 50–67.

3965    Chambers, G., Greasley, B. and Winter, C. (1993) 'The National Curriculum: modern foreign languages and geography' in Speak, C. and Wiegand, P. (eds) *International Understanding through Geography*. Sheffield: Geographical Association, pp. 18–21.

3966    Clarke, J. and Wrigley, K. (1988) *Humanities for All: Teaching Humanities in the Secondary School*. London: Cassell.

3967    Dove, J. and Owen, D. (1991) 'Teaching geography through music and sound', *Teaching Geography*, 16, 1, pp. 3–6.

3968    Driscoll, K. J. (1986) 'Geography in the humanities curriculum' in Driscoll, K. J. *Humanities Curriculum Guidelines for the Middle and Secondary Years*. London: Falmer Press, pp. 39–53.

3969    Flaim, M. L. and Chiodo, J. J. (1994) 'A novel approach to geographic education: using literature in the social studies', *Social Studies*, 85, 5, pp. 225–227.

3970    Fredrich, B. and Fuller, K. (1996) 'Linking geography and art: Inness *The Lackawanna Valley*', *Journal of Geography*, 95, 6, pp. 254–262.

3971    Gill, D. (1993) 'Geography' in Pumfrey, P. D. and Verma, G. K. (eds) *Cultural Diversity and the Curriculum, Volume 1: Cross-Curricular Contexts, Themes and Dimensions in Secondary Schools*. London: Falmer Press, pp. 148–160.

3972    Gordon, P. (ed) (1991) *Teaching the Humanities*. London: Woburn Press.

3973    Howlett, C. (1986) *An Investigation into the Conceptual Basis of Lower School Geography Texts as a Pre-requisite to Planning an Inter-disciplinary Humanities Curriculum*, unpublished MA dissertation. University of London Institute of Education.

3974 Huckle, J. (1982) 'Humanistic geography: an introduction' in Wiegand, P. and Orrell, K. *New Leads in Geographical Education*. Sheffield: Geographical Association, pp. 14–20.

3975 Jarrett, B. (1988) 'Drama and geography' in Mills, D. (ed) *Geographical Work in Primary and Middle Schools*. Sheffield: Geographical Association, pp. 56–58.

3976 Johnson, S. (1996) 'Towards 2000: a humanities entitlement at Key Stage 4', *Teaching Geography*, 21, 2, pp. 96–97.

3977 Johnson, T. and Hepple, B. (1978) 'Integrated humanities can work in practice', *Teaching Geography*, 4, 1, pp. 28–30.

3978 Johnston, R. J. (1974) 'Geography and the social sciences', *Geographical Education*, 2, 2, pp. 159–168.

3979 Keller, V. (1986) 'Geography and integration' in Holly, D. *Humanities in Adversity: Teachers' Experience of Integrated Humanities in the 1980s*. London: Falmer Press, pp. 107–121.

3980 Kelly, P. (1988) 'Geography within the humanities' in Mills, D. (ed) *Geographical Work in Primary and Middle Schools*. Sheffield: Geographical Association, pp. 223–230.

3981 Kimber, D., Clough, N., Forrest, M., Harnett, P., Menter, I. and Newman, E. (1995) 'People and place' in Kimber, D. *et al.* (ibid.) *Humanities in Primary Education*. London: David Fulton, pp. 36–60.

3982 Marsden, W. E. (1994) 'Linking geography with history and art: a focused topic work approach' in Marsden, W. E. and Hughes, J. (eds) *Primary School Geography*. London: David Fulton, pp. 107–120.

3983 Mathias, P. (1973) 'Relations with other subjects' in Mathias, P. *The Teachers' Handbook for Social Studies*. London: Blandford Press, pp. 101–136.

3984 Miller, C. R. (1986) *The Contribution of Geography to an Integrated Humanities Course for the Early Secondary Years: A Case Study of an Insider Curriculum Evaluation at the Departmental Level*, unpublished MA dissertation. University of London Institute of Education.

3985 Nicholson, H. N. (1992) *Geography and History in the National Curriculum*. Sheffield: Geographical Association.

3986 Nishi, M. (1973) 'Geographic guidelines for reconstructing the social studies curriculum' in Bale, J., Graves, N. and Walford, R. *Perspectives on Geographical Education*. Edinburgh: Oliver and Boyd, pp. 267–275.

3987 Norton, D. E. (1993) 'Circa 1492 and the integration of literature, reading, and geography (engaging children in literature)', *Reading Teacher*, 46, 7, pp. 610–614.

3988 Oden, P. (1989) 'Geography is everywhere in children's literature', *Journal of Geography*, 88, 3, pp. 151–158.

3989 Paterson, J. L. (1991) 'Putting pop into place: using popular music in the teaching of geography', *New Zealand Journal of Geography*, 92, pp. 18–19.

3990 Proctor, N. (1984) 'Art as graphicacy in the common curriculum', *Journal of Art and Design Education*, 3, 2, pp. 203–214.

3991 Proctor, N. (1987) 'History, geography and humanities: a geographer's interpretation', *Teaching History*, 48, pp. 8–12.

3992 Rainey, D. (1993) 'Foundation subject: geography' in Pumfrey, P. D. and Verma, G. K. (eds) *Cultural Diversity and the Curriculum, Volume 3: Cross-Curricular Contexts, Themes and Dimensions in Primary Schools*. London: Falmer Press, pp. 148–160.

3993 Ross, A. (1993) 'The subjects that dare not speak their name' in Campbell, J. (ed) *Breadth and Balance in the Primary Curriculum*. London: Falmer Press, pp. 137–156.

3994 Ross, A. (1995) 'The rise and fall of the social subjects in the curriculum' in Ahier, J. and Ross, A. (eds) *The Social Subjects within the Curriculum: Children's Social Learning in the National Curriculum*. London: Falmer Press, pp. 53–78.

3995 Schofield, A. (1993) 'Links between geography and history at secondary level' in Speak, C. and Wiegand, P. (eds) *International Understanding through Geography*. Sheffield: Geographical Association, pp. 26–29.

3996 Sharp, D. (1989) 'Geography and modular humanities' in Wiegand, P. (ed) *Managing the Geography Department*. Sheffield: Geographical Association, pp. 136–151.

3997 Slater, A. (1992) 'Sea, sand and haikus: linking geography with art and English', *Teaching Geography*, 17, 1, pp. 19–21.

3998 Smith, B. (1982) 'Geography in an 11–13 humanities course', *Teaching Geography*, 8, 1, pp. 35–36.

3999 Spillane, J. M. (1989) *Humanities 14–16: A Study of the Humanities Provision in Two LEAs and the Contribution of Geography to GCSE Humanities*, unpublished MA dissertation. University of London Institute of Education.

4000 Teather, E. K. (1991) 'Novels and drama in the teaching of geography', *Geographical Education*, 6, 3, pp. 38–43.

4001 Warn, C. (1987) 'Geography in a modular humanities scheme: the Manchester experience', *Teaching Geography*, 12, 3, pp. 106–109.

4002 Whitty, G. (1987) 'Integrated humanities: a curriculum context for ecology and development education' in Lacey, C. and Williams, M. (eds) *Education, Ecology and Development: The Case for an Education Network*. London: World Wildlife Fund/Kogan Page, pp. 129–145.

4003 Yee Sze-onn (1997) 'Make a joyful noise: teaching geography through songs', *Geographical Education*, 10, pp. 57–60.

## (b) Mathematics and science

4004 Adamczyk, P., Binns, T., Brown, A., Cross, S. and Magson, Y. (1994) 'The geography-science interface: a focus for collaboration', *Teaching Geography*, 19, 1, pp. 11–14.

4005 Boardman, D. (1989) 'The mathematics curriculum: implications for teaching map skills', *Teaching Geography*, 14, 3, pp. 116–119.

4006 Burt, T. (1989) 'Science and fieldwork in physical geography', *Teaching Geography*, 14, 4, pp. 151–154.

4007 Clare, P. H. (1977) *A Consideration of the Place of Mathematical Concepts in the Teaching and Learning of Geography at Secondary School Level*, unpublished MSc (Ed) dissertation. University of Southampton.

4008 Girkin, K. G. (1970) *The Relationships between Mathematics and New Developments in Secondary School Geography*, unpublished MA dissertation. University of London Institute of Education.

4009 Goodson, I. F. (1983) 'The defence of geography and biology' in Goodson, I. F. *School Subjects and Curriculum Change: Case Studies in Curriculum History*. London: Croom Helm, pp. 154–171.

4010    Gwilliam, P. (1988) 'Beyond numeracy: practical mathematics through geography' in Mills, D. (ed) *Geographical Work in Primary and Middle Schools*. Sheffield: Geographical Association, pp. 48–55.

4011    Hawley, D. (1997) 'Cross-curricular concerns in geography: earth science and physical geography' in Tilbury, D. and Williams, M. (eds) *Teaching and Learning Geography*. London: Routledge, pp. 80–92.

4012    Henrie, R. L. (1977) 'Geography and the science curriculum' in Manson, G. A. and Ridd, M. K. (eds) *New Perspectives on Geographic Education: Putting Theory into Practice*. Dubuque, IA: Kendall/Hunt, pp. 85–98.

4013    Hilton, K. (1996) 'Physical geography: science or extinction?' in Kent, A., Lambert, D., Naish, M. and Slater, F. (eds) *Geography in Education: Viewpoints on Teaching and Learning*. Cambridge: Cambridge University Press, pp. 3–21.

4014    Jones, P. F. (1974) 'O level geology and A level geography', *Geography*, 59, 2, pp. 155–157.

4015    Kenyon, J. (1994) 'Linking geography with mathematics and science: curriculum integration in a primary school' in Marsden, W. E. and Hughes, J. (eds) *Primary School Geography*. London: David Fulton, pp. 121–155.

4016    Mottershead, D. and Hewitt, M. (1989) Geography and the science National Curriculum', *Teaching Geography*, 14, 4, pp. 156–157.

4017    Parsons, T. and Knight, P. (1991) 'Finding out in physical geography: a question of science?', *Teaching Geography*, 16, 1, pp. 15–17.

4018    Selkirk, K. (1981) 'The mathematical content of some recent geography books for the 11–16 age-group', *Teaching Geography*, 6, 4, pp. 180–185.

4019    Shea, J. H. (1987) 'Science, geology, geography and "cultural literacy"', *Journal of Geological Education*, 35, 5, pp. 244–245.

4020    Thomas, H. and Tidswell, V. (1979) 'Functional adjacency: how can the mathematician help the geographer?', *Teaching Geography*, 5, 1, pp. 31–34.

4021    Trend, R. D. (1992) 'Curricular possibilities at the geography/science interface' in Golby, M. and Appleby, R. (eds) *The Making of the National Curriculum*. Tiverton: Fairway Publications, pp. 39–45.

4022    Trend, R. D. (1992) *Earth Science and Physical Geography in the Secondary School Curriculum*, unpublished PhD thesis. University of Exeter.

4023    Trend, R. D. (1993) 'International understanding: science and geography working together' in Speak, C. and Wiegand, P. (eds) *International Understanding through Geography*. Sheffield: Geographical Association, pp. 22–25.

4024    Trend, R. D. (1994) 'Joint response to SCAA on draft proposals for geography and science from ASE, ESTA and GA', *Teaching Earth Sciences*, 19, 3, pp. 101–103.

4025    Trend, R. D. (1995) *Geography and Science: Forging Links at Key Stage 3*. Sheffield: Geographical Association.

4026    Walker, G. and Winbourne, P. (1993) 'Linking geography and mathematics at Key Stage 3', *Teaching Geography*, 18, 1, pp. 21–23.

4027    Wedden, D. and Wilson, P. A. (1974) 'Geology teaching for geographers in secondary schools' in Long, M. (ed) *Handbook for Geography Teachers*. London: Methuen, pp. 128–134.

# (c) Geography and curriculum integration

4028    Archer, J. E. (1972) *Projects in Geography for the Secondary School*. London: B. T. Batsford.

4029    Aspinall, S. (1978) 'Integration for and against: the case in favour', *Teaching Geography*, 3, 4, pp. 166–168.

4030    Bailey, P. (1987) 'Combined courses and the geographer: some suggested principles for course design' in Bailey, P. and Binns, T. (eds) *A Case for Geography*. Sheffield: Geographical Association, pp. 55–58.

4031    Bailey, P. (1988) 'Combined courses and the geographer: some questions for course planners', *Teaching Geography*, 13, 2, pp. 74–75.

4032    Bull, G. B. G. (1974) 'Geography in integrated studies' in Long, M. (ed) *Handbook for Geography Teachers*. London: Methuen, pp. 87–98.

4033    Carter, R. and Bailey, P. (1996) 'Geography in the whole curriculum' in Bailey, P. and Fox, P. (eds) *Geography Teachers' Handbook*. Sheffield: Geographical Association, pp. 11–27.

4034    Catling, S. (1988) 'On the move' in Tann, C. S. (ed) *Developing Topic Work in the Primary School*. London: Falmer Press, pp. 149–165.

4035    Cleverley, P. (1991) 'Geography: safe if separate?' in Walford, R. (ed) *Viewpoints on Geography Teaching*. Harlow: Longman, pp. 78–79.

4036    Cracknell, R. (1981) 'Project work for the 5–13s' in Mills, D. (ed) *Geographical Work in Primary and Middle Schools*. Sheffield: Geographical Association, pp. 151–161.

4037    Daugherty, R. (1980) '"Integration" through key subjects: key to what?', *Teaching Geography*, 5, 3, pp. 134–135.

4038    Elliott, G. G. (1974) 'Integrated studies: some problems and possibilities for the geographer' in Williams, M. (ed) (1976) *Geography and the Integrated Curriculum: A Reader*. London: Heinemann, pp. 160–165.

4039    Holcroft, F. (1978) 'In favour of teaching geography separately', *Teaching Geography*, 4, 2, pp. 81–82.

4040    Jones, D. (1979) 'Subject integration: geographers need not be defensive', *Teaching Geography*, 4, 3, pp. 113–115.

4041    Mills, D. (1981) 'The teaching of geography as a separate subject' in Mills, D. (ed) *Geographical Work in Primary and Middle Schools*. Sheffield: Geographical Association, pp. 162–175.

4042    Naish, M. (1972) 'Geography in the integrated curriculum' in Graves, N. (ed) *New Movements in the Study and Teaching of Geography*. London: Temple Smith, pp. 55–71.

4043    Phillips, H. (1978) 'Justifications for a single subject approach', *Teaching Geography*, 4, 2, pp. 82–83.

4044    Proctor, N. (1984) 'Geography and the common curriculum', *Geography*, 69, 1, pp. 38–45.

4045    Rawling, E. (1991) 'Geography and cross-curricular themes', *Teaching Geography*, 16, 4, pp. 147–154.

4046    Robinson, R. (1994) 'Cross-curricular benefits for classroom geography', *Teaching Geography*, 19, 4, pp. 178–179.

4047   Seaden-Jones, P. T. (1982) *Geography and Integrated Studies in the Lower Secondary School*, unpublished MA dissertation. University of London Institute of Education.

4048   Skelton, I. A. N. (1977) *A Case Study of Curriculum Integration in the Lower Years of the Secondary School: A Geographer's Evaluation*, unpublished MSc (Ed) dissertation. University of Southampton.

4049   Williams, M. (ed) (1976) *Geography and the Integrated Curriculum: A Reader*. London: Heinemann.

4050   Williams, M. (1984) *Designing and Teaching Integrated Courses*. Sheffield: Geographical Association.

4051   Williams, M. (1986) 'Planning combined studies' in Boardman, D. (ed) *Handbook for Geography Teachers*. Sheffield: Geographical Association, pp. 219–226.

4052   Williams, M. (1992) 'Geography and cross-curricularity' in Hill, A. D. (ed) *International Perspectives on Geographic Education*. Boulder, CO/Skokie, IL: IGUCGE/Rand, McNally and Co., pp. 101–110.

# 12. Managing Geography

4053   Bailey, P. (1972) 'The organisation and management of geography departments in comprehensive schools', *Geography*, 57, 3, pp. 226–231.

4054   Bailey, P. (1981) 'Appraising the performance of departments in maintained secondary schools: concepts and approaches' in Ribbins, P. and Thomas, H. (eds) *Research in Educational Management and Administration (BEMAS Occasional Paper)*. Sheffield: BEMAS.

4055   Bailey, P. (1983) 'Greater than the sum of its parts?: making the most of the geography department', *Teaching Geography*, 8, 3, pp. 98–99.

4056   Bailey, P. and Fox, P. (eds) (1996) *Geography Teachers' Handbook*. Sheffield: Geographical Association.

4057   Bramley, W. and Wood, P. (1982) 'Collaboration, consultation and conflict: the process of change in a teaching department', *Journal of Geography in Higher Education*, 5, pp. 45–54.

4058   Brown, B. (1989) 'Management strategies for meeting increased enrolments in introductory college geography courses', *Journal of Geography in Higher Education*, 8, pp. 226–229.

4059   Brunn, S. D. (1990) 'Hiring, evaluation, promotion and tenure decisions in a US geography department', *Journal of Geography in Higher Education*, 14, 2, pp. 111–122.

4060   Burke, M. (1990) *After the Elton Report: An Investigation into the Initial Training of Geography Teachers in Classroom Management and Control*, unpublished MA dissertation. University of London Institute of Education.

4061   Cambers, G. (1996) 'Managing the departmental team, and departmental self-assessment' in Bailey, P. and Fox, P. (eds) *Geography Teachers' Handbook*. Sheffield: Geographical Association, pp. 279–285.

4062   Campion, K., Carter, R. and Krause, J. (1997) 'OFSTED revisited: how to make the best use of prior experience', *Teaching Geography*, 22, 4, pp. 170–172.

4063    Cracknell, J. R. (1985) *The Setting Up and Evaluation of an In-service Course for Computer Assisted Learning in Geography*, unpublished MA dissertation. University of London Institute of Education.

4064    Dalton, T. H. (1988) *The Challenge of Curriculum Innovation: A Study of Ideology and Practice.* London: Falmer Press.

4065    Dove, M. J. (1987) *Opportunities and Obstacles: The Adoption of Computer-assisted Learning by Geography Teachers in Victoria, Australia*, unpublished MA dissertation. University of London Institute of Education.

4066    Gold, J. R., Jenkins, A., Lee, R., Monk, J., Riley, J., Shepherd, I. and Unwin, D. (1993) *Teaching Geography in Higher Education: A Manual of Good Practice.* Oxford: Blackwell/Institute of British Geographers.

4067    Harris, C. (1996) 'Managing, and benefiting from, an OFSTED inspection' in Bailey, P. and Fox, P. (eds) *Geography Teachers' Handbook.* Sheffield: Geographical Association, pp. 291–296.

4068    Kent, A. (1996) *Process and Pattern of a Curriculum Innovation*, unpublished PhD thesis. University of London Institute of Education.

4069    Kent, A. (1997) 'Challenging geography: a personal view', *Geography*, 82, 4, pp. 293–304.

4070    Luker, K. (1996) 'Managing resources' in Bailey, P. and Fox, P. (eds) *Geography Teachers' Handbook.* Sheffield: Geographical Association, pp. 287–289.

4071    Naish, M. (1990) 'Managing change in the geography curriculum: the case of Geography 16–19', *Asian Geographer*, 9, 2, pp. 123–129.

4072    Naish, M. (1996) 'Developing understanding of the dynamics of change in the geography curriculum' in van der Schee, J., Schoenmaker, G., Trimp, H. and van Westrhenen, H. (eds) *Innovation in Geographical Education (Netherlands Geographical Studies, 208).* Utrecht/Amsterdam: IGUCGE/Centrum voor Educatieve Geografie Vrije Universiteit Amsterdam, pp. 239–248.

4073    Parsons, C. (1987) *The Curriculum Change Game: A Longitudinal Study of the Schools Council 'Geography for the Young School Leaver' Project.* London: Falmer Press.

4074    Quinn, G. (1984) 'Department management' in Orrell, K. and Wiegand, P. (eds) *Evaluation and Assessment in Geography.* Sheffield: Geographical Association, pp. 7–8.

4075    Rawlings, J. (1980) 'Reflections on four years as head of department', *Teaching Geography*, 6, 1, pp. 33–34.

4076    Rogers, S. (1987) *The Constraining and Enabling Influences on the Take-up of CAL in Geography in Essex Secondary Schools*, unpublished MA dissertation. University of London Institute of Education.

4077    Siddelley, J. (1989) 'Managing advisers and HMI' in Wiegand, P. (ed) *Managing the Geography Department.* Sheffield: Geographical Association, pp. 103–106.

4078    Smith, P. (1997) 'Standards achieved: a review of geography in secondary schools in England, 1995–96', *Teaching Geography*, 22, 3, pp. 125–126.

4079    Tolley, H., Biddulph, M. and Fisher, T. (1996) *The Professional Development Management File.* Cambridge: Chris Kington Publishing.

4080    Wiegand, P. (ed) (1989) *Managing the Geography Department.* Sheffield: Geographical Association.

4081    Williams, M. (1983) 'Inactive heads of geography departments?', *Teaching Geography*, 7, pp. 21–23.

# C. GEOGRAPHICAL EDUCATION IN SOCIAL CONTEXT

## 1. Geography and Political Education

### (a) Geography and citizenship education

4082    Bailey, P. (1993) 'Citizenship and core and foundation subjects: geography' in Edwards, J. and Fogelman, K. (eds) *Developing Citizenship in the Curriculum*. London: David Fulton, pp. 58–61.

4083    Driver, F. and Maddrell, A. M. C. (1996) 'Geographical education and citizenship: introduction', *Journal of Historical Geography*, 22, 4, pp. 371–372.

4084    Edwards, J. and Trott, C. (1995) 'Education for citizenship in Key Stages 1 and 2', *Curriculum Journal*, 6, 3, pp. 395–408.

4085    Fogelman, K. (1992) 'Citizenship education and the National Curriculum', *Curriculum*, 13, 3, pp. 158–162.

4086    Gilbert, R. (1995) 'Education for citizenship and the problem of identity in post-modern political culture' in Ahier, J. and Ross, A. (eds) *The Social Subjects within the Curriculum*. London: Falmer Press, pp. 11–30.

4087    Grimshaw, P. M. and Briggs, K. (1970) 'Geography and citizenship: pupil participation in town and country planning', *Geography*, 55, 3, pp. 307–331.

4088    Huckle, J. (1988) 'Geography and world citizenship' in Fien, J. and Gerber, R. (eds) *Teaching Geography for a Better World*. Edinburgh: Oliver and Boyd, pp. 20–30.

4089    John, A. (1994) 'Geography and citizenship: cycling on the avenues', *Teaching Geography*, 19, 3, p. 126.

4090    Jones, E. B. and Jones, N. (eds) (1992) *Education for Citizenship: Ideas and Perspectives for Cross-curricular Study*. London: Kogan Page.

4091    Kerr, D. (1996) *Citizenship in Primary Schools*. London: Institute of Citizenship Studies.

4092    Machon, P. (1991) 'Subject or citizen', *Teaching Geography*, 16, 3, p. 128.

4093    Maddrell, A. M. C. (1996) 'Empire, emigration and school geography: changing discourses on imperial citizenship 1880–1925', *Journal of Historical Geography*, 22, 4, pp. 373–387.

4094    Martin, L. (1995) 'Citizenship, cultural diversity and the geography curriculum', *British Journal of Curriculum and Assessment*, 5, 2, pp. 30–31.

4095    Matless, D. (1996) 'Visual culture and geographical citizenship: England in the 1940s', *Journal of Historical Geography*, 22, 4, pp. 424–439.

4096    Nash, C. (1996) 'Geo-centric education and anti-imperialism: theosophy, geography and citizenship in the writings of J. H. Cousins', *Journal of Historical Geography*, 22, 4, pp. 399–411.

4097 Walford, R. (1996) 'Geographical education and citizenship: an afterword', *Journal of Historical Geography*, 22, 4, pp. 440–442.

4098 Wiegand, P. (1990) 'Geography, citizenship and international understanding' in Catling, S. (ed) *Some Issues for Geography within the National Curriculum*. Sheffield: Geographical Association, pp. 81–85.

4099 Wong, W. Y. and **Marsden**, W. E. (1993) 'Continuity and change in geography's contribution to citizenship education in England in the 19th and 20th centuries', *Paedagogica Historica*, 29, 2, pp. 483–502.

## (b) Geography and political literacy

4100 Barrs, D. (1982) 'The art of the gerrymander: a classroom exercise in political geography', *Teaching Politics*, 11, 1, pp. 86–98.

4101 **Birmingham Development Education Centre** (1996) *Where to Draw the Line: Studies in Political Development for A Level Geography*. Harlow/Birmingham: Longman/DEC.

4102 Butt, G. (1990) 'Political understanding through geography teaching', *Teaching Geography*, 15, 2, pp. 62–65.

4103 Conley, F. (1990) 'How can politics teachers help geographers?', *Teaching Geography*, 15, 2, pp. 58–59.

4104 Cook, I. and **Pepper**, D. (ed) (no date) 'Anarchism and geography', *Contemporary Issues in Geography and Education*, 3, 2 (whole issue).

4105 Crick, B. (1990) 'Politics and geography', *Teaching Geography*, 15, 2, pp. 51–52.

4106 Fien, J. (1991) 'Ideology, political education and teacher education: matching paradigms and models', *Journal of Curriculum Studies*, 23, 3, pp. 239–256.

4107 Fry, P. (1987) *Dealing with Political Bias through Geographical Education*, unpublished MA dissertation. University of London Institute of Education.

4108 Harwood, D. (1984) 'The World Studies 8–13 project and political education: some problems of dissemination', *Curriculum*, 5, 3, pp. 30–36.

4109 Hickling-Hudson, A. (1994) 'The environment as radical politics: can "Third World" education rise to the challenge?', *International Review of Education*, 40, 1, pp. 19–36.

4110 Hopkin, J. and **Serf**, J. (1986) 'Geography and political education', *Teaching Geography*, 11, 2, pp. 82–85.

4111 Huckle, J. (1983) 'Political education' in Huckle, J. (ed) *Geographical Education: Reflection and Action*. Oxford: Oxford University Press, pp. 82–88.

4112 Huckle, J. (1983) 'The politics of school geography' in Huckle, J. (ed) *Geographical Education: Reflection and Action*. Oxford: Oxford University Press, pp. 143–154.

4113 Huckle, J. (1984) 'Explaining unemployment: an example of political education through geography', *Teaching Geography*, 9, 3, pp. 99–103.

4114 Huckle, J. (1988) 'The Daintree rainforest: developing political literacy through an environmental issue' in Fien, J. and Gerber, R. (eds) *Teaching Geography for a Better World*. Edinburgh: Oliver and Boyd, pp. 45–60.

4115 Huckle, J. (1997) 'Towards a critical school geography' in Tilbury, D. and Williams, M. (eds) *Teaching and Learning Geography*. London: Routledge, pp. 241–252.

4116    Huckle, J. and Machon, P. (1990) 'Geography and political education in the National Curriculum: first you see it and then you don't!', *Teaching Geography*, 15, 2, pp. 53–57.

4117    McElroy, B. (1988) 'Learning geography: a route to political literacy' in Fien, J. and Gerber, R. (eds) *Teaching Geography for a Better World*. Edinburgh: Oliver and Boyd, pp. 31–42.

4118    Machon, P. (1991) 'Geography' in Conley, F. (ed) *Political Understanding Across the Curriculum*. London: Politics Association, pp. 57–76.

4119    Marvell, A. (1997) 'Social and political dimensions in post-16 geography' in Powell, A. (ed) *Handbook of Post-16 Geography*. Sheffield: Geographical Association, pp. 167–174.

4120    Morris, J. S. (1992) '"Back to the future": the impact of political ideology on the design and implementation of geography in the National Curriculum', *Curriculum Journal*, 3, 1, pp. 75–85.

4121    Osborne, K. (1991) 'Geography's contribution to political education', *Geographical Education*, 6, 3, pp. 25–28.

4122    Sandford, M. (1986) 'Geography's contribution to political and economic understanding', *Teaching Geography*, 11, 2, pp. 69–70.

4123    Short, J. (1985) 'The new political geography' in Kent, A. (ed) *Perspectives on a Changing Geography*. Sheffield: Geographical Association, pp. 76–79.

## 2. Geography and Equal Opportunities

### (a) Social justice/welfare issues

4124    Bale, J. (1981) 'Teaching welfare issues in urban geography: a work unit on externalities' in Walford, R. (ed) *Signposts for Geography Teaching*. Harlow: Longman, pp. 51–63.

4125    Bale, J. (1983) 'Welfare approaches to geography' in Huckle, J. (ed) *Geographical Education: Reflection and Action*. Oxford: Oxford University Press, pp. 63–73.

4126    Brooker-Gross, S. R. (1991) 'Teaching about race, gender, class and geography through fiction', *Journal of Geography in Higher Education*, 15, 1, pp. 35–47.

4127    Coates, B. E. (1982) 'Towards a geography of social well-being' in Wiegand, P. and Orrell, K. (eds) *New Leads in Geographical Education*. Sheffield: Geographical Association, pp. 21–26.

4128    Gilbert, R. and Singh, M. (1992) 'Geography teaching and social justice', *Geographical Education*, 6, 4, pp. 7–12.

4129    Hall, G. (1982) 'Spatial injustice in the city: a workshop based on GYSL material' in Wiegand, P. and Orrell, K. (eds) *New Leads in Geographical Education*. Sheffield: Geographical Association, pp. 59–62.

4130    Hammond, R. (1978) 'Externalities: the benefits and penalties of where you live', *Teaching Geography*, 4, 2, pp. 68–70.

4131    Knox, P. (1985) 'The geography of social concern' in Kent, A. (ed) *Perspectives on a Changing Geography*. Sheffield: Geographical Association, pp. 58–69.

4132    Lambert, D. (1992) 'Towards a geography of social concern' in Naish, M. (ed) *Geography and Education: National and International Perspectives*. London: University of London Institute of Education, pp. 144–159.

4133    Lee, R. (1983) 'Teaching geography: the dialectic of structure and agency' in Boardman, D. (ed) *New Directions in Geographical Education*. London: Falmer Press, pp. 199–216.

4134    Simpson, A. (1984) 'The rich as a minority group', *Contemporary Issues in Geography and Education*, 1, 2, pp. 18–21.

4135    Smith, D. L. (1974) 'Social relevance in geographical education: relevance for whom? relevance for when?', *Geographical Education*, 2, 2, pp. 173–184.

4136    Storm, M. (1973) 'Schools and the community: an issue based approach' in Bale, J., Graves, N. and Walford, R. (eds) *Perspectives in Geographical Education*. Edinburgh: Oliver and Boyd, pp. 289–304.

## (b) Multi-cultural issues

4137    Barrett, H. (1996) 'Education without prejudice' in Bailey, P. and Fox, P. (eds) *Geography Teachers' Handbook*. Sheffield: Geographical Association, pp. 29–37.

4138    Brooker-Gross, S. R. (1991) 'Teaching about race, gender, class and geography through fiction', *Journal of Geography in Higher Education*, 15, 1, pp. 35–47.

4139    Carter, D. (1987) 'Resources for multicultural education: a view from the primary school', *Teaching Geography*, 12, 4, pp. 52–153.

4140    Gill, D. (1982) 'The contribution of secondary school geography to multicultural education: a critical review of some materials', *Multiracial Education*, 10, 3, pp. 13–26.

4141    Gill, D. (1983) 'Anti-racism education: of what relevance to the geography curriculum?', *Contemporary Issues in Geography and Education*, 1, 1, pp. 6–10.

4142    Gill, D. (1983) 'Anti-racist teaching through geography', *Contemporary Issues in Geography and Education*, 1, 1, pp. 34–36.

4143    Gill, D. (1985) 'Geographical education for a multicultural society' in Straber-Welds, M. (ed) *Education for a Multicultural Society: A Case Study in ILEA Schools*. London: Bell and Hyman, pp. 58–69.

4144    Gonzalez, B. and Gonzalez, E. (1997) 'Equal opportunity and the teaching of geography' in Tilbury, D. and Williams, M. (eds) *Teaching and Learning Geography*. London: Routledge, pp. 117–132.

4145    Hacking, E. (1991) 'Preparing for life in a multi-cultural society' in Walford, R. (ed) *Viewpoints on Geographical Education*. Harlow: Longman, pp. 85–88.

4146    Hicks, D. (1981) 'The contribution of geography to multicultural misunderstanding', *Teaching Geography*, 7, 2, pp. 64–67.

4147    Hicks, D. (1981) *Minorities: A Teacher's Resource Book for the Multi-ethnic Curriculum*. London: Routledge.

4148    Jackson, P. (1989) 'Challenging racism through geography teaching', *Journal of Geography in Higher Education*, 13, 1, pp. 5–14.

4149    Marsden, W. E. (1990) 'Rooting racism into the educational experience of childhood and youth in the nineteenth and twentieth centuries', *History of Education*, 19, 4, pp. 333–353.

4150     Mills, C. (1988) 'Geography teaching within a multi-ethnic society' in Mills, D. (ed) *Geographical Work in Primary and Middle Schools*. Sheffield: Geographical Association, pp. 58–61.

4151     Preiswerk, R. (ed) (1980) *The Slant of the Pen*. Geneva: World Council of Churches.

4152     Singh, M. (1991) 'Geography's contribution to multicultural education', *Geographical Education*, 6, 3, pp. 9–13.

4153     Walford, R. (1985) *Geographical Education for a Multi-cultural Society*. Sheffield: Geographical Association.

4154     Walford, R. (1993) 'Geography' in King, A. and Reiss, M. (eds) *The Multicultural Dimension of the National Curriculum*. London: Falmer Press, pp. 91–108.

4155     Wright, D. (1983) 'A portrait of racism in geography', *Education Journal*, 5, 2, pp. 1–5.

4156     Wright, D. (1985) 'In black and white: racist bias in textbooks', *Geographical Education*, 5, 1, pp. 13–17.

4157     Wright, D. (1986) 'Racism in school textbooks' in Punter, D. (ed) *Introduction to Contemporary Cultural Studies*. London: Longman, pp. 223–236.

## (c) Gender issues

4158     Atkinson, J. (1992) 'How are women in the Third World portrayed in geography textbooks?', *Teaching Geography*, 17, 4, pp. 179–180.

4159     Bale, J. (1982) 'Sexism in geographical education' in Kent, A. (ed) *Bias in Geographical Education*. Sheffield: Geographical Association, pp. 3–10.

4160     Beatty, W. W. and Troster, A. I. (1987) 'Gender differences in geographical knowledge', *Sex Roles*, 16, 11/12, pp. 565–590.

4161     Bowlby, S. (1992) 'Feminist geography and the changing curriculum', *Geography*, 77, 4, pp. 349–360.

4162     Boardman, D. (1990) 'Graphicacy revisited: mapping abilities and gender differences', *Educational Review*, 42, 1, pp. 57–64.

4163     Bramwell, J. (1987) 'Pupils' attitudes towards geography in the lower school: an investigation into gender issues', *Geography*, 72, 1, pp. 46–48.

4164     Brooker-Gross, S. R. (1991) 'Teaching about race, gender, class and geography through fiction', *Journal of Geography in Higher Education*, 15, 1, pp. 35–47.

4165     Connolly, J. (1992) 'Geography: equal opportunities and the National Curriculum' in Myers, K. (ed) *Genderwatch*, Cambridge: Cambridge University Press, pp. 143–146.

4166     Connolly, J. (1993) 'Gender balanced geography: have we got it right yet?', *Teaching Geography*, 16, 2, pp. 61–64.

4167     Franchi, N. M. (1987) *Gender and Geography: The Need for Anti-sexist Teaching Resources*, unpublished MA dissertation. University of London Institute of Education.

4168     Larsen, B. (ed) (no date) 'Gender bias and the GCSE', *Contemporary Issues in Geography and Education*, 3, 1, pp. 80–84.

4169     Larsen, B. (1983) 'Geography' in Whyld, J. (ed) *Sexism in the Secondary Curriculum*. London: Harper and Row, pp. 165–178.

4170    Loyd, B. and Rengert, A. (eds) (1978) 'Women in geographic curricula', *Journal of Geography*, 77, 5, pp. 164–191.

4171    Marriott, A. (1985) 'Geography as a girls' subject', *Teaching Geography*, 11, 1, p. 29.

4172    Matthews, M. H. (1984) 'Cognitive mapping abilities of young boys and girls', *Geography*, 69, 4, pp. 327–336.

4173    Matthews, M. H. (1986) 'Gender, graphicacy and geography', *Educational Review*, 38, 3, pp. 259–271.

4174    Matthews, M. H. (1987) 'Gender, home range and environmental cognition', *Transactions of the Institute of British Geographers*, 12, 1, pp. 43–56.

4175    Monk, J. (1988) 'Engendering a new geographic vision' in Fien, J. and Gerber, R. (eds) *Teaching Geography for a Better World*. Edinburgh: Oliver and Boyd, pp. 91–103.

4176    Monk, J. (1996) 'Partial truths: feminist perspectives on ends and means' in Williams, M. (ed) *Understanding Geographical and Environmental Education: The Role of Research*. London: Cassell, pp. 274–286.

4177    Riding, R. J. and Boardman, D. (1983) 'The relationship between sex and learning style and graphicacy in 14-year-old children', *Educational Review*, 35, 1, pp. 69–79.

4178    Self, C. M., Gopal, S., Golledge, R. G. and Fenstermaker, S. (1992) 'Gender-related differences in spatial abilities', *Progress in Human Geography*, 16, 3, pp. 315–342.

4179    Slater, F. (1983) 'Sexism and racism: parallel experiences: an exploration', *Contemporary Issues in Geography and Education*, 1, 1, pp. 26–31.

4180    Townsend, J. G. and Townsend, A. R. (1988) 'Teaching gender: north–south', *Geography*, 73, 2, pp. 193–201.

4181    Warner, H. (1993) 'Equal opportunities: IT and gender', *Teaching Geography*, 18, 3, pp. 134–135.

4182    Wiegand, P. (1986) 'Sex bias and differentiation' in Boardman, D. (ed) *Handbook for Geography Teachers*. Sheffield: Geographical Association, pp. 193–197.

4183    Williamson-Fien, J. (1988) 'Limits to growth: a feminist perspective' in Fien, J. and Gerber, R. (eds) *Teaching Geography for a Better World*. Edinburgh: Oliver and Boyd, pp. 104–116.

4184    Wright, D. (1985) 'Are geography textbooks sexist?', *Teaching Geography*, 10, 2, pp. 81–84.

## (d) Age issues

4185    Gant, R. (1997) 'Elderly people, personal mobility and local environment', *Geography*, 82, 3, pp. 207–217.

4186    Gant, R. (1997) 'Geographical investigations with elderly people' in Naish, M. (ed) *Values in Geography Education*. London: University of London Institute of Education, pp. 76–80.

4187    Haddock, K. C. (1993) 'Teaching geography of the aged: a suggested resource', *Journal of Geography*, 92, 3, pp. 118–120.

4188    Haddock, K. C. and Mulvihili, J. L. (1981) 'Assessing the locational attributes of housing for the elderly through classroom and field studies', *Journal of Geography*, 80, 4, pp. 136–141.

4189    Harper, S. and Laws, G. (1995) 'Rethinking the geography of ageing', *Progress in Human Geography*, 19, 2, pp. 199–221.

4190    Marsden, W. E. (1988) 'The age aspect in human rights geography in school', *Teaching Geography*, 13, 4, pp. 146–148.

4191    Rowles, G. D. (1980) 'Toward a geography of growing old' in Buttimer, A. and Seamon, D. (eds) *The Human Experience of Place and Space*. London: Croom Helm, pp. 55–72.

4192    Warnes, A. M. (1981) 'Towards a geographical contribution to gerontology', *Progress in Human Geography*, 5, 3, pp. 317–341.

4193    Warnes, A. M. (1982) *Geographical Perspectives on the Elderly*. London: John Wiley and Sons.

# 3. Geography and Economic and Industrial Awareness

See also Part B Sub-section 6e.

4194    Butt, G. (1992) 'Education through industrial visits', *Teaching Geography*, 17, 2, pp. 78–80.

4195    Carter, R. (1991) 'Industrial and economic understanding: a matter of values', *Teaching Geography*, 16, 1, p. 30.

4196    Carter, R. (1993) 'Recent developments in geography and economic and industrial understanding', *Teaching Geography*, 18, 1, p. 34.

4197    Corney, G. (1985) *Geography, Schools and Industry*. Sheffield: Geographical Association.

4198    Corney, G. (1986) 'Teaching for economic understanding', *Teaching Geography*, 11, 3, pp. 106–110.

4199    Corney, G. (1987) 'Economic processes and policies in teaching geography: the example of the Geographical Association's Geography, Schools and Industry Project' in Bailey, P. and Binns, T. (eds) *A Case for Geography*. Sheffield: Geographical Association, pp. 45–47.

4200    Corney, G. (1989) *Geography and Economic Understanding: A Paper on Behalf of the Geographical Association Submitted to the National Curriculum Geography Working Group*. Sheffield: Geographical Association.

4201    Corney, G. (1990) *Teaching Geography for Economic Understanding: The Experience of GSIP*. Sheffield: Geographical Association.

4202    Corney, G. (1991) 'The Geography, Schools and Industry Project' in Walford, R. (ed) *Viewpoints on Geography Teaching*. Harlow: Longman, pp. 48–51.

4203    Corney, G. (1992) *Teaching Economic Understanding through Geography*. Sheffield: Geographical Association.

4204    Curriculum Council for Wales (1994) *Developing Economic and Industrial Understanding through Geography and History*. Cardiff: CCW.

4205    Davies, P. (1993) 'Handling economic ideas and values in geography teaching', *Economic Awareness*, 6, 1, pp. 3–8.

4206    Hawkes, D. S. (1986) *Geography, Schools and Industry: An Investigation of Employers' Perceptions*, unpublished MA dissertation. University of London Institute of Education.

4207     Kelly, J. (1986) 'GSIP: action and involvement', *Teaching Geography*, 11, 3, pp. 115–117.

4208     Kemp, R. (1985) 'Is what you teach about industry really relevant?', *Teaching Geography*, 10, 2, pp. 54–55.

4209     Lambert, D. (1989) 'Working with industry producing classroom materials', *Teaching Geography*, 14, 1, pp. 6–7.

4210     National Curriculum Council (1992) *Geography and Economic Understanding at Key Stages 3 and 4*. York: NCC.

4211     Rawling, E. (1988) 'Geography for economic understanding', *Teaching Geography*, 13, 2, p. 50.

4212     Rawling, E. (1989) 'Geography for economic understanding: in Cheshire', *Teaching Geography*, 14, 2, p. 80.

4213     Rawling, E. (1990) 'Geography: working with the community to study a local issue', *Economic Awareness*, 2, 3, pp. 9–14.

4214     Rawling, E. (1991) 'Education for economic understanding through geography', *Geographical Education*, 6, 3, pp. 29–34.

4215     Rawling, E. and Davies, P. (1991) *Economic Awareness Guide: Geography*. Harlow: Longman/Economics Association.

4216     Ross, A. and Hutchings, M. (1990) *Enterprise, Economic and Industrial Understanding in the Curriculum (Primary Enterprise Pack)*. London: Enterprise Awareness in Teacher Education/PNL Press.

4217     Sandford, M. (1986) 'Geography's contribution to political and economic understanding', *Teaching Geography*, 11, 2, pp. 69–70.

4218     Williams, M. and Khalid, K. (1994) 'Geography as a vehicle for economic and industrial understanding: a comparative study of England, Wales and Malaysia', *IRGEE*, 3, 1, pp. 19–30.

## 4. Geography and the European Dimension

4219     Audigier, F. (1992) *The European Dimension in Geography: One Level amongst Others (Council of Europe Seminar Report)*. Strasbourg: CEC.

4220     Beasley, K. (1997) 'The European dimension: organising a "Europe Day"', *Teaching Geography*, 22, 1, pp. 33–34.

4221     Bell, G. H. (1991) *Developing a European Dimension in Primary Schools*. London: David Fulton.

4222     Bell, G. H. (1991) 'European citizenship: 1992 and beyond', *Westminster Studies in Education*, 14, pp. 15–25.

4223     Bell, G. H. (1995) *Educating European Citizens*. London: David Fulton.

4224     Bell, G. H. (1995) 'Towards a European dimension in the early years curriculum', *Early Years*, 12, 2, pp. 22–28.

4225    Biilmann, O. and **Williams, M.** (1984) 'Studies of pupils' private geography in the context of the "European Dimension in Geographical Education" project' in Haubrich, H. (ed) *Perception of People and Places through Media, Volume 1.* Freiburg: IGUCGE/Pädagogische Hochschule Freiburg, pp. 164–199.

4226    **Blackwell, M.** (1992) 'Geography and ERASMUS in the United Kingdom', *Journal of Geography in Higher Education*, 16, 1, pp. 76–83.

4227    **Campbell, R., Clary, M., Convey, A., Haubrich, H., Hodgson, K.** and **Wetzler, H.** (1997) *ENVERS: Towards Environmental Education in European Schools.* Brussels: European Commission.

4228    **Central Bureau for Educational Visits and Exchanges** (1991) *Making the Most of your Partner School Abroad.* London: Central Bureau.

4229    **Central Bureau for Educational Visits and Exchanges** (1993) *European Dimension in Teaching.* London: Central Bureau.

4230    **Convey, A.** (1988) *The European Dimension in Initial Teacher Training Courses in the UK: A Survey with Recommendations.* London: UK Centre for European Education.

4231    **Convey, A.** (1989) *Teacher Training and 1992.* London: UK Centre for European Education/Central Bureau.

4232    **Convey, A.** (1992) *Approaches to the European Dimension in Teacher Education.* London: UK Centre for European Education/Central Bureau.

4233    **Convey, A.** (1995) 'The European dimension in teacher education' in Phillips, D. (ed) *Aspects of Education and the European Union (Oxford Studies in Comparative Education*, 5, 2; special edition). Wallingford: Triangle Journals, pp. 77–98.

4234    **Convey, A.** (1996) 'Achieving a European dimension in the training of geography teachers: review and future perspective' in van der Zijpp, T., van der Schee, J. and Trimp, H. (eds) *Innovation in Geographical Education: Proceedings of the 28th International Geographical Congress Commission on Geographical Education.* Amsterdam: IGUCGE/Centrum voor Educatieve Geografie Vrije Universiteit Amsterdam, pp. 211–219.

4235    **Convey, A.** (1997) 'The case for the European dimension', *Primary Geographer*, 29, pp. 4–6.

4236    **Convey, A.** (1997) 'Know your European population geography' in Convey, A. and Nolzen, H. (eds) *Geography and Education (Münchner Studien zur Didaktik der Geographie, Band 10).* Munich: Lehrstuhl für Didaktik der Geographie der Universität München, pp. 69–76.

4237    **Convey, A., Evans, M., Green, S., Macaro, E.** and **Mellor, J.** (1997) *Pupils' Perceptions of Europe: Identity and Education.* London: Cassell.

4238    **Convey, A., Greasley, B.** and **Winter, C.** (1993) 'Geography and the European dimension in the National Curriculum' in Speak, C. and Wiegand, P. (eds) *International Understanding through Geography.* Sheffield: Geographical Association, pp. 30–37.

4239    **Convey, A.** and **Speak, C.** (1994) *A European Dimension in the Teaching of Geography: An Introduction.* Sheffield: Geographical Association.

4240    **Council of Europe** (1993) *The European Dimension of Environmental Education in Secondary Schools.* Strasbourg: CEC.

4241    **Department of Education and Science** (1991) *The European Dimension in Education.* London: DES.

4242    Donert, K. (1997) 'Exploiting your European dimension', *Teaching Geography*, 22, 3, pp. 134–137.

4243    Dussart, G. B. J. (1990) 'Environmental education in Europe: a synoptic view', *Environmental Education and Information*, 9, 2, pp. 59–72.

4244    Farroni, T. and Barret, M. (1996) 'English and Italian children's knowledge of European geography', *British Journal of Developmental Psychology*, 14, 3, pp. 257–273.

4245    Freeman, P. and Nicholas, H. (eds) (1977) *European Studies Handbook*. London: Longman.

4246    Gale, P. and Hunt, J. (1993) *Into Europe: Planning and Delivering the Curriculum in the 90s*. Lancaster: Framework.

4247    Goodson, F. and McGivney, V. (1985) *The European Dimension in the Secondary School Curriculum*. London: Falmer Press.

4248    Halocha, J. (1997) 'The European dimension in primary education' in Tilbury, D. and Williams, M. (eds) *Teaching and Learning Geography*. London: Routledge, pp. 231–240.

4249    Haubrich, H. (1997) 'Identity, solidarity and the new geography of Europe: teaching ideas and materials', *Geography*, 82, 1, pp. 45–57.

4250    Hughes, J. and Paterson, K. (1994) 'Primary geography and the European dimension' in Marsden, W. E. and Hughes, J. (eds) *Primary School Geography*. London: David Fulton, pp. 156–169.

4251    James, C. V. (1973) 'European studies and the study of Europe' in Williams, M. (ed) *Geography and the Integrated Curriculum: A Reader*. London: Heinemann, pp. 200–209.

4252    Kirschberg, G. (1990) 'Europe in geography teaching: didactic considerations on a new stage in European integration', *Geographische Rundschau*, 42, 4, pp. 225–228.

4253    Lee, R. (1992) 'The Europe of geography: UK perspectives on the ERASMUS scheme', *Journal of Geography in Higher Education*, 16, 1, pp. 71–75.

4254    Lowe, J. (1992) 'Education and European integration', *International Review of Education*, 38, 6, pp. 579–590.

4255    Marchant, E. C. (1971) *Education in Europe: The Teaching of Geography in Secondary Schools*. London/Strasbourg: George Harrop/Council of Europe.

4256    Marsden, W. E. (1990) 'The Euro-tunnel as a case study: past and present', *Teaching Geography*, 15, 3, pp. 122–123.

4257    Marsden, W. E. (1994) 'Introducing European awareness into primary phase geography' in Haubrich, H. (ed) *Europe and the World in Geography Education (Geographiedidaktische Forschungen, Band 22)*. Nuremberg: IGUCGE, pp. 85–95.

4258    Nicol, E. (1992) 'The European dimension, internationalization, education for citizenship and human rights in the early years', *Early Years*, 12, 2, pp. 3–17.

4259    Osler, A., Rathenow, H.-F. and Starkey, H. (eds) (1995) *Teaching for Citizenship in Europe*. Stoke-on-Trent: Trentham Books.

4260    Peacock, D. (ed) (1982) *Europe in Secondary School Curricula: Aims, Approaches and Problems*. Strasbourg: Council of Europe.

4261    Preston, D. (1992) 'Using Europe for education: the experience of geographers at the University of Leeds', *Journal of Geography in Higher Education*, 16, 1, pp. 94–98.

4262    **Sayer, J.** (1995) *Developing Schools for Democracy in Europe: An Example of Trans-European Cooperation in Education.* Wallingford: Triangle Books.

4263    **Shennan, M.** (1991) *Teaching about Europe.* London: Cassell.

4264    **Starkey, H.** (1995) 'Re-inventing citizenship education in a new Europe', *Oxford Studies in Comparative Education*, 5, 1, pp. 213–226.

4265    **Taylor, W. H.** (1993) 'Educating British children for European citizenship', *European Journal of Education*, 28, 4, pp. 437–444.

4266    **Tomlinson, H.** (1993) 'European community understanding' in Verma, G. K. and Pumfrey, P. D. (eds) *Cultural Diversity and the Curriculum, Volume 2: Cross-Curricular Contexts, Themes and Dimensions in Secondary Schools.* London: Falmer Press, pp. 180–191.

4267    **van der Schee, J.** and **Huigen, P. J.** (1992) 'International understanding and geography teaching about Europe: a Dutch perspective' in Hill, A. D. (ed) *International Perspectives on Geographical Education.* Boulder, CO/Skokie, IL: IGUCGE/Rand, McNally and Co., pp. 221–228.

4268    **Wake, R. A.** (1973) 'Reflections on European studies', *Trends in Education*, Special Europe Issue, pp. 9–14.

4269    **Weinbrenner, U.** (1997) 'Education for Europe by means of geography school textbooks?', *IRGEE*, 6, 1, pp. 93–97.

4270    **Wiegand, P.** (1992) *The New Europe in the Teaching of Geography (Council of Europe Symposium Report).* Strasbourg: CEC.

4271    **Williams, G.** (1997) 'European Education Project: a case study', *Teaching Geography*, 22, 4, pp. 186–189.

4272    **Williams, M.** (1977) *Teaching European Studies.* London: Heinemann.

4273    **Williams, M.** (1982) 'Europe in school geography', *Teaching about Europe*, 9, 2, pp. 1–4.

4274    **Williams, M.** (1982) 'Geography with a European dimension', *International Schools Journal*, 3, 1, pp. 35–41.

4275    **Williams, M.** (1983) 'Europe in the geography curriculum of pupils aged 11–14 years in England and Wales', *Teaching Geography*, 9, 5, pp. 196–198.

4276    **Williams, M.** (1993) 'Researching the European dimension in school geography' in Convey, A. and Speak, C. (eds) (1994) *A European Dimension in the Teaching of Geography: An Introduction.* Sheffield: Geographical Association, pp. 5–7.

4277    **Williams, M.** (1995) 'European dimensions: rhetoric and realities' in Gordon, P. (ed) *The Study of Education (Inaugural Lectures, Volume 4).* London: Woburn Press, pp. 105–121.

# 5. Geography and International Understanding

## (a) Bias and stereotyping

4278   Barret, M. and **Short**, J. (1992) 'Images of European people in a group of 5–10 year old English schoolchildren', *British Journal of Developmental Psychology*, 10, 4, pp. 339–363.

4279   Biilmann, O. and **Williams**, M. (1984) 'Studies of pupils' private geography in the context of the "European Dimension in Geographical Education" project' in Haubrich, H. (ed) *Perception of People and Places through Media, Volume 1*. Freiburg: IGUCGE/Pädagogische Hochschule Freiburg, pp. 164–199.

4280   Binns, J. A. (1979) 'How "we" see "them": some thoughts on Third World teaching', *Teaching Geography*, 4, 4, pp. 176–177.

4281   Carnie, J. (1972) 'Children's attitudes to other nationalities' in Graves, N. (ed) *New Movements in the Study and Teaching of Geography*. London: Temple Smith, pp. 121–134.

4282   Carnie, J. (1973) 'The development of national concepts in primary school children' in Bale, J., Graves, N. and Walford, R. (eds) *Perspectives on Geographical Education*. Edinburgh: Oliver and Boyd, pp. 101–118.

4283   Fien, J. (1984) 'Structural silence: aborigines in Australian geography textbooks', *Contemporary Issues in Geography and Education*, 1, 2, pp. 22–25.

4284   Franchi, N. M. (ed) (no date) 'Gender bias and geography: the need for anti-sexist teaching resources', *Contemporary Issues in Geography and Education*, 3, 1, pp. 93–101.

4285   Fry, P. (1987) *Dealing with Political Bias through Geographical Education*, unpublished MA dissertation. University of London Institute of Education.

4286   Gill, D. (1983) 'GYSL: education or indoctrination?', *Contemporary Issues in Geography and Education*, 1, 1, pp. 34–35.

4287   Haubrich, H. (ed) (1987) *How I See my Country: Personal Views of 15-year-olds from 28 Countries*. Freiburg: IGUCGE/Pädagogische Hochschule Freiburg.

4288   Haubrich, H. (ed) (1987) *Where and How I Live: 10-year-olds Write for Children in the World*. Freiburg: IGUCGE/Pädagogische Hochschule Freiburg.

4289   Hibbard, D. (1983) 'Children's images of the Third World', *Teaching Geography*, 9, 2, pp. 68–71.

4290   Hicks, D. (1979) *Bias in Geography Textbooks: Images of the Third World and Multi-ethnic Britain (Working Paper No. 1)*. London: University of London Institute of Education.

4291   Hicks, D. (1980) 'Bias in books', *World Studies Journal*, 1, 3, pp. 14–22.

4292   Hicks, D. (1981) 'Images of the world: what do geography text-books actually teach about development?', *Cambridge Journal of Education*, 11, 1, pp. 15–35.

4293   Hicks, D. (1981) 'Teaching about other peoples: how biased are school books?', *Education 3–13*, 9, 2, pp. 14–19.

4294    Hicks, D. (1983) 'The use of checklists' in Bale, J. (ed) *The Third World: Issues and Approaches*. Sheffield: Geographical Association, p. 73.

4295    Hodgkinson, K. (1987) 'Eurocentric world views: the hidden curriculum of humanities maps and atlases', *Multicultural Teaching*, 5, 2, pp. 27–31.

4296    Hodgkinson, K. (1991) 'Standing the world on its head: a review of Eurocentrism in humanities maps and atlases', *Teaching History*, 62, pp. 19–23.

4297    Huckle, J. and **Slater, F.** (1980) 'Choosing among countries: the preferences of English school children' in Slater, F. and Spicer, B. (eds) *Perception and Preference Studies at the International Level*. Tokyo: IGUCGE/AIP, pp. 184–197.

4298    Jungkunz, T. (1987) *How School Children View Third World Countries: A Preliminary Investigation into Research Methodologies*. Oxford: Oxford Development Education Unit.

4299    Kent, A. (ed) (1982) *Bias in Geographical Education*. Sheffield: Geographical Association.

4300    Kent, A. (1992) 'Images of people, environment and life' in Hill, A. D. (ed) *International Perspectives on Geographical Education*. Boulder, CO/Skokie, IL: IGUCGE/Rand, McNally and Co., pp. 37–48.

4301    Lambert, D. (1997) 'Opening minds' in Slater, F., Lambert, D. and Lines, D. (eds) *Education, Environment and Economy: Reporting Research in a New Academic Grouping (Bedford Way Papers)*. London: University of London Institute of Education, pp. 9–36.

4302    Lambert, D. and **Slater, F.** (1992) 'Sharing our sense of the world' in Hill, A. D. (ed) *International Perspectives on Geographic Education*. Boulder, CO/Skokie, IL: IGUCGE/Rand, McNally and Co., pp. 257–264.

4303    Leigh, M. and **Snellock, K.** (1991) 'Five years on: school pupils' perceptions of the USSR', *Teaching Geography*, 16, 3, pp. 125–126.

4304    Marsden, W. E. (1976) 'Stereotyping and Third World geography', *Teaching Geography*, 1, 5, pp. 228–231.

4305    Marsden, W. E. (1984) 'Paradigms, pedagogics, politics and some problems of stereotyping in school geography' in Haubrich, H. (ed) *Perception of People and Places through Media, Volume 1*. Freiburg: IGUCGE/Pädagogische Hochschule Freiburg, pp. 402–418.

4306    Marsden, W. E. (1992) 'Cartoon geography: the new stereotyping?', *Teaching Geography*, 17, 3, pp. 128–130.

4307    Paterson, J. (1981) *The Image in Geographical Education, with Special Reference to Stereotyped Images of Place*, unpublished MSc (Ed) dissertation. University of Southampton.

4308    Robinson, R. (1987) 'Exploring students' images of the developing world', *Geographical Education*, 5, 3, pp. 48–52.

4309    Royle, S. A. (1986) 'Place, perception and propaganda: American students' images of Belfast', *Teaching Geography*, 11, 4, pp. 155–159.

4310    Rupar, T. (1982) *Middle Class Images of the Third World*, unpublished MA dissertation. University of London Institute of Education.

4311    Slater, F. and Spicer, B. (eds) (1980) *Perception and Preference Studies at the International Level*. Tokyo: IGUCGE/AIP.

4312 Slater, F. and Spicer, B. (1980) 'The development of perception and preference exercises at the international level: how do we see and how are we seen?' in Slater, F. and Spicer, B. (eds) *Perception and Preference Studies at the International Level*. Tokyo: IGUCGE/AIP, pp. 57–62.

4313 Spicer, B. (1980) 'Do we see ourselves as others see us?' in Slater, F. and Spicer, B. (eds) *Perception and Preference Studies at the International Level*. Tokyo: IGUCGE/AIP, pp. 207–223.

4314 Thiel, T. (1977) *An Investigation into Stereotyping in Relation to Personal Contact in a School Setting*, unpublished MA dissertation. University of London Institute of Education.

4315 Thomas, O. G. and Chapman, J. (1991) *14 Year Olds' Images of 'Third World' Countries: A Comparison of Two Research Methodologies*. Oxford: Oxford Development Education Unit.

4316 van Ginkel, H. and Paul, L. (1990) 'The changing view of the world in major geographical textbooks' in Johnston, R., Hauer, J. and Hoekveld, G. A. (eds) *Regional Geography: Current Developments and Future Prospects*. London: Routledge, pp. 32–49.

4317 Walton, M. (1984) 'The influence of the World Cup on international stereotypes', *Teaching Geography*, 9, 5, pp. 203–207.

4318 Wickert, P. J. (1981) *A Comparison of Children's Stereotyped Images Using Data from the Soviet Union, the United States and Great Britain*, unpublished MA dissertation. University of London Institute of Education.

4319 Wiegand, P. (1986) 'Sex bias and differentiation' in Boardman, D. (ed) *Handbook for Geography Teachers*. Sheffield: Geographical Association, pp. 193–197.

4320 Wiegand, P. (1991) 'Does travel broaden the mind?', *Education 3–13*, 19, 1, pp. 54–58.

4321 Williams, M., Biilmann, O., Harn, R. and van Westrhenen, J. (1984) 'A cross-national study of children's attitudes' in Haubrich, H. (ed) *Perception of People and Places through Media, Volume 1*. Freiburg: IGUCGE/Pädagogische Hochschule Freiburg, pp. 137–163.

4322 Worster, M., Lawrence, S. and Lugg, S. (1986) 'Weather, war and furry hats: high school pupils' perceptions of the USSR', *Teaching Geography*, 11, 4, pp. 152–154.

4323 Wright, D. (1979) 'Visual images in geography textbooks: the case of Africa', *Geography*, 64, 3, pp. 205–210.

4324 Wright, D. (1982) '"Colourful South Africa"?: an analysis of textbook images', *Multiracial Education*, 10, 3, pp. 27–36.

4325 Wright, D. (1983) 'They have no need of transport: a study of attitudes to black people in three geography textbooks', *Contemporary Issues in Geography and Education*, 1, 1, pp. 11–14.

4326 Wright, D. (1989) 'Changing images of Australia in UK geography textbooks', *Geographical Education*, 6, 1, pp. 43–44.

## (b) Development education

4327 Al-Ghasm, A. M. A. (1986) *An Investigation into the Nature, Purpose and Significance of Development Education in the Context of the Emerging Transnational World System*, unpublished PhD thesis. University of London Institute of Education.

4328 Bale, J. (ed) (1983) *The Third World: Issues and Approaches*. Sheffield: Geographical Association.

4329 Barrs, D. (1995) 'Educating succeeding generations', *Teaching Geography*, 20, 4, pp. 161–167.

4330 Binns, T. (1995) 'Geography in development: development in geography', *Geography*, 80, 4, pp. 303–332.

4331 Birmingham Development Education Centre (1992) *Developing Geography*. Birmingham: DEC.

4332 Bowen, P. (1983) 'Geographical approaches to development' in Bale, J. (ed) *The Third World: Issues and Approaches*. Sheffield: Geographical Association, pp. 10–13.

4333 Bowen, P. (1983) Geography and development education: a publisher's view' in Bale, J. (ed) *The Third World: Issues and Approaches*. Sheffield: Geographical Association, pp. 70–73.

4334 Button, J. (ed) (1989) *The Primary School in a Changing World*. London: Centre for World Development Education.

4335 Courtenay, P. P. (1995) 'Geography, development and an uncertain world', *Geographical Education*, 8, 3, pp. 27–30.

4336 Crane, C. R. (1982) *The Design and Development of a Unit of Development Education in a Comprehensive School*, unpublished MEd dissertation. University of Wales Cardiff.

4337 Crew, J. (1979) *Perspectives on Third World Geography*, unpublished MA dissertation. University of London Institute of Education.

4338 Drake, M. (1992) *Development Education and National Curriculum Geography: Introduction and Resources Guide for Use at Key Stages 1 and 2*. Sheffield: Geographical Association.

4339 Harber, C. (1986) 'Development education in context: an evaluation of the West Midlands–West Africa project', *International Journal of Educational Development*, 6, 2, pp. 133–141.

4340 Hickling-Hudson, A. (1994) 'The environment as radical politics: can "Third World" education rise to the challenge?', *International Review of Education*, 40, 1, pp. 19–36.

4341 Hicks, D. (1977) 'The Third World: what should we be teaching?', *Teaching Geography*, 3, 1, pp. 22–24.

4342 Hicks, D. (1983) 'Development education' in Huckle, J. (ed) *Geographical Education: Reflection and Action*. Oxford: Oxford University Press, pp. 89–98.

4343 Hicks, D. (1986) 'Other worlds: what should we be teaching?, *Teaching Geography*, 11, 4, pp. 160–162.

4344 Hopkin, J. (1988) 'Geography 5–16: a global dimension?', *Teaching Geography*, 13, 1, p. 8.

4345 Hopkin, J. (1994) 'Geography and development education' in Osler, A. (ed) *Development Education: Global Studies in the Curriculum*. London: Cassell, pp. 65–90.

4346 Huckle, J. (1987) 'Environment and development issues in the curriculum: the experience of one curriculum project' in Lacey, C. and Williams, M. (eds) *Education, Ecology and Development: The Case for an Education Network*. London: World Wildlife Fund/Kogan Page, pp. 129–147.

4347    Jones, B., Swift, D. and Vickers, D. (1997) 'Writing about development', *Teaching Geography*, 22, 1, pp. 5–10.

4348    Kendrick, C. F. W. (1987) *Trends in Development Education: An Initial Survey of Practice, Theory and Issues in Avon Secondary Schools with Special Reference to Geography*, unpublished MPhil thesis. University of Bristol.

4349    King, R. (1976) 'Alternative approaches to the geography of development', *Teaching Geography*, 2, 2, pp. 81–83.

4350    Knamiller, G. W. (1981) 'Environmental education and the north–south dialogue', *Comparative Education*, 17, 1, pp. 87–94.

4351    Lines, D. (1997) 'Development education, initial teacher education and the school curriculum: a programme for action research' in Slater, F., Lambert, D. and Lines, D. (eds) *Education, Environment and Economy: Reporting Research in a New Academic Grouping (Bedford Way Papers)*. London: University of London Institute of Education, pp. 71–94.

4352    Marshall, L. D. (1985) *An Analysis of Factors Influencing the Nature of Third World Studies in the Geography Curriculum*, unpublished MPhil thesis. University of London, King's College.

4353    Mason, P. (1989) 'Geography and development education: recent teaching and future strategies', *Teaching Geography*, 14, 1, pp. 2–5.

4354    Mitchell, D. J. (1987) *Development Education in Geography*, unpublished MA dissertation. University of London Institute of Education.

4355    Morrish, M. (1986) 'Third World studies' in Boardman, D. (ed) *Handbook for Geography Teachers*. Sheffield: Geographical Association, pp. 185–192.

4356    Owen, R. (1980) 'Third World studies: pitfalls to be avoided', *Teaching Geography*, 5, 3, pp. 116–117.

4357    Robinson, R. (1986) 'Geography teachers' reflections on their teaching about development', *Journal of Curriculum Studies*, 18, 4, pp. 409–427.

4358    Robinson, R. (1988) 'Development issues: sympathy and paternalism, empathy and realism' in Gerber, R. and Lidstone, J. (eds) *Developing Skills in Geographical Education*. Brisbane: IGUCGE/Jacaranda Press, pp. 152–155.

4359    Robinson, R. (1988) 'Teaching development issues', *Teaching Geography*, 13, 1, p. 7.

4360    Robinson, R. (1991) 'Strength from partnership: school geography and development education' in Walford, R. (ed) *Viewpoints on Geographical Education*. Harlow: Longman, pp. 55–56.

4361    Robinson, R. (1993) 'Geography, development education and international understanding in the cross-curricular themes' in Speak, C. and Wiegand, P. (eds) *International Understanding through Geography*. Sheffield: Geographical Association, pp. 15–17.

4362    Scott, J. R. (1985) *Development Education in Geography*, unpublished MEd dissertation. University of Wales Cardiff.

4363    Serf, J. and Sinclair, S. (eds) (1992) *Developing Geography: A Development Education Approach to Key Stage 3*. Birmingham: Development Education Centre.

4364    Smith, R. (1988) 'An outsider's view of development education', *Teaching Geography*, 13, 1, pp. 8–9.

4365   Steel, R. W. (1971) 'The challenge of the tropics in our teaching of geography', *Geography*, 56, 1, pp. 15–23.

4366   Steel, R. W., Wright, D., Hore, P. and Storm, M. (1975) 'Teaching about the Third World: a report of a symposium', *Geography*, 60, 1, pp. 52–58.

4367   Storm, M. (1983) 'Geography and development education', *Economics*, 19, 1, pp. 27–28.

4368   Storm, M. (1983) 'A short history of development education' in Bale, J. (ed) *The Third World: Issues and Approaches*. Sheffield: Geographical Association, pp. 18–20.

4369   Storm, M. (1983) 'Geographical development education: a metropolitan view' in Bale, J. (ed) *The Third World: Issues and Approaches*. Sheffield: Geographical Association, pp. 31–39.

4370   Storm, M. (1983) 'Perceptions of the Third World' in Bale, J. (ed) *The Third World: Issues and Approaches*. Sheffield: Geographical Association, pp. 40–43.

4371   Storm, M. and Tinline, E. (1983) 'Some definitions and dilemmas' in Bale, J. (ed) *The Third World: Issues and Approaches*. Sheffield: Geographical Association, pp. 6–9.

4372   Swee-Hin, T. (1988) 'Justice and development' in Hicks, D. (ed) *Education for Peace: Issues, Principles and Practice in the Classroom*. London: Routledge, pp. 196–213.

4373   Swee-Hin, T. (1988) 'Third World studies: conscientisation in the geography classroom' in Fien, J. and Gerber, R. (eds) *Teaching Geography for a Better World*. Edinburgh: Oliver and Boyd, pp. 117–139.

4374   Tilbury, D. (1997) 'Environmental education and development education: teaching geography for a sustainable world' in Tilbury, D. and Williams, M. (eds) *Teaching and Learning Geography*. London: Routledge, pp. 105–116.

4375   Trainer, T. (1994) 'What is development?', *Geographical Education*, 7, 2, pp. 9–21.

4376   Vicars, A. (1990) 'How well do we teach students about the developing world?', *Teaching Geography*, 15, 1, pp. 30–33.

4377   Villars, R. (1988) 'Global perspectives on the curriculum', *World Studies Journal*, 7, 1, pp. 25–28.

4378   Waterman, S. and Maitland, S. (1984) 'Value positions in teaching about development', *Teaching Geography*, 9, 3, pp. 104–105.

4379   Wright, D. (1983) 'Some initiatives' in Bale, J. (ed) *The Third World: Issues and Approaches*. Sheffield: Geographical Association, pp. 3–5.

4380   Wright, D. (1983) 'Third World teaching: which way now?' in Bale, J. (ed) *The Third World: Issues and Approaches*. Sheffield: Geographical Association, pp. 14–17.

4381   Wright, D. (1983) 'Development education in a 16-plus examination' in Bale, J. (ed) *The Third World: Issues and Approaches*. Sheffield: Geographical Association, pp. 62–63.

4382   Wright, D. (1983) 'Some resources for Third World teaching' in Bale, J. (ed) *The Third World: Issues and Approaches*. Sheffield: Geographical Association, pp. 75–77.

4383   Yangopoulos, S. (1997) 'Developing sixth form students' understanding of the relationships between environment and development issues' in Slater, F., Lambert, D. and Lines, D. (eds) *Education, Environment and Economy: Reporting Research in a New Academic Grouping (Bedford Way Papers)*. London: University of London Institute of Education, pp. 135–156.

## (c) Peace and human rights education

4384    Barrs, D. (1993) 'The National Curriculum, geography teaching and the United Nations' in Speak, C. and Wiegand, P. (eds) *International Understanding through Geography*. Sheffield: Geographical Association, pp. 45–49.

4385    Burnley, J. (1988) 'Teaching for human rights in geography' in Fien, J. and Gerber, R. (eds) *Teaching Geography for a Better World*. Edinburgh: Oliver and Boyd, pp. 61–79.

4386    Fien, J. (1991) 'Education for peace in the secondary school: the contribution of one subject to an across-the-curriculum perspective', *International Review of Education*, 37, 3, pp. 335–350.

4387    Fien, J. (1992) 'Education for peace through geography' in Naish, M. (ed) *Geography and Education: National and International Perspectives*. London: University of London Institute of Education, pp. 114–130.

4388    Hall, R. (1987) 'More conflict over peace', *Contemporary Issues in Geography and Education*, 2, 3, pp. 60–69.

4389    Harwood, D. (1987) 'Peace education in schools: demise or development in the late '80s', *Teaching Politics*, 16, 2, pp. 147–169.

4390    Hicks, D. (1987) 'Education for peace: principles into practice', *Cambridge Journal of Education*, 17, 1, pp. 3–12.

4391    Hicks, D. (ed) (1988) *Education for Peace: Issues, Principles and Practice in the Classroom*. London: Routledge.

4392    Hicks, D. (1988) 'The geography of war and peace' in Fien, J. and Gerber, R. (eds) *Teaching Geography for a Better World*. Edinburgh: Oliver and Boyd, pp. 140–152.

4393    Hicks, D. (1991) 'The Centre for Peace Studies: 1980–89', *Westminster Studies in Education*, 14, pp. 37–49.

4394    Pepper, D. (1987) 'Weapons technology, geographical space and environment: some war and peace themes for geography classes', *Contemporary Issues in Geography and Education*, 2, 3, pp. 28–40.

4395    Randle, D. (1983) 'Environmental issues and peace education', *World Studies Journal*, 4, 4, pp. 16–22.

4396    Serf, J. and Hoyte, V. (1988) 'South Africa: geography and human rights', *Teaching Geography*, 13, 1, pp. 10–13.

4397    Starkey, H. (1991) *The Challenge of Human Rights Education*. London: Cassell/Council of Europe.

## (d) Global studies and international understanding

4398    Bale, J. (ed) (1983) *The Third World: Issues and Approaches*. Sheffield: Geographical Association.

4399    Binns, T. (1993) 'The international dimension in the geography National Curriculum' in Speak, C. and Wiegand, P. (eds) *International Understanding through Geography*. Sheffield: Geographical Association, pp. 7–10.

4400    Boden, P. (1977) *Promoting International Understanding through School Textbooks: A Case Study*. Brunswick: Georg Eckert Institute for International Textbook Research.

4401 Bridges, D. (1975) 'Education and international understanding' in Elliott, J. and Pring, R. (eds) *Social Education and Social Understanding.* London: University of London Press, pp. 104–125.

4402 Catling, S. (1993) 'The whole world in our hands', *Geography*, 78, 4, pp. 340–358.

4403 Cox, B. (1988) 'Reflections on teaching geography for a better world' in Fien, J. and Gerber, R. (eds) *Teaching Geography for a Better World.* Edinburgh: Oliver and Boyd, pp. 181–187.

4404 Creighton, C. (1984) 'Teaching geography: the global perspective', *Social Studies Review*, 24, 1, pp. 19–25.

4405 Fagan, M. W. (1992) 'Teaching world issues in a secondary school' in Hill, A. D. (ed) *International Perspectives on Geographical Education.* Boulder, CO/Skokie, IL: IGUCGE/Rand, McNally and Co., pp. 197–207.

4406 Fien, J. (1980) 'International understanding: some classroom implications' in Slater, F. and Spicer, B. (eds) *Perception and Preference Studies at the International Level.* Tokyo: IGUCGE/AIP, pp. 255–270.

4407 Fien, J. and Gerber, R. (eds) (1988) *Teaching Geography for a Better World.* Edinburgh: Oliver and Boyd.

4408 Fisher, S. and Hicks, D. (1985) *World Studies 8–13: A Teacher's Handbook.* Edinburgh: Oliver and Boyd.

4409 Goldschmidt, C. (1993) 'A global planning education information system', *Environment and Planning B: Planning and Design*, 20, 5, pp. 577–583.

4410 Graves, N. (1981) 'International aspects of geography education', *Journal of Geography*, 80, 3, pp. 84–86.

4411 Graves, N. (1985) 'International understanding through geography', *Terra*, 97, 1, pp. 45–49.

4412 Hartoonian, H. M. (1992) 'Territory and thinking: national consciousness in a global community' in Hill, A. D. (ed) *International Perspectives on Geographical Education.* Boulder, CO/Skokie, IL: IGUCGE/Rand, McNally and Co., pp. 179–183.

4413 Harwood, D. (1995) 'The pedagogy of the World Studies 8–13 project: the influence of the presence/absence of the teacher upon primary children's collaborative groupwork', *British Educational Research Journal*, 21, 5, pp. 587–611.

4414 Harwood, D. (1997) 'Teacher roles in world studies democratic pedagogy', *Evaluation and Research in Education*, 11, 2, pp. 1–26.

4415 Haubrich, H. (1992) 'National identification and international understanding' in Naish, M. (ed) *Geography and Education: National and International Perspectives.* London: University of London Institute of Education, pp. 131–143.

4416 Haubrich, H. (1996) 'Global ethics in geographical education' in Gerber, R. and Lidstone, J. (eds) *Developments and Directions in Geographical Education.* Clevedon: Channel View Publications, pp. 163–174.

4417 Haubrich, H. (1996) 'International understanding and cooperation through geographical education' in van der Schee, J., Schoenmaker, G., Trimp, H. and van Westrhenen, H. (eds) *Innovation in Geographical Education (Netherlands Geographical Studies, 208).* Utrecht/Amsterdam: IGUCGE/Centrum voor Educatieve Geografie Vrije Universiteit Amsterdam, pp. 219–234.

4418    Heater, D. (1980) *Education for International Understanding in Britain*. London: Harrap.

4419    Hicks, D. (1988) 'Teaching geography for a better world' in Fien, J. and Gerber, R. (eds) *Teaching Geography for a Better World*. Edinburgh: Oliver and Boyd, pp. 13-19.

4420    Hicks, D. (1989) 'World studies: the global dimension' in Campbell, J. and Little, V. (eds) *Humanities in the Primary School*. London: Falmer Press, pp. 121-134.

4421    Hicks, D. (1990) 'Lessons from global education: avoiding a nationalistic curriculum', *Education 3-13*, 18, 3, pp. 29-45.

4422    Hicks, D. and Fisher, S. (1982) 'World studies: a global perspective on the curriculum', *Curriculum*, 3, 2, pp. 6-12.

4423    Hicks, D. and Fisher, S. (eds) (1985) *World Studies: A Teacher's Handbook*. Edinburgh: Oliver and Boyd.

4424    Hicks, D. and Steiner, M. (eds) (1989) *Making Global Connections: A World Studies Workbook*, Edinburgh: Oliver and Boyd.

4425    Hicks, D. and Townley, C. (eds) (1982) *Teaching World Studies: An Introduction to Global Perspectives on the Curriculum*. Harlow: Longman.

4426    Hill, D. (1996) 'Geographic Inquiry into Global Issues (GIGI)' in van der Schee, J., Schoenmaker, G., Trimp, H. and van Westrhenen, H. (eds) *Innovation in Geographical Education (Netherlands Geographical Studies, 208)*. Utrecht/Amsterdam: IGUCGE/Centrum voor Educatieve Geografie Vrije Universiteit Amsterdam, pp. 270-272.

4427    International Geographical Union Commission on Geographical Education (1992) *International Charter on Geographical Education*. Freiburg: IGUCGE.

4428    International Geographical Union Commission on Geographical Education (1995) 'International Charter on Geographical Education' (reprint), *Teaching Geography*, 20, 2, pp. 95-98.

4429    Jarvis, H. (1992) *Education for International Understanding: How Far have we Come? What Needs to be Done?*, unpublished MA thesis. University of London Institute of Education.

4430    Lambert, S. and Wiegand, P. (1990) 'The beginnings of international understanding', *New Era*, 71, 3, pp. 90-93.

4431    Lidstone, J. (1992) 'Natural disasters: promoting international perspectives through geographical education' in Hill, A. D. (ed) *International Perspectives on Geographical Education*. Boulder, CO/Skokie, IL: IGUCGE/Rand, McNally and Co., pp. 209-220.

4432    Lidstone, J. (1995) 'Global education, global change and disaster education' in Lidstone, J., Romanova, E. and Kondakov, A. (eds) *Global Change and Geographical Education*. Brisbane/Moscow: IGUCGE/Queensland University of Technology/Moscow State University, pp. 13-30.

4433    Lidstone, J., Romanova, E. and Kondakov, A. (eds) (1995) *Global Change and Geographical Education*. Brisbane/Moscow: IGUCGE/Queensland University of Technology/Moscow State University.

4434    McFarlane, C. (ed) (1986) *Theme Work: Approaches for Teaching with a Global Perspective*. Birmingham: Development Education Centre.

4435    McFarlane, C. (ed) (1991) *Theme Work: A Global Perspective in the Primary Curriculum in the '90s*. Birmingham: Development Education Centre.

4436 Manshard, W. (1993) 'Geography and the international global change programs', *European Review*, 1, 4, pp. 309–317.

4437 Marsden, W. E. (1992) 'W(h)ither international understanding' in Hall, G. (ed) *Themes and Dimensions of the National Curriculum: Implications for Policy and Practice.* London: Kogan Page, pp. 101–115.

4438 Marsden, W. E. (1997) 'From pre- to anti-modern: versions of teaching geography for a better world' in Convey, A. and Nolzen, H. (eds) *Geography and Education (Münchner Studien zur Didaktik der Geographie, Band 10).* Munich: Lehrstuhl für Didaktik der Geographie der Universität München, pp. 189–198.

4439 Meijer, H. (1984) 'Geographical textbooks, information and international understanding' in Haubrich, H. (ed) *Perception of People and Places through Media, Volume 1.* Freiburg: IGUCGE/Pädagogische Hochschule Freiburg, pp. 439–448.

4440 Pike, G. (1990) 'Global education: learning in a world of change' in Dufour, B. (ed) *The New Social Curriculum: A Guide to Cross-curricular Issues.* Cambridge: Cambridge University Press, pp. 133–149.

4441 Pike, G. and Selby, D. (1988) *Global Teacher, Global Learner.* London: Hodder and Stoughton.

4442 Pradervand, P. (1987) 'Global education: towards a world that works for all', *Geographical Education*, 5, 1, pp. 12–18.

4443 Robinson, R. (1997) 'Global shopping mall and global city slum', *Teaching Geography*, 22, 2, pp. 85–87.

4444 Robinson, R. and Serf, J. (1997) *Global Geography: Learning through Development Education at Key Stage 3.* Sheffield/Birmingham: Geographical Association/Development Education Centre.

4445 Scarfe, N. V. (1978) 'International understanding', *Geography*, 63, 2, pp. 85–87.

4446 Selby, D. (1991) 'Towards an irreducible global perspective in schools', *Westminster Studies in Education*, 14, pp. 27–35.

4447 Sinclair, S. (1997) 'Going global', *Teaching Geography*, 22, 4, pp. 160–164.

4448 Smeaton, M. (1988) 'Geography and world studies' in Mills, D. (ed) *Geographical Work in Primary and Middle Schools.* Sheffield: Geographical Association, pp. 209–212.

4449 Speak, C. and Wiegand, P. (eds) (1993) *International Understanding through Geography: International Understanding and the National Curriculum.* Sheffield: Geographical Association.

4450 Speak, C. and Wiegand, P. (eds) (1993) *International Understanding through Geography: Issues.* Sheffield: Geographical Association.

4451 Steiner, M. (1993) *Learning from Experience: World Studies in the Primary Curriculum.* Stoke-on-Trent: Trentham Books/World Studies Trust.

4452 Steiner, M. (1996) 'Matching practice and vision: evaluating global education' in Williams, M. (ed) *Understanding Geographical and Environmental Education: The Role of Research.* London: Cassell, pp. 196–219.

4453 Storm, M. (1989) 'World view: geography', *Teacher*, 45, pp. 12–14.

4454 Swee-Hin, T. (1993) 'Bringing the world into the classroom', *Geographical Education*, pp. 13–22.

4455   Webb, D. and **Cogan, J.** (1982) 'A global approach for the school curriculum', *Curriculum*, 3, 2, pp. 13–17.

4456   **Williams, M.** (1986*) Geography and International Understanding in Primary Schools: Report of a European Teachers' Seminar Organised by the Council for Cultural Cooperation.* Strasbourg: Council of Europe.

4457   **Williams, M.** (1997) 'From the local to the international: passion, action and identity in geographical education' in Convey, A. and Nolzen, H. (eds) *Geography and Education (Münchner Studien zur Didaktik der Geographie, Band 10).* Munich: Lehrstuhl für Didaktik der Geographie der Universität München, pp. 293–301.

4458   **Wise, M.** (1992) 'International geography: the IGU Commission on Geographical Education' in Naish, M. (ed) *Geography and Education: National and International Perspectives.* London: University of London Institute of Education, pp. 233–246.

4459   **Zin, F. D., Lyons, T. S.** and **Hinojosa, R. C.** (1993) 'Bringing a global approach to education: the case of urban planning', *Environment and Planning B: Planning and Design*, 20, 5, pp. 557–565.

# 6. Geography and Careers

## (a) Geography and vocational education

4460   Anson, R. (1976) 'Jobs for geographers: in cartography', *Teaching Geography*, 2, 1, pp. 33–35.

4461   Bailey, P. (1977) 'Jobs for geographers: what is the Dip HE?', *Teaching Geography*, 2, 4, p. 178.

4462   Bale, J. (1987) *Geography and TVEI.* Sheffield: Geographical Association.

4463   Birchall, P. (1991) 'Careers education and guidance: a problem of time', *Teaching Geography*, 16, 1, p. 31.

4464   Butt, G. (1994) 'Geography, vocational education and assessment', *Teaching Geography*, 19, 4, pp. 182–183.

4465   Butt, G. (1996) 'Developments in geography 14–19: a changing system' in Rawling, E. and Daugherty, R. (eds) *Geography into the Twenty-first Century.* Chichester: John Wiley, pp. 173–193.

4466   Carter, R. (1985) 'TVEI: a place for geography', *Teaching Geography*, 10, 2, pp. 51–53.

4467   Caswell, P. (1980) 'The employment of university graduates', *Teaching Geography*, 5, 3, pp. 136–140.

4468   Church, A. and Bull, P. (1995) 'Evaluating and assessing student oral presentation: a limited but effective role for employers in the geography curriculum', *Journal of Geography in Higher Education*, 19, 2, pp. 191–202.

4469   Davidson, G. (1984) 'Geography and the challenge of TVEI', *Teaching Geography*, 9, 1, pp. 3–5.

4470   Devereux, M. (1975) 'Careers for geographers: the British geographer in the Third World', *Teaching Geography*, 1, 5, pp. 231–233.

4471    Devereux, M. (1975) 'Jobs for geographers: the outlook for university graduates', *Teaching Geography*, 1, 1, p. 35.

4472    Devereux, M. (1976) 'Jobs for geographers: in chartered surveying', *Teaching Geography*, 2, 2, pp. 84–85.

4473    Devereux, M. and Stichbury, M. (1975) 'Jobs for geographers: town and country planning', *Teaching Geography*, 1, 4, pp. 184–187.

4474    Fowler, G. (1976) 'TVEI: some questions to ask', *Teaching Geography*, 13, 2, pp. 79–80.

4475    Fox, P. (1996) 'Where can you go with geography?' in Bailey, P. and Fox, P. (eds) *Geography Teachers' Handbook*. Sheffield: Geographical Association, pp. 325–335.

4476    Geographical Association (1982) *The Contribution of Geography to 17+ Courses*. Sheffield: Geographical Association.

4477    Graves, N. (ed) (1982) *The Contribution of Geography to 17+ Courses: A Report by the GA Working Party on Examinations*. Sheffield: Geographical Association.

4478    Hart, C. (ed) (1981) *A Basis for Choice? Geography and Pre-Employment Courses in the Sixth Form: A Joint Geography 16–19 and Sheffield LEA Initiative Concerned with the Contribution of Geographical Education to the Proposed 17+ Pre-Employment Examination*. London/Sheffield: Schools Council/Sheffield LEA.

4479    Hart, C. (ed) (1981) *Geography and Pre-employment Courses in the Sixth Form*. London: Geography 16–19 Project, University of London Institute of Education.

4480    Hart, C. (1983) 'Putting geography to work at 17+', *Teaching Geography*, 8, 3, pp. 112–113.

4481    Hart, C. (1986) 'Pre-vocational education' in Boardman, D. (ed) *Handbook for Geography Teachers*. Sheffield: Geographical Association, pp. 198–204.

4482    Hebden, R. (1982) 'Careers profiles of geography graduates part 1: what can I do with a degree in geography?', *Teaching Geography*, 8, 2, pp. 86–87.

4483    Hebden, R. (1983) 'Careers profiles of geography graduates part 2', *Teaching Geography*, 8, 3, pp. 115–116.

4484    Hebden, R. (1983) 'Careers profiles of geography graduates part 3', *Teaching Geography*, 8, 4, pp. 179–180.

4485    Hebden, R. (1987) 'How employable are geography graduates?', *Journal of Geography in Higher Education*, 11, 2, pp. 171–172.

4486    Hodkinson, P. (1985) 'Piloting CPVE: a geographer's experience', *Teaching Geography*, 10, 4, pp. 152–157.

4487    Jenkins, A. and Healey, M. (1995) 'Linking the geography curriculum to the worlds of industry, commerce and public authorities', *Journal of Geography in Higher Education*, 19, 2, pp. 177–181.

4488    Johnston, R. J. (1990) 'What can I do with a geography degree?', *Teaching Geography*, 15, 4, pp. 159–161.

4489    Marchant, E. C. (1972) 'Geography for careers: report of the findings of a working group of the Geographical Association and Royal Geographical Society', *Geography*, 57, 4, pp. 327–332.

4490    Marvell, A. (1994) 'Should your department consider GNVQ Leisure and Tourism?', *Teaching Geography*, 19, 4, pp. 175–176.

4491    Milton, M., Laws, S., Davey, J. and Milne, P. (1985) 'Geography and TVEI: a strategy for inclusion', *Teaching Geography*, 11, 1, pp. 18–19.

4492    Rawling, E. (1997) 'Geography and vocationalism: opportunity or threat?', *Geography*, 82, 1, pp. 163–178.

4493    Regan, P. and Hyde, D. (1978) 'Jobs for geographers: teaching', *Teaching Geography*, 4, 1, p. 36.

4494    Sheridan, P. (1981) 'How can I use my geography if I leave school at 16?', *Teaching Geography*, 6, 3, pp. 103–105.

4495    Stevens, B. (1986) 'Geography: a qualification for what?', *Teaching Geography*, 11, 3, pp. 118–119.

4496    Stichbury, M. (1975) 'Jobs for geographers: geography is an academic subject not a job!', *Teaching Geography*, 1, 2, pp. 87–88.

4497    Sutton, A. (1996) 'The post-16 pre-vocational strand' in Bailey, P. and Fox, P. (eds) *Geography Teachers' Handbook*. Sheffield: Geographical Association, pp. 299–307.

4498    Swift, D. (1994) 'Points to help your department's discussion on GNVQs', *Teaching Geography*, 19, 4, p. 177.

4499    Walmsley, F. (1977) 'Jobs for geographers: the work of the Countryside Commission', *Teaching Geography*, 3, 1, pp. 34–36.

4500    Westwood, S. (1987) *The Contribution of Geography to Pre-vocational Education*, unpublished MA dissertation. University of London Institute of Education.

4501    Woolway, P. (1975) 'Jobs for geographers: geography for careers?', *Teaching Geography*, 1, 3, pp. 138–140.

## (b) Becoming a geography teacher

4502    Bale, J. and McPartland, M. (1986) 'Johnstonian anarchy, inspectorial interest and the undergraduate education of PGCE geography students', *Journal of Geography in Higher Education*, 10, 1, pp. 61–70.

4503    Black, S. (1987) 'A note on the shortage of geography teachers', *Geography*, 72, 2, pp. 151–152.

4504    Butt, G. (1994) 'Assessment through residential field-study in a geography PGCE' in Butterfield, S. (ed) *Qualifying Teachers: Assessing Professional Work (Educational Review Publications 2)*. Birmingham: University of Birmingham, pp. 29–35.

4505    Corney, G. (1981) *Teacher Education and Geography 16–19 (Geography 16–19 Occasional Paper No. 1)*. London: University of London Institute of Education.

4506    Corney, G. (1983) 'A conversation with an old student', *Journal of Geography in Higher Education*, 7, 1, pp. 85–89.

4507    Ellis, B. (1993) 'Training geography teachers: an increased role for schools', *Teaching Geography*, 18, 3, pp. 129–131.

4508    Ellis, B. (ed) (1997) *Working Together: Partnership in the Education of Geography Teachers*. Sheffield: Geographical Association.

4509    Foskett, N. (1994) 'What are we going to do with our student teacher?', *Teaching Geography*, 19, 1, pp. 26–29.

4510    Gerber, R. and **Williams, M.** (eds) (1992) *Distance Education and Geography Teaching.* Brisbane: IGUCGE/Queensland University of Technology.

4511    Graves, N. (1978) 'Changes of attitude towards the training of teachers of geography', *Geography*, 63, 1, pp. 75–84.

4512    Graves, N. (1984) 'Educating geography teachers: the experience of England and Wales' in Marsden, W. E. (ed) *Teacher Education Models in Geography: An International Comparison.* Kalamazoo, MI: IGUCGE/Western Michigan University, pp. 35–43.

4513    Graves, N. (1997) 'Some thoughts on the education of geography teachers' in Convey, A. and Nolzen, H. (eds) *Geography and Education (Münchner Studien zur Didaktik der Geographie, Band 10).* Munich: Lehrstuhl für Didaktik der Geographie der Universität München, pp. 111–118.

4514    Hacking, E. (1996) 'Novice teachers and their geographical persuasions', *IRGEE*, 5, 1, pp. 77–86.

4515    Hacking, E. and **Robinson, L.** (1994) 'Beginning teachers and the National Curriculum' in Walford, R. and Machon, P. (eds) *Challenging Times: Implementing the National Curriculum in Geography.* Cambridge: Cambridge Publishing Services, pp. 65–67.

4516    Hall, D. (1994) 'Postgraduate understanding and awareness of the specifics and professional dimensions of the new National Curriculum in England and Wales' in Haubrich, H. (ed) *Europe and the World in Geography Education (Geographiedidaktische Forschungen, Band 22).* Nuremberg: IGUCGE, pp. 297–324.

4517    Hebden, R. and **Wholmsley, J. P.** (1983) 'Teacher training and the future of geography', *Area*, 15, 4, pp. 285–288.

4518    Hones, G. (1992) 'Teacher education and classroom reality' in Naish, M. (ed) *Geography and Education: National and International Perspectives.* London: University of London Institute of Education, pp. 61–71.

4519    Hughes, M. (1994) 'School-based teacher training: "like learning through fieldwork"', *Teaching Geography*, 19, 4, pp. 171–173.

4520    Ince, C. (1994) 'Appointing newly qualified mature geography teachers', *Teaching Geography*, 19, 2, pp. 81–82.

4521    Johnston, R. J. (1995) 'Who teaches geography?', *Geography*, 80, 2, p. 192.

4522    Lambert, D. (1996) 'Understanding and improving school geography: the training of beginning teachers' in Williams, M. (ed) *Understanding Geographical and Environmental Education: The Role of Research.* London: Cassell, pp. 230–241.

4523    Leat, D. (1996) 'Geography student teachers and their images of teaching', *IRGEE*, 5, 1, pp. 63–68.

4524    Lee, R. (1985) 'Where have all the geographers gone?', *Geography*, 70, 1, pp. 45–59.

4525    McPartland, M. (1995) 'On being a geography mentor', *Teaching Geography*, 20, 1, pp. 35–37.

4526    McPartland, M. (1996) 'Walking in our own footsteps: autobiographical memories of the teaching of geography', *IRGEE*, 5, 1, pp. 57–62.

4527    Marsden, W. E. (1984) 'Teacher education in geography: the comparative view' in Marsden, W. E. (ed) *Teacher Education Models in Geography: An International Comparison.* Kalamazoo, MI: IGUCGE/Western Michigan University, pp. 1–3.

4528    Marsden, W. E. (1994) 'Geography in primary initial teacher education: the developing agenda' in Ellis, B. (ed) *Issues and Challenges for ITE in Geography: Geographical Association Teacher Education Working Group.* Sheffield: Geographical Association, pp. 6–8.

4529    Naish, M. (1996) 'Forum: *recherche du temps perdu*', *IRGEE*, 5, 1, pp. 55–56.

4530    Robbins, D. and Butt, G. (1994) 'What do children really think about student teachers?', *Teaching Geography*, 19, 3, pp. 131–133.

4531    Roberts, M. (1996) 'Teacher education and training' in Bailey, P. and Fox, P. (eds) *Geography Teachers' Handbook.* Sheffield: Geographical Association, pp. 315–323.

4532    Russell, J. (1987) 'Training to teach geography: some observations on the numbers game', *Geography*, 72, 4, pp. 323–327.

4533    Rynne, E. and Lambert, D. (1997) 'The continuing mismatch between students' undergraduate experiences and the teaching demands of the geography classroom: experience of pre-service geography teachers', *Journal of Geography in Higher Education*, 21, 1, pp. 65–77.

4534    Skinner, D. (1989) 'Student teachers' in Wiegand, P. (ed) *Managing the Geography Department.* Sheffield: Geographical Association, pp. 48–63.

4535    Slater, F. and Rask, R. (1983) 'Geography teacher education', *European Journal of Teacher Education*, 6, 2, pp. 183–189.

4536    Thomas, D. (1983) 'The transition to teaching', *Teaching Geography*, 9, 1, p. 5.

4537    Tuffin, B. (1989) 'Teacher training: the school's role' in Wiegand, P. (ed) *Managing the Geography Department.* Sheffield: Geographical Association, pp. 48–63.

4538    Unwin, T. (1986) 'Attitudes towards geographers in the graduate labour market', *Journal of Geography in Higher Education*, 10, 2, pp. 149–157.

4539    Walford, R. (1996) 'What is geography?: an analysis of definitions provided by prospective teachers of the subject', *IRGEE*, 5, 1, pp. 69–76.

4540    Wholmsley, J. P. (1984) 'Who trains the teachers and for what?', *Geography*, 69, 1, pp. 56–60.

4541    Williams, M. and Tilbury, D. (ed) (1996) 'Conceptual aspects of geographical and environmental education in teacher education' in van der Zijpp, T., van der Schee, J. and Trimp, H. (eds) *Innovation in Geographical Education: Proceedings of the 28th International Geographical Congress Commission on Geographical Education.* Amsterdam: Centrum voor Educatieve Geografie Vrije Universiteit Amsterdam, pp. 89–94.

4542    Wright, D. (1988) 'Destroying the seedcorn: is there a crisis in the training of geography teachers in England?', *Journal of Geography in Higher Education*, 12, 2, pp. 210–213.

## (c) In-service education of teachers

4543    Barron, A. and Bloomer, G. (1975) 'Geography in the south: work in secondary schools and in-service needs', *British Journal of In-service Education*, 1, 2, pp. 36–40.

4544    Hall, D. (1976) 'A framework for in-service expansion' in Hall, D. *Geography and the Geography Teacher.* London: George Allen and Unwin, pp. 286–306.

4545    Marsden, W. E. (1996) 'The in-service education of generalist primary teachers in geography in England' in van der Zijpp, T., van der Schee, J. and Trimp, H. (eds) *Innovation in Geographical Education: Proceedings of the 28th International Geographical Congress Commission on Geographical Education.* Amsterdam: IGUCGE/Centrum voor Educatieve Geografie Vrije Universiteit Amsterdam, pp. 307–311.

4546    Naish, S. and Naish, M. (1988) 'Continuing education of geography teachers: reflections on experience' in Gerber, R. and Lidstone, J. (eds) *Skills in Geographical Education Symposium '88, Volume 2.* Brisbane: IGUCGE/Brisbane College of Advanced Education, pp. 430–440.

4547    Williams, M. (1988) 'Continuing education of geography teachers' in Gerber, R. and Lidstone, J. (eds) *Developing Skills in Geographical Education.* Brisbane: IGUCGE/Jacaranda Press, pp. 231–244.

4548    Williams, M. (1988) 'Models of in-service and continuing education of geography teachers' in Williams, M., Biilmann, O. and Gerber, R. (eds) *Towards Models for the Continuing Education of Geography Teachers.* Brisbane: IGUCGE/Brisbane College of Advanced Education, pp. 2–40.

4549    Williams, M. (1988) 'The in-service education and training of geography teachers in England and Wales' in Williams, M., Biilmann, O. and Gerber, R. (eds) *Towards Models for the Continuing Education of Geography Teachers.* Brisbane: IGUCGE/Brisbane College of Advanced Education, pp. 131–150.

4550    Williams, M. (1991) 'Staff development and INSET' in Wiegand, P. (ed) *Managing the Geography Department.* Sheffield: Geographical Association, pp. 91–102.

4551    Yockney, J. (1986) 'Preparing for GCSE: an in-service programme for geography teachers', *Education for Development*, 10, 2, pp. 3–15.

# 7. Lifelong Geographical and Environmental Education

4552    Awolola, M. D. (1991) 'Adult education: an agent of environmental awareness', *Environmental Education and Information*, 10, 3, pp. 175–182.

4553    Chapman, D. (1993) 'Adult education and our common future: the impact of environmental concerns', *Adults Learning*, 4, 8, pp. 222–223.

4554    Clark, C. and Higgitt, M. (1997) 'Geography and lifelong learning: a report on a survey of geography graduates', *Journal of Geography in Higher Education*, 21, 2, pp. 199–213.

4555    Department for Education (1993) *The Environment (PICKUP Sector Guide No. 3).* London: Department for Education.

4556    Field, J. (1989) 'Is the future for adult education green?: opportunities in environmentalism', *Adults Learning*, 1, 1, pp. 24–26.

4557    Field, J. (1993) 'Environmental education and training: the current situation', *Adults Learning*, 4, 8, pp. 210–211.

4558    Field, J. (ed) (1995) *The Environment Agenda: Taking Responsibility: Adult Continuing Education.* London: Pluto Press.

4559    Finger, M. (1989) 'Environmental adult education from the perspective of the adult learner', *Convergence*, 22, 4, pp. 25–32.

4560    Fraser, M. (1987) 'Environmental education as a continuing process', *Scottish Journal of Adult Education*, 8, 2, pp. 20–21.

4561    Geography Education Standards Project (1994) *Geography for Life*. Washington, DC: National Geographic Society.

4562    Gerber, R. (1995) 'A geographical education for life based on technological and graphic literacy', *Geographical Education*, 8, 3, pp. 50–56, 64.

4563    Gerber, R. (1997) 'Geography, work and lifelong learning', *Geographical Education*, 10, pp. 38–44.

4564    Gerber, R. (1997) 'Lifelong learning and the relevance of geography for work' in Convey, A. and Nolzen, H. (eds) *Geography and Education (Münchner Studien zur Didaktik der Geographie, Band 10)*. Munich: Lehrstuhl für Didaktik der Geographie der Universität München, pp. 101–110.

4565    Gerber, R. (1997) 'Valuing the concept of work in geographical education' in Naish, M. (ed) *Values in Geography Education: Proceedings*. London: IGUCGE/University of London Institute of Education, pp. 1–14.

4566    Gerber, R. and Williams, M. (1992) *Distance Education and Geography Teaching*. Swansea: IGUCGE/University of Wales Swansea.

4567    Grant, R. (1977) 'The Countryside Commission for Scotland: its training function', *Scottish Journal of Adult Education*, 2, 4, pp. 13–18.

4568    Gray, F. and Tivers, J. (1987) 'Distant relatives and poor cousins: geography in university adult education', *Area*, 19, 3, pp. 207–213.

4569    Gronemeyer, M. (1987) 'Ecological education a failing practice? or: is the ecological movement an educational movement?' in Leirman, W. and Kulich, J. (eds) *Adult Education and the Challenge of the 1990s*. London: Croom Helm, pp. 70–83.

4570    Harvey, B. (1977) 'Environmental education and university extra-mural departments', *Scottish Journal of Adult Education*, 2, 4, pp. 19–24.

4571    Hill, A. D. (1995) 'Geography standards, instruction and competencies for the new world of work', *Geographical Education*, 8, 3, pp. 47–49, 63.

4572    Lindsay, M. (1977) 'Education and the Scottish Civic Trust', *Scottish Journal of Adult Education*, 2, 4, pp. 5–12.

4573    Marriott, A. (1991) 'Geography in adult education', *Geography*, 76, 3, pp. 229–234.

4574    National Institute for Adult Continuing Education (1993) *Learning for the Future: Adult Learning and the Environment: Report of the Working Party on Environmental Adult Education*. Leicester: NIACE.

4575    Parker, J. (1993) 'Environmental ethics: questions for adult education', *Adults Learning*, 4, 8, pp. 216–217.

4576    Sommerville, A. (1980) 'Natural history, conservation and education', *Scottish Journal of Adult Education*, 4, 4, pp. 37–41.

4577    Thomas, P. A. (1993) 'The place of ecology in adult education' in Hale, M. (ed) *Ecology in Education*. Cambridge: Cambridge University Press, pp. 35–44.

4578    Verduin-Muller, H. (1984) 'Information theory and geography education' in Haubrich, H. (ed) *Perception of People and Places through Media, Volume 2*. Freiburg: IGUCGE/Pädagogische Hochschule Freiburg, pp. 208–219, 468–488.

4579    Welsh, R. (1993) 'Education for the urban environment', *Adults Learning*, 4, 8, pp. 212–213.

4580    White, S. and Senior, J. (1994) 'The ripple effect: a new approach to environmental education for adults', *Adults Learning*, 5, 8, pp. 214–215.

4581    Whitington, J. (1993) 'Environmentally speaking', *Adults Learning*, 4, 8, pp. 218–219.

# D. ENVIRONMENTAL EDUCATION

## 1. Environmental Education

4582    Agyeman, J. (1997) 'The multi-cultural city ecosystem' in Slater, F., Lambert, D. and Lines, D. (eds) *Education, Environment and Economy: Reporting Research in a New Academic Grouping (Bedford Way Papers)*. London: University of London Institute of Education, pp. 99–114.

4583    Ahier, J. (1995) 'Hidden controversies in two cross-curricular themes' in Ahier, J. and Ross, A. (eds) *The Social Subjects within the Curriculum: Children's Social Learning in the National Curriculum*. London: Falmer Press, pp. 139–156.

4584    Aho, L. (1984) 'A theoretical framework for research into environmental education', *International Review of Education*, 30, 2, pp. 183–191.

4585    Aldrich-Moodie, B. and Kwong, J. (1997) *Environmental Education*. London: Institute of Economic Affairs.

4586    Altman, I. and Wohwill, J. F. (eds) (1978) *Children and the Environment*. New York: Plenum Publishers.

4587    Anderson, S. and Moss, B. (1993) 'How wetland habitats are perceived by children: consequences for children's education and wetland conservation', *International Journal of Science Education*, 15, 5, pp. 473–485.

4588    Andrew, J., Jickling, B. and Robottom, I. (1996) 'Ethics, education and wildlife issues', *IRGEE*, 5, 1, pp. 31–44.

4589    Andrews, R. (1996) 'Spiritual and religious perspectives on the environment and their implications for education', *New Era*, 77, 3, pp. 72–79.

4590    Arnfield, S. B. (1983) *A Study of Some of the Factors affecting the Inclusion of Environmental Education in the Curriculum of Secondary Schools in England*, unpublished MPhil thesis. University of Reading.

4591    Bachiorri, A. and Vezzosi, C. (1997) 'Outcome research in environmental education: a case study', *Environmental Education and Information*, 16, 2, pp. 141–150.

4592    Baczala, K. (1992) *Towards a School Policy for Environmental Education: An Environmental Audit*. Walsall: National Association for Environmental Education (UK).

4593    Baez, A. V., Knamiller, G. W. and Smyth, J. C. (1987) *The Environment and Science and Technology and Education*. Oxford: Pergamon Press.

4594    Bak, N. (1995) 'Green doesn't always mean "go": possible tensions in the desirability and implementation of environmental education', *Environmental Education Research*, 1, 3, pp. 315–352.

4595    Bakshi, T. S. and Naveh, Z. (1980) *Environmental Education: Principles, Methods and Applications*. New York: Plenum Press.

4596    Ballantyne, R. (1995) 'Environmental teacher education: constraints, approaches and course design', *Environmental Education and Information*, 14, 2, pp. 115–128.

4597    Ballantyne, R. and Parker, J. (1996) 'Teaching and learning in environmental education: developing environmental conceptions', *Journal of Environmental Education*, 27, 2, pp. 25–32.

4598    Ballantyne, R. and Uzzell, D. (1994) 'A checklist for the critical evaluation of informal environmental learning experience', *Environmental Education and Information*, 13, 2, pp. 111–124.

4599    Ballantyne, R. and Witney, E. (1996) 'Using a phenomenographic approach to determine students' conceptions of environmental issues' in Gerber, R. and Williams, M. (eds) *Qualitative Research in Geographical Education*. Armidale, NSW: IGUCGE/University of New England Press, pp. 73–83.

4600    Batterham, D., Stanistreet, M. and Boyes, E. (1996) 'Kids, cars and conservation: children's ideas about the environmental impact of motor cars', *International Journal of Science Education*, 18, 3, pp. 347–354.

4601    Beal, W. K. (1973) 'Conservation and the schools', *Trends in Education*, 29, pp. 27–32.

4602    Berkowitz, A. R. (1993) 'New opportunities for ecology education in the United States' in Hale, M. (ed) *Ecology in Education*. Cambridge: Cambridge University Press, pp. 45–59.

4603    Billimore, B. (1990) *The Outdoor Classroom*. London: HMSO.

4604    Bolwell, L. H. (1973) 'A case for environmental education in schools', *Educational Development*, 13, 1, pp. 21–23.

4605    Bolwell, L. H. and Lines, C. J. (1973) 'The place of environmental studies in remedial work with older pupils', *Remedial Education*, 8, 3, pp. 31–34.

4606    Booth, R. (1990) *Ecology in the National Curriculum: A Practical Guide to Using School Grounds*. Winchester: Learning through Landscapes Trust.

4607    Boschhuizen, R. and Brinkman, F. G. (1991) 'A proposal for a teaching strategy based on pre-instructional ideas of pupils: environmental education: the use of pupils' ideas about cycles of nature and health', *European Journal of Teacher Education*, 14, 1, pp. 45–56.

4608    Bowers, C. A. (1993) *Education, Cultural Myths, and the Ecological Crisis*. Albany: SUNY Press.

4609    Bowlby, S. and Lowe, M. (1992) 'Environmental and green movements' in Mannion, A. M. and Bowlby, S. (eds) *Environmental Issues in the 1990s*. Chichester: Wiley, pp. 161–174.

4610    Boyes, E. and Stanistreet, M. (1992) 'Students' perceptions of global warming', *International Journal of Environmental Studies*, 42, pp. 287–300.

4611    Boyes, E. and Stanistreet, M. (1993) 'The "greenhouse effect": children's perceptions of causes, consequences and cures', *International Journal of Science Education*, 15, 5, pp. 531–552.

4612    Boyes, E. and Stanistreet, M. (1994) 'The ideas of secondary school children concerning ozone layer damage', *Global Environmental Change*, 4, 4, pp. 311–324.

4613    Boyes, E. and Stanistreet, M. (1996) 'Threats to the global atmospheric environment: the extent of pupil understanding', *IRGEE*, 5, 3, pp. 186–195.

4614    Braham, M. (1988) 'The ecology of education' in Briceno, S. and Pitt, D. C. (eds) *New Ideas in Environmental Education*. London: Croom Helm, pp. 3–32.

4615  Brainerd, J. W. (1971) *Nature Study for Conservation: A Handbook for Environmental Education*. New York: Macmillan.

4616  Brennan, A. (1991) 'Environmental awareness and liberal education', *British Journal of Educational Studies*, 39, 3, pp. 279–296.

4617  Briceno, S. and Pitt, D. C. (1988) *New Ideas in Environmental Education*. London: Croom Helm.

4618  Brinkman, F. G. and Scott, W. H. (1996) 'Reviewing a European Union initiative on environmental education within programmes of pre-service teacher education', *Environmental Education Research*, 2, 1, pp. 5–16.

4619  Brown, L. (1987) *Conservation and Practical Morality: Challenges to Education and Reform*. London: Macmillan.

4620  Brown, M. R. (1975) 'Toward an environmental ethic', *New Era*, 56, 1, pp. 31–33.

4621  Brown, M. R. (1980) 'A challenge for educators: education for a global economy environmentally oriented', *New Era*, 61, 4, pp. 128–129.

4622  Caduto, M. (1983) 'A review of environmental values education', *Journal of Environmental Education*, 14, 3, pp. 13–21.

4623  Caduto, M. (1983) 'Towards a comprehensive strategy for environmental values education', *Journal of Environmental Education*, 14, 4, pp. 12–18.

4624  Carson, S. McB. (ed) (1978) *Environmental Education: Principles and Practice*. London: Edward Arnold.

4625  Cave, B. (1990) 'Environmental education: a cross-curricular theme in the National Curriculum', *Values*, 5, 1, pp. 8–10.

4626  Centre for Educational Research and Innovation (1974) *Environmental Education at Post-Secondary Level*. Paris: Organisation for Economic Cooperation and Development.

4627  Centre for Educational Research and Innovation (1974) *Environmental Education at Post-Secondary Level: The Training of Generalists and Specialists, Volumes 1 and 2*. Paris: Organisation for Economic Cooperation and Development.

4628  Cerovsky, J. (1973) 'Environmental education as an integrating concept in science teaching' in Richmond, P. E. (ed) *New Trends in Integrated Science Teaching, Volume 2*. Paris: UNESCO, pp. 127–141.

4629  Charles, C. (1996) 'Ecological literacy is not enough', *IRGEE*, 5, 2, pp. 133–135.

4630  Chidley, L. (1990) 'Panda, people and plant: the work of the WWF Education Department', *Journal of Biological Education*, 24, 3, pp. 149–152.

4631  Childress, R. B. (1978) 'Public school environmental education curricula: a national profile', *Journal of Environmental Education*, 9, 3, pp. 2–11.

4632  Clarke, J. (1993) 'Education, population, environment and sustainable development', *International Review of Education*, 39, 1/2, pp. 53–61.

4633  Clary, M. (1996) 'Environmental education: an active learning' in van der Zijpp, T., van der Schee, J. and Trimp, H. (eds) *Innovation in Geographical Education: Proceedings of the 28th International Geographical Congress Commission on Geographical Education*. Amsterdam: Centrum voor Educatieve Geografie Vrije Universiteit Amsterdam, pp. 97–101.

4634  Collins, J. D. (1990) *Mathematics and Environmental Education*. Godalming: World Wildlife Fund (UK).

4635 Collis, M. (1977) 'Environmental education: ten years post-Plowden', *Education 3–13*, 5, 1, pp. 31–36.

4636 Colwell, T. (1997) 'The nature–nurture controversy and the future of environmental education', *Journal of Environmental Education*, 28, 4, pp. 4–8.

4637 Convey, A. (1994) 'Environmental education: international approaches and policies', *IRGEE*, 2, 1, pp. 92–96.

4638 Cooper, G. (1991) 'The role of outdoor and field study centres in educating for the environment', *Journal of Adventure Education and Outdoor Leadership*, 8, 2, pp. 78–83.

4639 Copland, W. O. (1976) 'Environmental education in secondary schools', *Trends in Education*, June 1976, pp. 41–43.

4640 Corney, G. (1997) 'Conceptions of environmental education' in Slater, F., Lambert, D. and Lines, D. (eds) *Education, Environment and Economy: Reporting Research in a New Academic Grouping (Bedford Way Papers)*. London: University of London Institute of Education, pp. 37–56.

4641 Corney, G. and Middleton, N. (1996) 'Teaching environmental issues in schools and higher education' in Rawling, E. and Daugherty, R. (eds) *Geography into the Twenty-first Century*. Chichester: John Wiley, pp. 323–338.

4642 Council for Environmental Education (1991) *Teacher Education and Environmental Education*. Reading: CEE.

4643 Council for Environmental Education (1997) *INSET for Environmental Education 5–16*. Reading: CEE.

4644 Council of Europe (1988) *Resolution on Environmental Education*. Strasbourg, Council of Europe.

4645 Curriculum Council for Wales (1992) *Environmental Education: A Framework for the Development of a Cross-curricular Theme in Wales*. Cardiff: CCW.

4646 Department for Education (1993) *Environmental Responsibility: An Agenda for Further and Higher Education*. London: HMSO.

4647 Department for Education/Department of the Environment (1995) *Education and the Environment: The Way Forward*. London: DfE.

4648 Department of Education and Science (1977) *Environmental Education in the UK*. London: HMSO.

4649 Department of Education and Science (1981) *Environmental Education: A Review*. London: HMSO.

4650 Department of Education and Science (1989) *Environmental Education from 5 to 16: Curriculum Matters 13, an HMI Series*. London: HMSO.

4651 Department of the Environment (1979) *Environmental Education in Urban Areas*. London: HMSO.

4652 Development Education Centre (1992) *"It's Our World Too": A Local-Global Approach to Environmental Education at Key Stages 2 and 3*. Birmingham/Sheffield: Development Education Centres.

4653 Disinger, J. (1986) 'Current trends in environmental education', *Journal of Environmental Education*, 17, 2, pp. 1–3.

4654    Donoghue, R. B. (1991) 'Environmental education: the development of a curriculum through "grass-roots" reconstructive action', *International Journal of Science Education*, 13, 4, pp. 391–404.

4655    Dorion, C. (1994) *Planning and Evaluation of Environmental Education 11–16*. London: Worldwide Fund for Nature.

4656    Dove, J. (1996) 'Student misconceptions on the greenhouse effect, ozone depletion and acid rain', *Environmental Education Research*, 2, 1, pp. 89–100.

4657    Dussart, G. B. J. (1990) 'Environmental education in Europe: a synoptic view', *Environmental Education and Information*, 9, 2, pp. 59–72.

4658    Elliott, J. (1995) 'The politics of environmental education', *Curriculum Journal*, 6, 3, pp. 377–393.

4659    Elliott, J. (1997) *Implementing Environmental Education in Secondary Schools*, unpublished MA (Ed) dissertation. University of Southampton.

4660    Elstgeest, J. and Harlen, W. (1990) *Environmental Science in the Primary Curriculum*. London: Paul Chapman.

4661    Eulefeld, G. (1979) 'The UNESCO-UNEP programme in environmental education', *European Journal of Science Education*, 1, 1, pp. 113–118.

4662    Evans, S. M. (1988) 'Man and the environment: the need for a more realistic approach to teaching ecology', *Journal of Biological Education*, 22, 2, pp. 136–138.

4663    Evans, S. M., Gill, M. E. and Marchant, J. (1996) 'Schoolchildren as educators: the indirect influence of environmental education on parents' attitudes towards the environment', *Journal of Biological Education*, 30, 4, pp. 243–249.

4664    Falk, J. H. (1982) 'Environmental education: formal vs informal learning', *Environmental Education and Information*, 2, 3, pp. 171–178.

4665    Falk, J. H. (1983) 'Field trips: a look at environmental effects on learning', *Journal of Biological Education*, 17, 2, pp. 137–142.

4666    Fenwick, W. P. (1971) 'Education and environment', *The Ecologist*, 2, 1, pp. 7–10.

4667    Fien, J. (1983) '"Par for the course": a case study in urban environmental education', *Geographical Education*, 4, 2, pp. 107–115.

4668    Fien, J. (1991) 'Accepting the dual challenge for professional development in environmental education', *Environmental Education and Information*, 10, 1, pp. 1–18.

4669    Fien, J. (1993) *Education for the Environment: Critical Curriculum Thinking and Environmental Education*. Geelong: Deakin University Press.

4670    Fien, J. (ed) (1993) *Environmental Education: a Pathway to Sustainability*. Geelong: Deakin University Press.

4671    Fien, J. (1995) 'Teaching for a sustainable world: the environment and development education project', *Environmental Education Research*, 1, 1, pp. 21–33.

4672    Fien, J. (1996) 'Teaching to care: a case for commitment in teaching environmental values' in Gerber, R. and Lidstone, J. (eds) *Developments and Directions in Geographical Education*. Clevedon: Channel View Publications, pp. 77–91.

4673    Fien, J. and Ferreira, J.-A. (1997) 'Environmental education in Australia: a review', *IRGEE*, 6, 3, pp. 234–239.

4674    Firth, R. (1995) 'Postmodernity, rationality and teaching environmental education', *IRGEE*, 4, 2, pp. 44–64.

4675 Ford, P. (1981) *Principles and Practices of Outdoor Environmental Education.* New York: John Wiley.

4676 Francis, G. (1989) 'Tertiary environmental education in its second decade', *Caribbean Journal of Education*, 16, 1/2, pp. 17–80.

4677 Gayford, C. (1986) 'Environmental education and the secondary school curriculum', *Journal of Curriculum Studies*, 18, 2, pp. 147–157.

4678 Gayford, C. (1987) *Environmental Education: Experiences and Attitudes.* Reading: Council for Environmental Education.

4679 Gayford, C. (1987) 'Environmental indoctrination or environmental education', *Environmental Education*, 27, 1, pp. 8–9.

4680 Gayford, C. (1990) 'Environmental education in the National Curriculum: an update', *Environmental Education and Information*, 9, 1, pp. 11–13.

4681 Gayford, C. (1991) 'Environmental education: a question of emphasis in the school curriculum', *Cambridge Journal of Education*, 21, 1, pp. 73–79.

4682 Gayford, C. (1993) 'Environmental education' in Verma, G. K. and Pumfrey, P. D. (eds) *Cultural Diversity and the Curriculum, Volume 2: Cross-Curricular Contexts, Themes and Dimensions in Secondary Schools.* London: Falmer Press, pp. 94–109.

4683 Gayford, C. (1994) 'Environmental education 5–16: in-service training (INSET) for teachers', *Journal of Biological Education*, 28, 4, pp. 284–290.

4684 Gayford, C. and Dillon, P. J. (1995) 'Policy and practice of environmental education in England: a dilemma for teachers', *Environmental Education Research*, 1, 2, pp. 177–183.

4685 Gayford, C. and Dorion, C. (1992) 'Local support systems for teachers and the implementation of environmental education in the primary curriculum', *Cambridge Journal of Education*, 22, 2, pp. 193–199.

4686 Gerber, R. (1996) 'Environmental learning: knowing, experiencing and acting for the environment' in van der Zijpp, T., van der Schee, J. and Trimp, H. (eds) *Innovation in Geographical Education: Proceedings of the 28th International Geographical Congress Commission on Geographical Education.* Amsterdam: IGUCGE/Centrum voor Educatieve Geografie Vrije Universiteit Amsterdam, pp. 102–106.

4687 Gigliotti, L. M. (1990) 'Environmental education: what went wrong? what can be done?' *Journal of Environmental Education*, 22, 1, pp. 9–12.

4688 Gigliotti, L. M. (1992) 'Environmental attitudes: 20 years of change', *Journal of Environmental Education*, 24, 1, pp. 15–26.

4689 Glasgow, J. (1984) 'Report on the subregional workshop on teacher training in environmental education for the Caribbean', *Caribbean Journal of Education*, 11, 1, pp. 48–69.

4690 Glasgow, J. (1989) 'Environmental education: global concern, Caribbean focus', *Caribbean Journal of Education*, 16, 1/2, pp. 1–12.

4691 Gomez-Granell, C. and Cervera-March, S. (1993) 'Development of conceptual knowledge and attitudes about energy and the environment', *International Journal of Science Education*, 15, 5, pp. 553–565.

4692 Goodall, S. (ed) (1994) *Developing Environmental Education in the Curriculum.* London: David Fulton.

4693    Goodey, B. (1970) 'Environmental studies and interdisciplinary research', *Area*, 2, 2, pp. 16–18.

4694    Goodman, P. (1988) 'The world environmental studies project', *World Studies Journal*, 7, 1, pp. 30–32.

4695    Goodson, I. F. (1976) 'Environmental education for all: strategies for change', *Environmental Education*, 5, pp. 13–16.

4696    Goodson, I. F. (1983) 'Redefining rural studies: the genesis of environmental studies' in Goodson, I. F. *School Subjects and Curriculum Change: Case Studies in Curriculum History*. London: Croom Helm, pp. 124–139.

4697    Goodson, I. F. (1983) 'The negotiation of environmental studies' in Goodson, I. F. *School Subjects and Curriculum Change: Case Studies in Curriculum History*. London: Croom Helm, pp. 172–188.

4698    Gough, N. (1993) 'Environmental education, narrative complexity and post-modern science fiction', *International Journal of Science Education*, 15, 5, pp. 607–625.

4699    Graves, N. (1986) 'The environment under threat: a challenge to education', *New Era*, 67, 1, pp. 3–5.

4700    Greaves, E., Stanistreet, M., Boyes, E. and Williams, T. (1993) 'Children's ideas about rain forests', *Journal of Biological Education*, 27, 3, pp. 189–194.

4701    Greenall, A. (1981) 'Environmental education: a case study in national curriculum action', *Environmental Education and Information*, 1, 4, pp. 285–294.

4702    Greenall, A. (1986) 'Searching for a meaning: what is environmental education?', *Geographical Education*, 5, 2, pp. 9–12.

4703    Greenall Gough, A. (1993) *Founders in Environmental Education*. Geelong: Deakin University Press.

4704    Greenall Gough, A. and Robottom, I. (1993) 'Towards a socially critical environmental education: water quality studies in a coastal school', *Journal of Curriculum Studies*, 23, 4, pp. 301–316.

4705    Greig, S., Pike, G. and Selby, D. (1987) *Earthrights: Education as if the Planet Really Mattered*. London: Kogan Page/World Wildlife Fund (UK).

4706    Greig, S., Pike, G. and Selby, D. (1989) *Greenprints for Changing Schools*. London: Kogan Page/World Wildlife Fund (UK).

4707    Grove, R. H. (1990) 'The origins of environmentalism', *Nature*, 100, pp. 11–14.

4708    Gruffudd, P. (1996) 'The countryside as educator: schools, rurality and citizenship in inter-war Wales', *Journal of Historical Geography*, 22, 4, pp. 412–423.

4709    Grun, M. (1996) 'An analysis of the discursive production of environmental education: terrorism, archaism and transcendentalism', *Curriculum Studies*, 4, 3, pp. 329–347.

4710    Hale, M. (1986) 'Approaches to ecological teaching: the educational potential of the local environment', *Journal of Biological Education*, 20, 3, pp. 179–184.

4711    Hale, M. (ed) (1987) *Ecological and Environmental Education Initiatives in Britain*. London: Polytechnic of North London Press.

4712    Hale, M. (1991) 'Ecology in the National Curriculum', *Journal of Biological Education*, 25, 1, pp. 20–26.

4713    Hale, M. (ed) (1993) *Ecology in Education*. Cambridge: Cambridge University Press.

4714    Hale, M. (1993) 'Ecology and environmental education in the urban environment' in Hale, M. (ed) *Ecology in Education*. Cambridge: Cambridge University Press, pp. 131–144.

4715    Hale, M. (1993) 'Educating for sustainability in developing countries: the need for environmental education support', *Environmental Education and Information*, 12, 1, pp. 1–14.

4716    Hale, M. and Hardie, J. (1993) 'Ecology and environmental education in schools in Britain' in Hale, M. (ed) *Ecology in Education*. Cambridge: Cambridge University Press, pp. 10–22.

4717    Han, S. H. and Sewing, D. R. (1987/88) 'Barriers to environmental education', *Journal of Environmental Education*, 19, 2, pp. 25–33.

4718    Harrah, D. F. and Harrah, B. K. (1975) *Conservation/Ecology: Resources for Environmental Education*. Metuchen, NJ: Scarecrow Press.

4719    Harris, C. (1991) 'Environmental education in England and Wales: a brief review', *European Journal of Education*, 26, 4, pp. 287–290.

4720    Harrison, R. (1976) 'Environmental education: the historical perspective', *Environmental Education*, 5, pp. 8–12.

4721    Hawkins, G. (1985) 'The development of conceptual frameworks with reference to learning in the environment', *Environmental Education and Information*, 4, 4, pp. 252–263.

4722    Hawkins, G., Jones, N. and Montford, S. (1990/91) 'Curriculum guidance 7: environmental education', *Streetwise*, 5, pp. 5–7.

4723    Henning, D. H. (1990) 'Environmental education and national parks: the world conservation strategy, values and naturalist interpretive activities', *Environmental Education and Information*, 9, 1, pp. 1–14.

4724    Hickling-Hudson, A. (1994) 'The environment as radical politics: can 'Third World' education rise to the challenge?', *International Review of Education*, 40, 1, pp. 19–36.

4725    Hicks, D. (1995) *Visions of the Future: Why we Need to Teach for Tomorrow*. Stoke-on-Trent: Trentham Books.

4726    Hicks, D. (1996) 'Envisioning the future: the challenge for environmental education', *Environmental Education Research*, 2, 1, pp. 101–108.

4727    Hicks, D. and Holden, C. (1995) 'Exploring the future: a missing dimension in environmental education', *Environmental Education Research*, 1, 2, pp. 185–193.

4728    Hillcoat, J., Forge, K., Fien, J. and Baker, E. (1995) '"I think it's really great that someone is listening to us...": young people and the environment', *Environmental Education Research*, 1, 2, pp. 159–171.

4729    Hindle, A. (1974) 'The use of English in environmental education', *English in Education*, 8, 2, pp. 56–72.

4730    Hobart, W. L. (1972) 'What's wrong with conservation education?', *Journal of Environmental Education*, 3, 4, pp. 23–25.

4731    Howell, C. A. (1989) 'Emerging trends in environmental education in the English-speaking Caribbean', *Convergence*, 22, 4, pp. 45–53.

4732    Howell, C. A. (1995) 'Educating for sustainable development: an overview of environmental education programs in the Caribbean', *Environmental Education and Information*, 14, 4, pp. 419–432.

4733    Huckle, J. (1987) 'Environment and development issues in the curriculum: the experience of one curriculum project' in Lacey, C. and Williams, R. (eds) *Education, Ecology and Development: The Case for an Education Network*. London: Kogan Page/World Wildlife Fund (UK), pp. 147–156.

4734    Huckle, J. (1988) 'Environment' in Hicks, D. (ed) *Education for Peace: Issues, Principles and Practice in the Classroom*. London: Routledge, pp. 196–213.

4735    Huckle, J. (1990) 'Environmental education: teaching for a sustainable future' in Dufour, D. (ed) *The New Social Curriculum: A Guide to Cross-curricular Issues*. Cambridge: Cambridge University Press, pp. 150–566.

4736    Huckle, J. (1990) '"What we consume": the sustainable rationale', *Geographical Education*, 6, 2, pp. 31–36.

4737    Huckle, J. (1993) 'Environmental education and sustainability: a view from critical theory' in Fien, J. (ed) *Environmental Education: A Pathway to Sustainability*. Geelong: Deakin University Press, pp. 43–69.

4738    Huckle, J. (1994) 'Environmental education and the National Curriculum in England and Wales', *IRGEE*, 2, 1, pp. 101–104.

4739    Huckle, J. (1995) 'Using television critically in environmental education', *Environmental Education Research*, 1, 3, pp. 291–304.

4740    Huckle, J. and Sterling, S. (1996) *Education for Sustainability*. London: Earthscan.

4741    Hungerford, H., Peyton, R. and Wilke, R. (1980) 'Goals for curriculum development in environmental education', *Journal of Environmental Education*, 11, 3, pp. 42–47.

4742    International Union for the Conservation of Nature (1971) 'Environmental education: a step towards the solution of environmental problems by changing people's attitudes' in *Economic Commission for Europe Symposium on Problems relating to Environment*. New York: United Nations, pp. 231–234.

4743    Iozzi, L. A. (1989) 'What research says to the educator: environmental education and the affective domain', *Journal of Environmental Education*, 20, 3, pp. 3–9; 20, 4, pp. 6–13.

4744    Irwin, H. S. (1982) 'The ethical challenge of environmental education', *New Era*, 63, 1, pp. 1–9.

4745    Jacobson, S. K. and McDuff, M. D. (1997) 'Success factors and evaluation in conservation education programs', *IRGEE*, 6, 3, pp. 204–221.

4746    Jaus, H. H. (1984) 'The development and retention of environmental attitudes in school children', *Journal of Environmental Education*, 15, 3, pp. 33–36.

4747    Jones, J. F. (1996) *The World in our Hands: Environmental Education, Training and Awareness in England and Wales*. London: Department of the Environment.

4748    Keighley, P. W. S. (1997) 'The impact of experiences out-of-doors on personal development and environmental attitudes', *Horizons*, 2, pp. 27–28.

4749    Keliher, V. (1997) 'Children's perceptions of science and nature', *IRGEE*, 6, 3, pp. 240–243.

4750    Kelly, P. J. (1977) 'What do we really mean by environmental education?' in Hughes-Evans, D. (ed) *Environmental Education: Key Issues of the Future*, Oxford: Pergamon, pp. 61–66.

4751    Kimber, D., Clough, N., Forrest, M., Harnett, P., Menter, I. and Newman, E. (1995) 'Environmental education' in Kimber, D. *et al.* (ibid.) *Humanities in Primary Education.* London: David Fulton, pp. 81–106.

4752    Knamiller, G. W. (1981) 'Environmental education and the north–south dialogue', *Comparative Education*, 17, 1, pp. 87–94.

4753    Knapp, C. (1983) 'A curriculum model for environmental values education', *Journal of Environmental Education*, 14, 3, pp. 23–26.

4754    Lacey, C. (1987) 'Towards a general framework for a new curriculum and pedagogy: progress towards a socialist education' in Lacey, C. and Williams, R. (eds) *Education, Ecology and Development: The Case for an Education Network.* London: Kogan Page/World Wildlife Fund (UK), pp. 87–103.

4755    Lacey, C. and Williams, R. (eds) (1987) *Education, Ecology and Development: The Case for an Education Network.* London: Kogan Page/World Wildlife Fund (UK).

4756    Lavanchy, S. (1993) 'Environmental education: how should we face it in early childhood education?', *International Journal of Early Childhood*, 25, 1, pp. 37–41.

4757    Leal Filho, W. (1993) 'Field studies as a technique for environmental education in developed and developing nations' in Hale, M. (ed) *Ecology in Education.* Cambridge: Cambridge University Press, pp. 82–98.

4758    Leal Filho, W. (1994) *Promoting Environmental Education in Europe.* Bradford: ERTCEE.

4759    Leal Filho, W. (1996) 'An overview of current trends in European environmental education', *Journal of Environmental Education*, 28, 1, pp. 5–10.

4760    Leal Filho, W. and Hale, M. (eds) (1994) *Trends in Environmental Education Worldwide.* Bradford/London: European Research Unit on Environmental Education and Development/Guildhall University.

4761    Leal Filho, W., MacDermott, F. and Murphy, Z. (eds) (1995) *Practices of Environmental Education in Europe.* Bradford: ERTCEE.

4762    Lewis, R. and Reid, A. (1996) 'Discussing environmental education research: how do we speak with each other?', *Environmental Education Research*, 2, 1, pp. 123–126.

4763    Liepe, J. (1991) 'Environmental education in decay', *Streetwise*, 8, pp. 27–29.

4764    Lines, C. J. and Bolwell, L. H. (1971) *Teaching Environmental Studies in the Primary and Middle School.* London: Ginn and Co.

4765    Linke, R. D. (1974) 'The classification and analysis of environmental education' in Musgrave, P. W. (ed) *Contemporary Studies in the Curriculum.* Sydney: Angus and Robertson, pp. 200–214.

4766    Linke, R. D. (1976) 'A case for indoctrination in environmental education', *South Pacific Journal of Teacher Education*, 4, 2, pp. 125–129.

4767    Lob, R. E. (1992) 'Environmental education as a comprehensive and integral commitment of primary school education: a report from Germany', *Environmental Education and Information*, 11, 1, pp. 25–30.

4768    Lowenthal, D. (1970) 'Earth day', *Area*, 2, 1, pp. 1–9.

4769    Lucas, A. M. (1980) 'Science and environmental education: pious hopes, self praise and disciplinary chauvinism', *Studies in Science Education*, 7, 1, pp. 1–26.

4770 Maher, M. (1986) 'Environmental education: what are we fighting for?', *Geographical Education*, 5, 2, pp. 22–25.

4771 Mares, C. and Stephenson, R. (1988) *Inside Outside*. Brighton: Tidy Britain Group.

4772 Marriott, A. (1997) 'Greening schools and colleges' in Powell, A. (ed) *Handbook of Post-16 Geography*. Sheffield: Geographical Association, pp. 161–166.

4773 Marsden, W. E. (1971) 'Environmental studies courses in colleges of education', *Journal of Curriculum Studies*, 3, 2, pp. 163–178.

4774 Marsden, W. E. (1997) 'The book of nature and the stuff of epitaphs: religion, romanticism and some historical connections in environmental education', *Paradigm*, 24, pp. 4–15.

4775 Marsden, W. E. (1997) 'Environmental education: historical roots, comparative perspectives and current issues in Britain and the United States', *Journal of Curriculum and Supervision*, 13, 1, pp. 6–29.

4776 Martin, E. S., Lewis, D., Trumman, L. J., Smith, B. J. and Brown, P. (1993) 'Environmental education in Sweden', *Environmentalist*, 13, 3, pp. 221–227.

4777 Martin, G. C. and Wheeler, K. (eds) (1975) *Insights into Environmental Education*. Edinburgh: Oliver and Boyd.

4778 Martin, P. (1990) *First Steps to Sustainability: The School, Curriculum and the Environment*. London: Worldwide Fund for Nature.

4779 Masterton, T. H. (1973) *Environmental Studies: A Concentric Approach*. Edinburgh: Oliver and Boyd.

4780 Matthews, M. H. (1985) 'Environmental capability of the very young: some implications for environmental education in primary schools', *Educational Review*, 37, 3, pp. 227–239.

4781 Mays, P. (1985) *Teaching Children through the Environment*. London: Hodder and Stoughton.

4782 Mische, P. M. (1992) 'Towards a pedagogy of environmental responsibility: learning to reinhabit the earth', *Convergence*, 25, 2, pp. 9–25.

4783 Montefiore, H. (1990) 'Environmental dilemmas', *Values*, 5, 1, pp. 3–7.

4784 Morgan, J. (1997) 'Consumer culture and education for sustainability' in Slater, F., Lambert, D. and Lines, D. (eds) *Education, Environment and Economy: Reporting Research in a New Academic Grouping (Bedford Way Papers)*. London: University of London Institute of Education, pp. 161–172.

4785 Nagy, J. N. and Baird, J. C. (1978) 'Children as environmental planners' in Altman, I. and Wohwill, J. F. (eds) *Children and the Environment*. New York: Plenum Press, pp. 259–294.

4786 Namafe, C. (1997) 'Cultural differences in responses to environment' in Slater, F., Lambert, D. and Lines, D. (eds) *Education, Environment and Economy: Reporting Research in a New Academic Grouping (Bedford Way Papers)*. London: University of London Institute of Education, pp. 115–134.

4787 National Curriculum Council (1992) *Environmental Education: Curriculum Guidance 7*. York: NCC.

4788 Neal, P. and Palmer, J. (1990) *Environmental Education in the Primary School*. Oxford: Blackwell.

4789   Newman, P. W. G. (1981) 'The dilemma of the environmental educator: are we really needed?: some answers and examples in the affirmative', *Environmental Education and Information*, 1, 2, pp. 109–122.

4790   Nicholas, J., Oulton, C. R. and Scott, W. H. (1993) 'Teacher education for the environment: a comparative view from Australia and the UK', *International Journal of Science Education*, 15, 5, pp. 567–574.

4791   Nicholls, A. D. (1973) 'Environmental studies in schools', *Geography*, 58, 3, pp. 197–206.

4792   Norton, B. G. and Hannon, B. (1997) 'Environmental values: a place-based theory', *Environmental Ethics*, 19, 3, pp. 227–245.

4793   Numata, M. (1985) 'A survey on environmental science and environmental education', *Environmental Education and Information*, 4, 4, pp. 298–306.

4794   O'Hear, A. (1997) *NonSense about Nature*. London: The Social Affairs Unit.

4795   Ojala, J. (1997) 'Lost in space?: the concepts of planetary phenomena held by trainee primary teachers', *IRGEE*, 6, 3, pp. 183–203.

4796   Oldenski, T. E. (1991) 'What on earth are we doing with environmental themes in education?', *Environmental Education and Information*, 10, 2, pp. 67–76.

4797   Olina, Z. (1997) *Education and the Environment in Europe*. Strasbourg: Council of Europe.

4798   Ophuls, W. (1980) 'Citizenship and ecological education', *Teachers College Record*, 82, 2, pp. 217–242.

4799   O'Riordan, T. (1981) 'Environmentalism and education', *Journal of Geography in Higher Education*, 5, 1, pp. 3–17.

4800   Orr, D. W. (1992) *Ecological Literacy: Education and the Transition to a Postmodern World*. Albany: State University of New York Press.

4801   Orr, D. W. (1994) *Earth in Mind – on Education, Environment and the Human Prospect*. Washington, DC: Island Press.

4802   Oulton, C. R. and Scott, W. H. (1992) 'The inter-dependence of environmental education, economic and industrial understanding, and the cross-curricular themes within the school curriculum', *Environmental Education and Information*, 11, 1, pp. 1–10.

4803   Oulton, C. R. and Scott, W. H. (1995) 'The "environmental education teacher": an exploration of the implications of UNESCO-UNEP's ideas for pre-service teacher education programmes', *Environmental Education Research*, 1, 2, pp. 213–231.

4804   Palmer, J. (1991) 'Implementing CG7: policy into practice', *Environmental Education*, 36, pp. 9–10.

4805   Palmer, J. (1993) 'From Santa Claus to sustainability: emergent understanding of concepts and issues in environmental science', *International Journal of Science Education*, 15, 5, pp. 487–495.

4806   Palmer, J. (1995) 'Environmental thinking in the early years: understanding and misunderstanding of concepts related to waste management', *Environmental Education Research*, 1, 1, pp. 35–48.

4807   Palmer, J. and Neal, P. (1994) *The Handbook of Environmental Education*. London: Routledge.

4808    Palmer, J., Suggate, J. and Matthews, J. (1996) 'Environmental cognition: early ideas and misconceptions at the ages of four and six', *Environmental Education Research*, 2, 3, pp. 301–330.

4809    Park, C. C. (1984) 'Towards a philosophy of environmental education', *Environmental Education and Information*, 3, 1, pp. 3–15.

4810    Parry, M. (1988) *Planning and Implementing Environmental Curriculum Initiatives in Secondary Schools in England and Wales.* Walsall: National Association for Environmental Education (UK).

4811    Pascoe, I. (1986) 'Environmental education in Scotland', *New Era*, 67, 4, pp. 87–88.

4812    Peltonen, A. (1997) 'Reflections on STS discussions on the reform of Finnish "environmental-science" education', *IRGEE*, 6, 1, pp. 27–40.

4813    Pepper, D. (1984) *The Roots of Modern Environmentalism.* London: Routledge.

4814    Pepper, D. (1987) 'Red and green: educational perspectives', *Green Teacher*, 4, pp. 11–14.

4815    Pepper, D. (1987) 'The basis of a radical curriculum in environmental education' in Lacey, C. and Williams, R. (eds) *Education, Ecology and Development: The Case for an Education Network.* London: Kogan Page/World Wildlife Fund (UK), pp. 65–79.

4816    Pepper, D. (1993) *Eco-socialism: From Deep Ecology to Social Justice.* London: Routledge.

4817    Pepper, D. (1996) *Modern Environmentalism.* London: Routledge.

4818    Perry, G. A., Jones, K. and Hammersley, A. (1971) *The Teachers' Handbook for Environmental Studies.* London: Blandford.

4819    Plant, M. (1995) 'The riddle of sustainable development and the role of environmental education', *Environmental Education Research*, 1, 3, pp. 253–266.

4820    Porritt, J. (1988) 'Education for life on earth', *Geography*, 73, 1, pp. 1–8.

4821    Posch, P. (1990) 'New strategies for environmental education', *Streetwise*, 4, pp. 28–31.

4822    Posch, P. (1993) 'Action research in environmental education', *Educational Action Research*, 1, 3, pp. 447–455.

4823    Posch, P. (1993) 'Research issues in environmental education', *Studies in Science Education*, 21, pp. 21–48.

4824    Pozarnik, B. M. (1995) 'Probing into pupil's moral judgement in environmental dilemmas: a basis for "teaching values"', *Environmental Education Research*, 1, 1, pp. 47–58.

4825    Prakash, M. S. (1995) 'Ecological literacy for moral virtue: Orr on (moral) education for postmodern sustainability', *Journal of Moral Education*, 24, 1, pp. 3–18.

4826    Pullen, O. J. E. (1970) 'Schools and the countryside', *Trends in Education*, 7, pp. 30–35.

4827    Purcell, J. E. (1971) 'Environmental studies and conservation', *General Education*, 16, pp. 11–19.

4828    Qualter, A., Francis, C., Boyes, E. and Stanistreet, M. (1995) 'The greenhouse effect: what do primary children think?', *Education 3–13*, 23, 2, pp. 28–31.

4829    Ramsey, C. E. and Rickson, R. E. (1977) 'Environmental knowledge and attitudes', *Journal of Environmental Education*, 8, 1, pp. 6–18.

4830    Randle, D. (1983) 'Environmental issues and peace education', *World Studies Journal*, 4, 4, pp. 16–22.

4831    Revell, T., Stanistreet, M. and Boyes, E. (1994) 'Children's views about marine pollution', *International Journal of Environmental Studies*, 45, pp. 245–260.

4832    Robins, J. and Garratt, D. (1994) 'Interdependence and controversial issues: environmental education and economic and industrial understanding as cross-curricular themes', *Environmental Education and Information*, 13, 4, pp. 5–28.

4833    Robottom, I. (ed) (1987) *Environmental Education: Practice and Possibility*. Geelong: Deakin University Press.

4834    Robottom, I. (1989) 'Social critique or social control: some problems for evaluation in environmental education', *Journal of Research in Science Teaching*, 24, 5, pp. 435–444.

4835    Robottom, I. and Hart, P. (1993) *Research in Environmental Education: Engaging the Debate*. Geelong: Deakin University Press.

4836    Roth, R. E. (1970) 'Fundamental concepts for environmental management education', *Journal of Environmental Education*, 1, 3, pp. 65–74.

4837    Royal Society for the Protection of Birds (1996) *Our World – Our Responsibility: Environmental Education – A Practical Guide*. Sandy: RSPB.

4838    Royal Town Planning Institute (1979) *The Role of the Planner in Environmental Education*. London: RTPI.

4839    St Maurice, H. (1996) 'Nature's nature: ideas of nature in curricula for environmental education', *Environmental Education Research*, 2, 2, pp. 141–148.

4840    Sale, L. L. and Lee, E. W. (1972) *Environmental Education in the Elementary School*. New York: Holt Rinehart and Winston.

4841    Saveland, R. N. (ed) (1976) *Handbook of Environmental Education: with International Case Studies*. London: John Wiley and Sons.

4842    Schleicher, K. (1989) 'Beyond environmental education: the need for ecological awareness', *International Review of Education*, 35, 3, pp. 257–281.

4843    Schoenfeld, C. (1970) 'Toward a national strategy for environmental education', *Journal of Educational Research*, 64, 1, pp. 5–11.

4844    Schools Council Environmental Studies Project (1972) *A Teacher's Guide*. London: Rupert Hart-Davis.

4845    Schools Council (1974) *Project Environment: Education for the Environment*. London: Longman, for the Schools Council.

4846    School Curriculum and Assessment Authority (1996) *Teaching Environmental Matters through the National Curriculum*. London: SCAA.

4847    Scriven, M. (1970) 'Environmental education' in Johnson, H. D. (ed) *No Deposit – No Return: Man and his Environment: A View toward Survival*. Reading, MA: Addison-Wesley Publishing Company, pp. 242–249.

4848    Shirley, D. (1993) 'Ecological studies between schools in Europe and Scandinavia: the benefits to the curriculum of working across national boundaries' in Hale, M. (ed) *Ecology in Education*. Cambridge: Cambridge University Press, pp. 167–178.

4849    Shuman, D. K. and Ham, S. H. (1987) 'Toward a theory of commitment to environmental education teaching', *Environmental Education*, 28, 2, pp. 25–32.

4850    Simmons, D. A. (1988) 'Environmental education and environmental ethics: theory, practice and mixed messages', *Environmental Education and Information*, 7, 2, pp. 52–61.

4851    Simmons, I. G. and Simmons, C. M. (1973) 'Environmentalism and education: a context for "conservation"', *School Science Review*, 54, 188, pp. 574–579.

4852    Smyth, J. C. (1987) 'Another country: environmental education in Scottish schools', *Bulletin of Environmental Education*, 195/196, pp. 24–26.

4853    Smyth, J. C. (1988) 'What makes education environmental?' in Briceno, S. and Pitt, D. C. (eds) *New Ideas in Environmental Education*. London: Croom Helm, pp. 33–56.

4854    Smyth, J. C. (1995) 'Environment and education: a view of a changing scene', *Environmental Education Research*, 1, 1, pp. 3–20.

4855    Spencer, C., Mitchell, S. and Wisdom, J. (1984) 'Evaluating environmental education in nursery and primary schools', *Environmental Education and Information*, 3, 1, pp. 16–32.

4856    Stapp, W. (1974) 'Historical setting of environmental education' in Swan, J. and Stapp, W. (eds) *Environmental Education: Strategies Toward a More Livable Future*. New York: Sage Publications, pp. 42–49.

4857    Sterling, S. (1992) *Coming of Age: A Short History of Environmental Education (to 1989)*. Walsall: National Association for Environmental Education (UK).

4858    Sterling, S. and Cooper, G. (1992) *In Touch: Environmental Education for Europe*. Godalming: World Wildlife Fund (UK).

4859    Stevenson, R. B. (1993) 'Becoming compatible: curriculum and environmental thought', *Journal of Environmental Education*, 24, 2, pp. 4–9.

4860    Stillman, C. W. (1972) 'Reflections on environmental education', *Teachers College Record*, 74, 2, pp. 195–200.

4861    Stimpson, P. (1994) 'Environmental education and classroom practice: some implications for teacher education', *IRGEE*, 3, 2, pp. 22–34.

4862    Stoddart, D. (1970) 'Our environment', *Area*, 2, 1, pp. 1–3.

4863    Sutton, P. (1989) 'Environmental education: what can we teach?', *Convergence*, 22, 4, pp. 5–11.

4864    Swan, J. (1971) 'Environmental education: one approach to resolving the environmental crisis', *Environment and Behavior*, 3, 3, pp. 223–229.

4865    Swan, J. (1971) 'The challenge of environmental education' in Ball, J., Steinbrink, J. and Stoltman, J. (eds) *The Social Sciences and Geographical Education: A Reader*. New York: John Wiley and Sons, pp. 318–323.

4866    Swan, J. and Stapp, W. (eds) (1974) *Environmental Education: Strategies Toward a More Livable Future*. New York: Sage Publications.

4867    Terry, M. (1971) *Teaching for Survival*. New York: Friends of the Earth/Ballantine.

4868    Thomas, I. (1987) 'Distinguishing aspects of environmental education', *Environmental Education and Information*, 6, 3, pp. 181–188.

4869    Tickell, C. (1996) 'Education for sustainability' in Carnie, F., Tasker, M. and Large, M. (eds) *Freeing Education: Steps towards Real Choice and Diversity in Schools*. Stroud: Hawthorn Press, pp. 141–151.

4870    Tilbury, D. (1992) 'Environmental education within pre-service teacher education: the priority of priorities', *Environmental Education and Information*, 11, 4, pp. 267–280.

4871    Tilbury, D. (1994) 'The international development of environmental education: a basis for a teacher education model?', *Environmental Education and Information*, 13, 1, pp. 2–20.

4872    Tilbury, D. (1995) 'Environmental education for sustainability: defining the new focus of environmental education in the 1990s', *Environmental Education Research*, 1, 2, pp. 195–212.

4873    Tilbury, D. and Turner, K. (1997) 'Environmental education for sustainability in Europe: philosophy into practice', *Environmental Education and Information*, 16, 2, pp. 123–140.

4874    Tilbury, D. and Walford, R. (1996) 'Grounded theory: defying the dominant paradigm in environmental education research' in Williams, M. (ed) *Understanding Geographical and Environmental Education: The Role of Research*. London: Cassell, pp. 51–64.

4875    Tilling, S. (1993) 'Ecology education and field studies: historical trends and some present-day influences in Britain' in Hale, M. (ed) *Ecology in Education*. Cambridge: Cambridge University Press, pp. 60–81.

4876    Trainer, T. (1990) 'Rethinking sustainable development', *Geographical Education*, 6, 2, pp. 24–30.

4877    Troost, C. J. and Altman, H. (1972) *Environmental Education: A Sourcebook*. New York: John Wiley.

4878    Trudgill, S. (1991) 'Environmental education: priorities and participation', *Geography*, 76, 1, pp. 43–49.

4879    United Nations Educational, Scientific and Cultural Organisation (1975) *International Workshop on Environmental Education, Tbilisi*. Paris: UNESCO.

4880    United Nations Educational, Scientific and Cultural Organisation (1977) *Intergovernmental Conference on Environmental Education, Belgrade*. Paris: UNESCO.

4881    United Nations Educational, Scientific and Cultural Organisation (1977) *Trends in Environmental Education*. Paris: UNESCO.

4882    United Nations Educational, Scientific and Cultural Organisation (1980) *Environmental Education in the Light of the Tbilisi Conference*. Paris: UNESCO.

4883    United Nations Educational, Scientific and Cultural Organisation (1987) *Intergovernmental Conference on Environmental Education, Moscow*. Paris: UNESCO.

4884    United Nations Educational, Scientific and Cultural Organisation (1990) 'Environmentally educated teachers: the priority of priorities', *Connect (UNESCO-UNEP Environmental Education Newsletter)*, 15, 1, pp. 1–5.

4885    van Dijk, H. and Stomp, L. (1996) 'Involvement, the key to environmental education' in van der Schee, J., Schoenmaker, G., Trimp, H. and van Westrhenen, H. (eds) *Innovation in Geographical Education (Netherlands Geographical Studies, 208)*. Utrecht/Amsterdam: IGUCGE/Centrum voor Educatieve Geografie Vrije Universiteit Amsterdam, pp. 179–189.

4886    Viezzer, L. (1992) 'Learning for environmental action', *Convergence*, 25, 2, pp. 3–8.

4887    Vivian, V. E. (1973) *Sourcebook for Environmental Education*. Saint Louis, MO: The C. V. Mosby Company.

4888    Vulliamy, G. (1988) 'Introducing a global perspective on the environment in Third World schools', *World Studies Journal*, 7, 1, pp. 18–20.

4889    Walker, K. (1997) 'Environmental education and the school curriculum: the need for a coherent curriculum theory', *IRGEE*, 6, 3, pp. 252–255.

4890    Wals, A. (1990) 'Caretakers of the environment: a global network of teachers and students to save the earth', *Journal of Environmental Education*, 21, 3, pp. 3–7.

4891    Walton, B. (1989) 'Environment education', *Education*, 174, 14, pp. 295–301.

4892    Webster, P. J. (1981) *The Environment and Education: A Study of Policies of Selected Educational Institutions in South Wales*, unpublished MEd dissertation. University of Wales Cardiff.

4893    Wendt, N. (1988) 'Environmental education in the South Pacific' in Gerber, R. and Lidstone, J. (eds) *Skills in Geographical Education Symposium '88, Volume 1*. Brisbane: IGUCGE/Brisbane College of Advanced Education, pp. 214–226.

4894    Weston, J. (ed) (1986) *Red and Green: The New Politics of the Environment*. London: Pluto Press.

4895    Wheatley, D. (1992) 'Environmental education: an instrument for change?' in Hall, G. (ed) *Themes and Dimensions of the National Curriculum: Implications for Policy and Practice*. London: Kogan Page, pp. 28–43.

4896    Williams, M. and Bell, S. (1972) *Using the Urban Environment: A Guide for Primary Teachers*. London: Heinemann.

4897    Williams, R. (1989) *One Earth – Many Worlds*. Godalming: World Wildlife Fund (UK).

4898    Williams, R. (ed) (1992) *Environmental Education and Teacher Education: Preparing for Change and Participation*. Brighton: University of Sussex.

4899    Wilson, R. A. (1993) 'Education for earth: a guide for early childhood instruction', *Journal of Environmental Education*, 24, 2, pp. 15–21.

4900    World Commission on Environment and Development (1987) *Our Common Future*. Oxford: Oxford University Press.

4901    Yangopoulos, S. (1997) 'Developing sixth form students' understanding of the relationships between environment and development issues' in Slater, F., Lambert, D. and Lines, D. (eds) *Education, Environment and Economy: Reporting Research in a New Academic Grouping (Bedford Way Papers)*. London: University of London Institute of Education, pp. 135–156.

4902    Zoller, U. (1984) 'Strategies for environmental education within contemporary science education', *European Journal of Science Education*, 6, 4, pp. 361–368.

## 2. Environmental Geography

4903    Baines, J. (1981) 'Geography within environmental education' in Mills, D. (ed) *Geographical Work in Primary and Middle Schools*. Sheffield: Geographical Association, pp. 141–145.

4904    Barrs, D. (1995) 'Educating succeeding generations', *Teaching Geography*, 20, 4, pp. 161–167.

4905    Blachford, K. R. (1979) 'Morals and values in geographical education: toward a metaphysic of the environment', *Geographical Education*, 3, 4, pp. 423–457.

4906 Boardman, D. and Ranger, G. (1996) 'Teaching sustainable development', *Teaching Geography*, 21, 4, pp. 161–167.

4907 Brunsden, D. (1987) 'The science of the unknown', *Geography*, 72, 3, pp. 193–208.

4908 Catling, S. (1988) 'Geography within environmental studies' in Mills, D. (ed) *Geographical Work in Primary and Middle Schools*. Sheffield: Geographical Association, pp. 252–264.

4909 Chambers, B. (1991) 'Approaches to environmental education', *Teaching Geography*, 16, 2, pp. 80–82.

4910 Chambers, B. (1995) *Awareness into Action: Environmental Education in the Primary School*. Sheffield: Geographical Association.

4911 Chambers, B. (1996) 'Environmental quality and change', *Primary Geographer*, 27, pp. 4–7.

4912 Coppock, J. T. (1970) 'Geographers and conservation', *Area*, 2, 1, pp. 24–26.

4913 Corney, G. and Middleton, N. (1996) 'Teaching environmental issues in schools and higher education' in Rawling, E. and Daugherty, R. (eds) *Geography into the Twenty-first Century*. Chichester: John Wiley and Sons, pp. 323–338.

4914 Cox, M. (1997) 'To what extent does environmental concern influence the culture and lifestyle of A level geography students?' in Slater, F. (ed) *Reporting Research in Geographical Education, Research Monograph No. 4*. London: University of London Institute of Education, pp. 1–12.

4915 Cribb, M. (1983) *Geography and Environmental Education: Bibliographic Notes No. 22*. Sheffield: Geographical Association.

4916 Elam, M. W. (1975) 'The challenge of environmental education', *Journal of Geography*, 74, 9, pp. 518–519.

4917 Emery, J. S. (1976) 'Trends in environmental education in Australia: some implications for geography', *Geographical Education*, 2, 4, pp. 455–472.

4918 Emery, J. S. (1982) 'Environmental education through geography', *Philippines Geographical Journal*, 26, 2, pp. 53–67.

4919 Emery, J. S., Davey, C. and Milne, A. K. (1974) 'Environmental education: the geography teacher's contribution', *Journal of Geography*, 73, 4, pp. 8–17.

4920 Fien, J. (1985) 'Geography as environmental experience', *Teaching Geography*, 10, 4, pp. 148–151.

4921 Fien, J. (1991) 'Geography's contribution to environmental education', *Geographical Education*, 6, 3, pp. 14–18.

4922 Fien, J. and Hillcoat, J. (1996) 'The critical tradition in research in geographical and environmental education research' in Williams, M. (ed) *Understanding Geographical and Environmental Education: The Role of Research*. London: Cassell, pp. 26–40.

4923 Geographical Association (1974) *The Role of Geography in Environmental Education*. Sheffield: Geographical Association.

4924 Geographical Association Environmental Education Working Group (1980) 'Geography and environmental education: a discussion paper', *Teaching Geography*, 6, 1, pp. 35–37.

4925    Gerber, R. (1995) 'Students' understanding of the concept of global change in their geographical education' in Lidstone, J., Romanova, E. and Kondakov, A. (eds) *Global Change and Geographical Education*. Brisbane/Moscow: IGUCGE/Queensland University of Technology/Moscow State University, pp. 57–71.

4926    Gerber, R. (1996) 'Adolescents' perceptions of global change in their geographical education' in Gerber, R. and Williams, M. (eds) *Qualitative Research in Geographical Education*. Armidale, NSW: IGUCGE/University of New England Press, pp. 33–55.

4927    Gerber, R. (1996) 'Interpretive approaches to geographical and environmental education research' in Williams, M. (ed) *Understanding Geographical and Environmental Education: The Role of Research*. London: Cassell, pp. 12–25.

4928    Goodson, I. F. (1983) 'Defining and defending the subject: geography versus environmental studies' in Hammersley, M. and Hargreaves, A. (eds) *Curriculum Practice: Some Sociological Case Studies*. London: Falmer Press, pp. 89–106.

4929    Goodson, I. F. (1996) 'Curriculum contests: environmental studies versus geography', *Environmental Education Research*, 2, 1, pp. 71–88.

4930    Hellyer, M. J. (1974) 'Geography and environmental studies' in Long, M. (ed) *Handbook for Geography Teachers*. London: Methuen, pp. 78–86.

4931    Huckle, J. (1983) 'Environmental education' in Huckle, J. (ed) *Geographical Education: Reflection and Action*. Oxford: Oxford University Press, pp. 99–111.

4932    Huckle, J. (1985) 'Ecological crisis: some implications for geographical education', *Contemporary Issues in Geography and Education*, 2, 2, pp. 2–13.

4933    Huckle, J. (1986) 'Geographical education for environmental citizenship', *Geographical Education*, 5, 2, pp. 13–20.

4934    Huckle, J. (1990) '"What we consume": the curriculum rationale', *Geographical Education*, 6, 2, pp. 31–36.

4935    Job, D. (1996) 'Geography and environmental education: an exploration of perspectives and strategies' in Kent, A., Lambert, D., Naish, M. and Slater, F. (eds) *Geography in Education: Viewpoints on Teaching and Learning*. Cambridge: Cambridge University Press, pp. 22–49.

4936    Job, D. (1997) 'Geography and environmental education' in Powell, A. (ed) *Handbook of Post-16 Geography*. Sheffield: Geographical Association, pp. 147–160.

4937    Kelly, V. (1984) 'Geography and environmental education in schools', *Geography*, 69, 2, pp. 138–140.

4938    Kent, A. (1980) 'Geography and environmental education', *Geographical Viewpoint*, 9, pp. 19–28.

4939    Lee, J. Chi-kin (1993) 'Geography teaching in England and Hong Kong: contributions towards environmental education', *IRGEE*, 2, 1, pp. 25–40.

4940    Lee, J. Chi-kin (1994) 'Environmental education through geography in Hong Kong', *Geographical Education*, 7, 2, pp. 34–41.

4941    Lee, J. Chi-kin (1996) 'A study of environmental attitudes and concepts of geography student teachers: implications for teacher education', *IRGEE*, 5, 3, pp. 154–171.

4942 Lee, J. Chi-kin (1996) 'Geography teachers' receptivity to environmental education in Hong Kong' in van der Zijpp, T., van der Schee, J. and Trimp, H. (eds) *Innovation in Geographical Education: Proceedings of the 28th International Geographical Congress Commission on Geographical Education*. Amsterdam: IGUCGE/Centrum voor Educatieve Geografie Vrije Universiteit Amsterdam, pp. 141–145.

4943 Lidstone, J. (1995) 'Global education, global change and disaster education' in Lidstone, J., Romanova, E. and Kondakov, A. (eds) *Global Change and Geographical Education*. Brisbane/Moscow: IGUCGE/Queensland University of Technology/Moscow State University, pp. 13–30.

4944 Lidstone, J., Romanova, E. and Kondakov, A. (eds) (1995) *Global Change and Geographical Education*. Brisbane/Moscow: IGUCGE/Queensland University of Technology/Moscow State University.

4945 McArthur, J. L. (1980) 'Environmental science, environmental studies, earth science and physical geography: a comparative review', *Philippines Geographical Journal*, 24, 1, pp. 21–32.

4946 McDonald, G. T. (1995) 'Environment and society in spatial context: future directions in geography', *Geographical Education*, 8, 3, pp. 17–22.

4947 McKeown-Ice, R. (1994) 'Environmental education: a geographical perspective' in Bednarz, R. S. and Peterson, J. F. (eds) *A Decade of Reform in Geographical Education: Inventory and Prospect*. Indiana, PA: National Council for Geographic Education, pp. 59–65.

4948 Mason, P. F. and Kuhn, M. W. (1971) 'Geography and environmental studies: the fifth tradition?', *Journal of Geography*, 70, 2, pp. 91–94.

4949 Milne, A. K. (1983) 'The role of geography in environmental education', *Geographical Education*, 4, 3, pp. 87–92.

4950 Mottershead, D. (1987) 'People and environment: geography and human survival' in Bailey, P. and Binns, T. (eds) *A Case for Geography*. Sheffield: Geographical Association, pp. 42–44.

4951 Naish, M. (1995) 'Geography and environmental education: meeting the challenge through the Geography 16–19 project', *Geographical Education*, 5, 2, pp. 26–30.

4952 O'Riordan, T. (1970) 'New conservation and geography', *Area*, 2, 2, pp. 33–36.

4953 O'Riordan, T. (1996) 'Environmentalism and geography: a union still to be consummated' in Rawling, E. and Daugherty, R. (eds) *Geography into the Twenty-first Century*. Chichester: John Wiley and Sons, pp. 113–128.

4954 Percival, M. (1997) 'Sustaining an interest in "sustainability"', *Teaching Geography*, 22, 2, pp. 63–67.

4955 Preston-Whyte, R. A. (1983) 'Environmentalism in geography: the missing link', *South African Geographical Journal*, 65, 1, pp. 2–12.

4956 Ramutsindela, M. F. (1995) 'Global scale challenges in the teaching of geography' in Lidstone, J., Romanova, E. and Kondakov, A. (eds) *Global Change and Geographical Education*. Brisbane/Moscow: IGUCGE/Queensland University of Technology/Moscow State University, pp. 37–43.

4957 Ranger, G. (1993) 'Enhancing geography with environmental education', *Teaching Geography*, 18, 3, pp. 121–123.

4958    Ranger, G. and Reid, A. (1996) 'Developing environmental education through geography', *British Journal of Curriculum and Assessment*, 6, 2, pp. 29–32.

4959    Rawling, E. (1981) 'New opportunities in environmental education' in Walford, R. (ed) *Signposts for Geography Teaching.* Harlow: Longman, pp. 203–212.

4960    Reid, A. (1996) 'Exploring values in sustainable development', *Teaching Geography*, 21, 4, pp. 168–171.

4961    Reid, A., Scott, W. H. and Oulton, C. R. (1997) 'Contribution of geography teaching to pupils' environmental education: methodological considerations and issues for researching teachers' thinking about practice', *IRGEE*, 6, 3, pp. 222–233.

4962    Robert, B. (1997) The ecosystem approach to the development of a school atlas', *IRGEE*, 6, 1, pp. 68–71.

4963    Rosell, D. Z. (1979) 'Environmental studies: the fifth tradition of geography', *Philippines Geographical Journal*, 23, 2, pp. 50–57.

4964    Salita, D. C. (1976) 'Geography: the core of environmental education', *Philippines Geographical Journal*, 20, 3, pp. 87–93.

4965    Salita, D. C. (1979) 'Geography and environmental education', *Philippines Geographical Journal*, 23, 3, pp. 89–94.

4966    Scott, R. (1973) 'Geography, environmental studies and the curriculum', *Froebel Journal*, 26, pp. 26–29.

4967    Semple, S. (1995) 'Planning global studies in geography in a time of global change' in Lidstone, J., Romanova, E. and Kondakov, A. (eds) *Global Change and Geographical Education.* Brisbane/Moscow: IGUCGE/Queensland University of Technology/Moscow State University, pp. 31–35.

4968    Shortle, D. (1970) 'Towards a solution of the environmental crisis: the contribution of geographical education', *Geographical Education*, 1, 2, pp. 111–125.

4969    Shortle, D. (1971) 'Environmental quality and geographical education: charting a course for the 1970s', *Geographical Education*, 1, 3, pp. 253–277.

4970    Shortle, D. (1971) 'Environmental ethics and geographical education' in Biddle, D. S. and Deer, C. E. (eds) (1973) *Readings in Geographical Education: Selections from Australian and New Zealand Sources, Volume 2: 1966–1972.* Sydney: Australian Geography Teachers Association/Whitcombe and Tombs, pp. 51–68.

4971    Simmons, I. G. (1990) 'Ingredients of a green geography', *Geography*, 75, 2, pp. 98–105.

4972    Simmons, I. G. (1995) 'Green geography: an evolving recipe', *Geography*, 80, 2, pp. 139–145.

4973    Slater, F. (1989) 'Research in geography education in the areas of environmental education, values education, concept development and language' in Graves, N., Kent, A., Lambert, D., Naish, M. and Slater, F. *Research in Geographical Education: MA Dissertations 1968–1988.* London: University of London Institute of Education, pp. 44–79.

4974    Steinberg, P. E. (1997) 'Political geography and the environment', *Journal of Geography*, 96, 2, pp. 113–118.

4975    Thomas, P. (1977) 'Geography and environmental studies', *Trends in Education*, 3, pp. 13–20.

4976    Tilbury, D. (1997) 'Environmental education and development education: teaching geography for a sustainable world' in Tilbury, D. and Williams, M. (ed) *Teaching and Learning Geography*. London: Routledge, pp. 105–116.

4977    Tilbury, D. (1997) 'Teaching geography about and for sustainable development in Hong Kong', *Geographical Education*, 10, pp. 53–56.

4978    Towler, J. (1981) 'Geography and environmental education: a Canadian perspective', *Journal of Geography*, 80, 4, pp. 132–135.

4979    Towler, J. and Brenchley, D. L. (1975) 'Geography and environmental education: why aren't we involved?', *Journal of Geography*, 74, 9, pp. 520–524.

4980    van der Schee, J. (1997) 'A geographer's view of international fisheries and environmental education' in Convey, A. and Nolzen, H. (eds) *Geography and Education (Münchner Studien zur Didaktik der Geographie, Band 10)*. Munich: Lehrstuhl für Didaktik der Geographie der Universität München, pp. 243–249.

4981    Walker, G. T. (1976) 'Man, environment and environmental education: a geographical view', *Geographical Education*, 2, 4, pp. 473–486.

4982    Westaway, J. and Rawling, E. (1996) 'Contributing to environmental education through geography', *Teaching Geography*, 21, 4, pp. 193–199.

4983    Wheeler, K. and Waites, B. (1976) *Environmental Geography: A Handbook for Teachers*. St Albans: Hart-Davis Educational Limited.

4984    Wicks, L. M. (1974) *Environmental Studies: An Approach to Geography Teaching in the Primary School*, unpublished MA dissertation. University of London Institute of Education.

4985    Williams, A. (1997) 'A consideration of student attitudes towards the environment in the context of field experience' in Slater, F. (ed) *Reporting Research in Geography Education, Monograph No. 4*. London: University of London Institute of Education, pp. 13–32.

4986    Williams, M. (ed) (1996) *Understanding Geographical and Environmental Education: The Role of Research*. London: Cassell.

4987    Williams, M. and Tilbury, D. (eds) (1996) 'Conceptual aspects of geographical and environmental education in teacher education' in van der Zijpp, T., van der Schee, J. and Trimp, H. (eds) *Innovation in Geographical Education: Proceedings of the 28th International Geographical Congress Commission on Geographical Education*. Amsterdam: Centrum voor Educatieve Geografie Vrije Universiteit Amsterdam, pp. 89–94.

4988    Wise, M. (1973) 'Environmental studies: geographical objectives', *Geography*, 58, 4, pp. 293–300.

4989    Yangopoulos, S. (1996) 'Sustainable development and geography education', *New Era*, 77, 3, pp. 66–71.

4990    Yeung, S. Pui-ming (1995) 'Environmental consciousness and geography teaching in Hong Kong: an empirical study', *International Journal of Environmental Education and Information*, 14, 2, pp. 171–194.

4991    Yeung, S. Pui-ming (1996) 'Teaching environmental issues in school geography: the Hong Kong experience', *IRGEE*, 5, 2, pp. 117–130.

4992    Adams, E. (1989) 'Learning to see', *Journal of Art and Design Education*, 8, 2, pp. 183–196.

4993    Adams, E. (1990) 'Learning through landscapes: the learning environment', *Values*, 5, 1, pp. 11–14.

4994    Adams, E. (1992) 'Art in the National Curriculum: links with environmental education', *Streetwise*, 9, pp. 21–24.

4995    Adams, E. (1997) 'Public art: art, design and environment implications for the curriculum', *Journal of Art and Design Education*, 16, 3, pp. 231–239.

4996    Adams, E. and Ward, C. (1982) *Art and the Built Environment: A Teacher's Approach.* Harlow: Longman/Schools Council.

4997    Agar, N. (1973) 'The place of history in environmental education', *Teaching History*, 3, pp. 126–129.

4998    Barnett, S. (1989) 'The arts in environmental education', *Caribbean Journal of Education*, 16, 1/2, pp. 117–130.

4999    Copeland, T. (1993) *A Teacher's Guide to Geography and the Historic Environment.* London: English Heritage.

5000    Department of the Environment (1990) *This Common Inheritance: Britain's Environmental Strategy.* London: HMSO.

5001    Ellison, L. (1979) 'Landscape evaluation as a fieldwork technique', *Teaching Geography*, 5, 1, pp. 35–58.

5002    Ellison, L. (1982) 'Assessing environmental quality in the Victorian residential areas of a town', *Teaching Geography*, 8, 2, pp. 81–83.

5003    Featherstone, J. (1995) 'Streetwise: fieldwork in an urban environment' in De Villiers, M. (ed) *Developments in Primary Geography: Theory and Practice.* Sheffield: Geographical Association, pp. 35–36.

5004    Hall, R. (1981) 'Streetscape appreciation', *Geographical Education*, 3, 4, pp. 489–506.

5005    Hall, R. (1984) 'Developing sensory awareness and aesthetic appreciation of the environment' in Fien, J., Gerber, R. and Wilson, P. (eds) *The Geography Teacher's Guide to the Classroom.* Melbourne: Macmillan, pp. 44–62.

5006    Hewlett, M. (1971) 'Urban environmental studies' in Williams, M. (ed) (1976) *Geography and the Integrated Curriculum: A Reader.* London: Heinemann, pp. 171–177.

5007    Howard, P. (1979) 'Art, design and landscape: some practical ideas', *Teaching Geography*, 5, 2, pp. 84–86.

5008    Jennings, J. (1977) 'History and environmental studies', *Trends in Education*, 4, pp. 8–13.

5009    Joicey, H. B. (1986) *An Eye on the Environment: An Art Education Project.* London: Bell and Hyman/World Wildlife Fund (UK).

5010    Keane, P. (1991) 'Trails and tribulations: town trails as a teaching tool', *Streetwise*, 6, pp. 17–19.

5011    Knight, P. (1983) 'The Heritage Project and the management of externally prompted change in primary schools', *School Organisation*, 3, 2, pp. 109–119.

5012    McPartland, M. (1983) 'The use of topographic literature: an idea for a geography project', *Teaching Geography*, 8, 4, pp. 181–183.

5013    Mercer, J. J. (1986) 'Then and now: a sense of place', *Teaching Geography*, 12, 1, pp. 6–7.

5014    Montford, S. (1991–2) 'Percent for art and the art of townscape', *Streetwise*, 9, pp. 3–6.

5015    Neal, P. (1979) *Heritage Education*. Walsall: National Association for Environmental Education (UK).

5016    Palmer, J. and Wise, M. (1982) *The Good, the Bad and the Ugly: A Study of an Urban Housing Estate by a Primary School Class*. Sheffield: Geographical Association.

5017    Pooley, C. (1983) 'Understanding the Victorian city', *Teaching Geography*, 9, 1, pp. 20–25.

5018    Ranger, G. and Milford, S. (1991) 'Town trails and learning outcomes', *Streetwise*, 7, pp. 30–31.

5019    Stewart, L. W. (1972) 'History and the environment', *Teaching History*, 2, pp. 201–206.

5020    Tracy, J. (1991) 'Adapting towntrails to the National Curriculum', *Streetwise*, 6, pp. 20–23.

5021    Waites, B. (1975) 'Conservation studies in historic towns', *Teaching Geography*, 1, 2, pp. 67–70.

5022    Waites, B. (1975) 'Historic conservation education' in Martin, G. C. and Wheeler, K. (eds) *Insights into Environmental Education*. Edinburgh: Oliver and Boyd, pp. 55–70.

5023    Ward, C. and Chippendale, F. (1975) 'Architecture in environmental education' in Martin, G. C. and Wheeler, K. (eds) *Insights into Environmental Education*. Edinburgh: Oliver and Boyd, pp. 89–97.

5024    Ward, C. and Fyson, A. (1973) *Streetwork: the Exploding School*. London: Routledge and Kegan Paul.

5025    Wheeler, K. (1992) 'The built environment and environmental education', *Streetwise*, 10, pp. 33–34.

# E. GEOGRAPHICAL AND ENVIRONMENTAL EDUCATION IN OTHER COUNTRIES

## 1. Europe (excluding UK)

5026    Aerni, K. (1978) 'Problems of the geography 16–19 curriculum in Switzerland' in Graves, N. (ed) *Geographical Education: Curriculum Problems in Certain European Countries with Special Reference to the 16–19 Age Group*. London: IGUCGE/University of London Institute of Education, pp. 172–182.

5027    Albrecht, V. (1996) 'Teaching Europe in the multi-cultural societies of Europe' in van der Zijpp, T., van der Schee, J. and Trimp, H. (eds) *Innovation in Geographical Education: Proceedings of the 28th International Geographical Congress Commission on Geographical Education*. Amsterdam: IGUCGE/Centrum voor Educatieve Geografie Vrije Universiteit Amsterdam, pp. 9–13.

5028    Albrecht, V. (1997) 'Political geography and political education' in Convey, A. and Nolzen, H. (eds) *Geography and Education (Münchner Studien zur Didaktik der Geographie, Band 10)*. Munich: Lehrstuhl für Didaktik der Geographie der Universität München, pp. 15–23.

5029    Andersen, H. P. and Wennevold, S. (1997) 'Environmental education in Norway: some problems seen from the geographer's point of view', *IRGEE*, 6, 2, pp. 157–160.

5030    Barth, J. (1984) 'Geographical teacher education models in West Berlin' in Marsden, W. E. (ed) *Teacher Education Models in Geography: An International Comparison*. Kalamazoo, MI: IGUCGE/Western Michigan University, pp. 99–111.

5031    Belonso, B. (1992) 'The status of geography and the social sciences in schools of the USSR', *Social Education*, 56, 2, pp. 112–117.

5032    Benayas, J., Herrero, C., de Lucio, J. V., and de Blas, P. (1991) 'Some features of environmental education in Spain', *European Journal of Education*, 26, 4, pp. 315–323.

5033    Bennett, J. (1993) 'Geography textbooks in the Republic of Ireland 1973–1993', *Irish Journal of Education*, 27, 1/2, pp. 25–35.

5034    Bernadin, J.-M. (1997) 'Explanation and causality in year 12 French geography textbooks: an inevitable halo of common sense?', *IRGEE*, 6, 1, pp. 89–92.

5035    Biilmann, O. (1997) 'Geography textbook analysis: a Danish perspective', *IRGEE*, 6, 1, pp. 79–81.

5036    Biilmann, O. (1997) 'On the history of environmental education in Danish *Folkeskole*', *IRGEE*, 6, 2, pp. 153–156.

5037    Birkenhauer, J. (1997) 'Skills in geography: a systematic attempt' in Convey, A. and Nolzen, H. (eds) *Geography and Education (Münchner Studien zur Didaktik der Geographie, Band 10)*. Munich: Lehrstuhl für Didaktik der Geographie der Universität München, pp. 33–42.

5038    Birkenhauer, J. and Marsden, W. E. (eds) (1988) *German Didactics of Geography in the Seventies and Eighties: A Review of Trends and Endeavours.* Munich: IGUCGE/Lehrstuhl für Didaktik der Geographie der Universität München.

5039    Bohn, D. (1997) 'International education through international textbook cooperation' in Convey, A. and Nolzen, H. (eds) *Geography and Education (Münchner Studien zur Didaktik der Geographie, Band 10).* Munich: Lehrstuhl für Didaktik der Geographie der Universität München, pp. 33–42.

5040    Bolscho, D. (1990) 'Environmental education in practice in the Federal Republic of Germany: an empirical study', *International Journal of Science Education*, 12, 2, pp. 133–146.

5041    Brady, B. M. (1991) 'Environmental education in Ireland', *Environmental Education and Information*, 10, 2, pp. 77–86.

5042    Brijker, M., De Jong, R. and Swaan, M. (1995) 'The need for support for secondary schools in the Netherlands in the implementation of environmental education', *Environmental Education Research*, 1, 1, pp. 99–107.

5043    Claval, P. (1978) 'The aims of the teaching of geography in the second stage of French secondary education' in Graves, N. (ed) *Geographical Education: Curriculum Problems in Certain European Countries with Special Reference to the 16–19 Age Group.* London: IGUCGE/University of London Institute of Education, pp. 159–166.

5044    Closs, H.-M. (1984) 'Geography teacher education in West Germany, with special reference to Rheinland-Pfalz' in Marsden, W. E. (ed) *Teacher Education Models in Geography: An International Comparison.* Kalamazoo, MI: IGUCGE/Western Michigan University, pp. 113–131.

5045    Cortés, C. E. and Fleming, D. B. (1986) 'Introduction: global education and textbooks', *Social Education*, 50, 5, pp. 340–344.

5046    Cortés, C. E. and Fleming, D. B. (1986) 'Changing global perspectives in textbooks', *Social Education*, 50, 5, pp. 376–384.

5047    Council of Europe (1988) *Resolution on Environmental Education.* Strasbourg: CEC.

5048    Curran, D. (1978) 'Observations on the French geographical curriculum' in Graves, N. (ed) *Geographical Education: Curriculum Problems in Certain European Countries with Special Reference to the 16–19 Age Group.* London: IGUCGE/University of London Institute of Education, pp. 100–103.

5049    Dussart, G. B. J. (1990) 'Environmental education in Europe: a synoptic view', *Environmental Education and Information*, 9, 2, pp. 59–72.

5050    Eulefeld, G. (1991) 'Environmental education in the Federal Republic of Germany', *European Journal of Education*, 26, 4, pp. 301–306.

5051    Fahy, G. (1979) 'Geography and geographic education in Ireland from early Christian times to 1960', *Geographical Viewpoint*, 10, pp. 5–30.

5052    Ferreira, M. (1995) 'Some aspects of the evaluation of geographical education in Portugal: the secondary school curriculum: its historical developments' in Slater, F. (ed) *Reporting Research in Geographical Education: Monograph No. 2.* London: University of London Institute of Education, pp. 9–27.

5053    Ferreira, M. (1997) 'The United Kingdom in Portuguese geography textbooks from 1836 to 1974', *IRGEE*, 6, 1, pp. 72–78.

5054    Fiori, M. (1997) 'Research on geography textbooks in Italy', *IRGEE*, 6, 1, pp. 82–85.

5055    Flogaitis, E. and Alexopoulos, I. (1991) 'Environmental education in Greece', *European Journal of Education*, 26, 4, pp. 339–345.

5056    Frederiksen, R. (1978) 'Denmark: geography in the curriculum of the 16–19 age group' in Graves, N. (ed) *Geographical Education: Curriculum Problems in Certain European Countries with Special Reference to the 16–19 Age Group*. London: IGUCGE/University of London Institute of Education, pp. 70–73.

5057    Fuchs, F. (1978) 'The teaching unit of the regional RCFP group in Frankfurt in relation to the aims of the RCFP and the new 16–19 curriculum' in Graves, N. (ed) *Geographical Education: Curriculum Problems in Certain European Countries with Special Reference to the 16–19 Age Group*. London: IGUCGE/University of London Institute of Education, pp. 90–103.

5058    Garcia-Ramon, M. D. (1989) 'Geography and gender in Spain: new lines of research and teaching', *Journal of Geography in Higher Education*, 13, 1, pp. 110–112.

5059    Geipel, R. (1978) 'The aims and organization of the RCFP of the Federal German Republic' in Graves, N. (ed) *Geographical Education: Curriculum Problems in Certain European Countries with Special Reference to the 16–19 Age Group*. London: IGUCGE/University of London Institute of Education, pp. 74–89.

5060    Gillmore, D. A. (1978) 'Geographic education in the Republic of Ireland', *Journal of Geography*, 77, 3, pp. 103–108.

5061    Giolitto, P. and Souchon, C. (1991) 'Environmental education in France: assessment and outlook', *European Journal of Education*, 26, 4, pp. 307–313.

5062    Goffin, L. (1991) 'Current trends in environmental education in the French-speaking areas of Belgium', *European Journal of Education*, 26, 4, pp. 291–300.

5063    Gorbanyov, V. (1995) 'The renovation of geographical education in Russian secondary schools' in Lidstone, J., Romanova, E. and Kondakov, A. (eds) *Global Change and Geographical Education*. Brisbane/Moscow: IGUCGE/Queensland University of Technology/Moscow State University, pp. 113–117.

5064    Graves, N. (1980) 'Paul Vidal de la Blache and geographical education in France' in Marsden, W. E. (ed) *Historical Perspectives on Geographical Education*. London: IGUCGE/University of London Institute of Education, pp. 8–17.

5065    Gunterman, B. and van Meegan, J. (1996) 'Geography for a better world: experiencing schools in Turkey' in van der Zijpp, T., van der Schee, J. and Trimp, H. (eds) *Innovation in Geographical Education: Proceedings of the 28th International Geographical Congress Commission on Geographical Education*. Amsterdam: IGUCGE/Centrum voor Educatieve Geografie Vrije Universiteit Amsterdam, pp. 24–26.

5066    Hallinen, M. (1980) 'New geography curricula and teaching opportunities', *Geographical Viewpoint*, 9, pp. 5–18.

5067    Hallinen, M. (1981) 'The evolution of the geography syllabus in Irish secondary education since 1961', *Geographical Viewpoint*, 10, pp. 56–62.

5068    Haubrich, H. (ed) (1982) *International Focus on Geographical Education*. Brunswick: Georg Eckert Institute for International Textbook Research.

5069    Haubrich, H. (ed) (1987) *International Trends in Geographical Education*. Freiburg: IGUCGE.

5070    Haubrich, H. (1991) 'Centralisation or decentralisation of geography curricula: an international perspective', *Geography*, 76, 3, pp. 209–218.

5071 Haubrich, H. (1992) 'Auto- and heterostereotypes of French, Swiss and German students' in Hill, A. D. (ed) *International Perspectives on Geographical Education*. Boulder, CO/Skokie, IL: IGUCGE/Rand, McNally and Co., pp. 31–37.

5072 Haubrich, H. (1992) 'Geographical education research 2000: some personal views', *IRGEE*, 1, 1, pp. 52–57.

5073 Haubrich, H. (ed) (1994) *Europe and the World in Geography Education (Geographiedidaktische Forschungen, Band 22)*. Nuremberg: IGUCGE.

5074 Haubrich, H. (1996) 'State of the art in geographical education 1996' in van der Zijpp, T., van der Schee, J. and Trimp, H. (eds) *Innovation in Geographical Education: Proceedings of the 28th International Geographical Congress Commission on Geographical Education*. Amsterdam: IGUCGE/Centrum voor Educatieve Geografie Vrije Universiteit Amsterdam, pp. 3–6.

5075 Hernando, A. (1986) *Geographical Education and Society*. Barcelona: IGUCGE.

5076 Hernando, A. (1997) 'Geography textbooks in Spanish schools: caught between traditional and innovatory forces', *IRGEE*, 6, 1, pp. 98–105.

5077 Hindson, J. and Thomas, T. (1992) 'Environmental education in Hungary', *Streetwise*, 10, pp. 28–32.

5078 Holland, E. (1981) 'Geography in secondary schools: some changes in methodology during the last twenty years', *Geographical Viewpoint*, 10, pp. 63–73.

5079 Houtsonen, L. (1997) 'Environmental education and research in the Nordic and Baltic countries from a geography teaching perspective', *IRGEE*, 6, 2, pp. 148–152.

5080 Houtsonen, L. (1997) 'Education for environmental sensitivity: the experienced urban environment in Finnish teacher education', *IRGEE*, 6, 2, pp. 161–169.

5081 Hurley, K. (1981) 'Geography in the primary school', *Geographical Viewpoint*, 10, pp. 44–55.

5082 Kaminske, V. (1997) 'Geographical concepts: their complexity and their grading', *IRGEE*, 6, 1, pp. 4–26.

5083 Kirschberg, G. (1990) 'Regional and general geography in geography teaching: a report on syllabus development in the Federal Republic of Germany', *Geographica*, 25, 1, pp. 47–63.

5084 Kosonen, O. (1992) 'Some learning outcomes in school geography from the viewpoint of realisation and development of curricular aims', *Terra*, 104, 3, pp. 156–158.

5085 Kuhnlova, H. (1991) 'Didactic geography and geographical education in Czechoslovakia', *Geographica*, 26, 1, pp. 53–68.

5086 Kunaver, J. (1997) 'Recent trends in geography teaching in Slovenia: a transitional and European perspective' in Convey, A. and Nolzen, H. (eds) *Geography and Education (Münchner Studien zur Didaktik der Geographie, Band 10)*. Munich: Lehrstuhl für Didaktik der Geographie der Universität München, pp. 159–168.

5087 Langridge, D. (1973) *The Development of Geography Teaching in Ireland*, unpublished PhD thesis. University of Ireland Cork.

5088 Leal Filho, W. (1994) *Promoting Environmental Education in Europe*. Bradford: ERTCEE.

5089 Leal Filho, W. (1996) 'An overview of current trends in European environmental education', *Journal of Environmental Education*, 28, 1, pp. 5–10.

5090    Leal Filho, W., MacDermott, F. and Murphy, Z. (eds) (1995) *Practices of Environmental Education in Europe.* Bradford: ERTCEE.

5091    Liiber, U. (1997) 'The development of school geography and environmental education in Estonia', *IRGEE*, 6, 2, pp. 170–175.

5092    Lob, R. E. (1989) 'Environmental education in the Federal Republic of Germany: an inventory', *Environmental Education and Information*, 8, 2, pp. 81–89.

5093    Lob, R. E. (1989) 'New approaches in environmental education: current developments in non-scientific school subjects of the Federal Republic of Germany: results of a research study', *Environmental Education and Information*, 8, 2, pp. 90–95.

5094    Lob, R. E. (1992) 'Environmental education as a comprehensive and integral commitment of primary school education: a report from Germany', *Environmental Education and Information*, 11, 1, pp. 25–30.

5095    McGloin, P. and Heywood, J. (1984) 'Teacher education in geography in the Republic of Ireland' in Marsden, W. E. (ed) *Teacher Education Models in Geography: An International Comparison.* Kalamazoo, MI: IGUCGE/Western Michigan University, pp. 57–65.

5096    Maksakovsky, V. P. (1978) 'Secondary school geographical education in the USSR' in Graves, N. (ed) *Geographical Education: Curriculum Problems in Certain European Countries with Special Reference to the 16–19 Age Group.* London: IGUCGE/University of London Institute of Education, pp. 182–187.

5097    Maksakovsky, V. P. (1995) 'Modern problems of school geography in Russia' in Lidstone, J., Romanova, E. and Kondakov, A. (eds) *Global Change and Geographical Education.* Brisbane/Moscow: IGUCGE/Queensland University of Technology/Moscow State University, pp. 107–108.

5098    Marbeau, L. (1978) 'Geography for the 16–19 age group in French Lycées' in Graves, N. (ed) *Geographical Education: Curriculum Problems in Certain European Countries with Special Reference to the 16–19 Age Group.* London: IGUCGE/University of London Institute of Education, pp. 114–133.

5099    Marbeau, L. (1988) 'History and geography in elementary school: for a change (France)', *Western European Education*, 20, 2, pp. 14–43.

5100    Marbeau, L. (1992) 'The need for curriculum research in geography: the case of France' in Naish, M. (ed) *Geography and Education: National and International Perspectives.* London: University of London Institute of Education, pp. 80–94.

5101    Martin, E. S., Lewis, D., Trumman, L. J., Smith, B. J. and Brown, P. (1993) 'Environmental education in Sweden', *Environmentalist*, 13, 3, pp. 221–227.

5102    Meijer, H. and Wiegand, P. (1990) *Dutch–British Conference on the Revision of Geography Textbooks.* Utrecht: Information and Documentation Centre for the Geography of the Netherlands.

5103    Merenne-Schoumaker, B. (1997) 'School geography textbooks in Francophone Belgium', *IRGEE*, 6, 1, pp. 86–88.

5104    Mikkelson, K. (1992) 'Environmental and adult education: towards a Danish dimension', *Convergence,* 25, 2, pp. 71–74.

5105    Niemz, G. (1996) 'Trends in German geography education for the turn of the millennium', *International Journal of Social Education*, 10, 2, pp. 45–52.

5106 Nolzen, H. (1979) 'The integration of the natural sciences into geography education: the example of the RCF Project of the Central Association of German Geographers', *European Journal of Science Education*, 1, 2, pp. 147–155.

5107 Olina, Z. (1997) *Education and the Environment in Europe*. Strasbourg: Council of Europe.

5108 Ophuls, W. (1980) 'Citizenship and ecological education', *Teachers College Record*, 82, 2, pp. 217–242.

5109 Oscarsson, V. (1996) 'Pupils' views on the future in Sweden', *Environmental Education Research*, 2, 3, pp. 261–278.

5110 Overjordet, A. H. (1984) 'Children's views of the world during an international media covered conflict' in Haubrich, H. (ed) *Perception of People and Places through Media, Volume 1*. Freiburg: IGUCGE/Pädagogische Hochschule Freiburg, pp. 208–219.

5111 Pancheshnikova, L. (1984) 'The system of preparing teachers at the pedagogical institutes for geography teaching, USSR' in Marsden, W. E. (ed) *Teacher Education Models in Geography: An International Comparison*. London: IGUCGE/University of London Institute of Education, pp. 151–155.

5112 Pawlowski, A. (1996) 'Perception of environmental problems by young people in Poland', *Environmental Education Research*, 2, 3, pp. 279–286.

5113 Peltonen, A. (1997) 'Reflections on STS discussions on the reform of Finnish "environmental-science" education', *IRGEE*, 6, 1, pp. 27–40.

5114 Rikkinen, H. (1992) 'Recent developments in geographical curricula in Finland', *Terra*, 104, 3, pp. 149–155.

5115 Rikkinen, H. (1994) 'Finnish self-image and stereotypes of its neighbours' in Haubrich, H. (ed) *Europe and the World in Geography Education (Geographiedidaktische Forschungen, Band 22)*. Nuremberg: IGUCGE, pp. 59–66.

5116 Rikkinen, H. (1996) 'Auto- and heterostereotypes of Finnish students' in van der Zijpp, T., van der Schee, J. and Trimp, H. (eds) *Innovation in Geographical Education: Proceedings of the 28th International Geographical Congress Commission on Geographical Education*. Amsterdam: IGUCGE/Centrum voor Educatieve Geografie Vrije Universiteit Amsterdam, pp. 31–35.

5117 Rikkinen, H. (1996) 'The living environment of 7–12-year-old pupils in Finland', *IRGEE*, 5, 2, pp. 107–116.

5118 Rohwer, G. (1996) 'How to encourage intercultural learning in geography lessons' in van der Zijpp, T., van der Schee, J. and Trimp, H. (eds) *Innovation in Geographical Education: Proceedings of the 28th International Geographical Congress Commission on Geographical Education*. Amsterdam: IGUCGE/Centrum voor Educatieve Geografie Vrije Universiteit Amsterdam, pp. 36–40.

5119 Schrettenbrunner, H. (1980) 'German school children's perception of countries' in Slater, F. and Spicer, B. (eds) *Perception and Preference Studies at the International Level*. Tokyo: IGUCGE/AIP, pp. 103–113.

5120 Schrettenbrunner, H. (1985) 'Geography: educational programs' in Husen, T. and Postlethwaite, T. N. (eds) *International Encyclopaedia of Education*. Oxford: Pergamon Press, pp. 2017–2022.

5121 Schrettenbrunner, H. (1994) 'Quantitative empirical research in the didactics of geography' in Haubrich, H. (ed) *Europe and the World in Geographical Education (Geographiedidaktische Forschungen, Band 22)*. Nuremberg: IGUCGE, pp. 383–386.

5122 Schrettenbrunner, H. and van Westrhenen, H. (eds) (1992) *Empirical Research and Geography Teaching (Netherlands Geographical Studies, 142)*. Amsterdam: IGUCGE/Centrum voor Educatieve Geografie Vrije Universiteit Amsterdam.

5123 Shirley, D. (1993) 'Ecological studies between schools in Europe and Scandinavia: the benefits to the curriculum of working across national boundaries' in Hale, M. (ed) *Ecology in Education*. Cambridge: Cambridge University Press, pp. 167–178.

5124 Shkarban, N. V. (1991) 'The ecological transformation of geography', *Soviet Education*, 33, 1, pp. 55–63.

5125 Sitte, W. (1978) 'The renewal of geography teaching to the 15–18 age group in Austria' in Graves, N. (ed) *Geographical Education: Curriculum Problems in Certain European Countries with Special Reference to the 16–19 Age Group*. London: IGUCGE/University of London Institute of Education, pp. 167–171.

5126 Slater, F. and Ferreira, M. (1996) 'A comparison of secondary school teacher attitudes to national curricula in England and Portugal' in van der Zijpp, T., van der Schee, J. and Trimp, H. (eds) *Innovation in Geographical Education: Proceedings of the 28th International Geographical Congress Commission on Geographical Education*. Amsterdam: IGUCGE/Centrum voor Educatieve Geografie Vrije Universiteit Amsterdam, pp. 321–325.

5127 Sperling, W. (1984) 'Present state, development and tasks of bibliography and documentation on didactics of geography' in Haubrich, H. (ed) *Perception of People and Places through Media, Volume 2*. Freiburg: IGUCGE/Pädagogische Hochschule Freiburg, pp. 908–927.

5128 Szekely, B. B. (1987) 'The new Soviet secondary school geography curriculum', *Soviet Education*, 29, 4, pp. 3–99.

5129 Truper, M. and Hustedde, M. (1990) 'Geographical education in West German high schools: do four years make a difference?', *Journal of Geography*, 89, 3, pp. 109–112.

5130 van der Schee, J. (1997) 'A geographer's view of international fisheries and environmental education' in Convey, A. and Nolzen, H. (eds) *Geography and Education (Münchner Studien zur Didaktik der Geographie, Band 10)*. Munich: Lehrstuhl für Didaktik der Geographie der Universität München, pp. 243–249.

5131 van der Schee, J. and Huigen, P. J. (1992) 'International understanding and geography teaching about Europe: a Dutch perspective' in Hill, A. D. (ed) *International Perspectives on Geographical Education*. Boulder, CO/Skokie, IL: IGUCGE/Rand, McNally and Co., pp. 221–228.

5132 van der Schee, J., Schoenmaker, G., Trimp, H. and van Westrhenen, H. (eds) (1996) *Innovation in Geographical Education (Netherlands Geographical Studies, 208)*. Utrecht/Amsterdam: IGUCGE/Centrum voor Educatieve Geografie Vrije Universiteit Amsterdam.

5133 van der Zijpp, T., van der Schee, J. and Trimp, H. (eds) (1996) *Innovation in Geographical Education: Proceedings of the 28th International Geographical Congress Commission on Geographical Education*. Amsterdam: IGUCGE/Centrum voor Educatieve Geografie Vrije Universiteit Amsterdam.

5134 van Westrhenen, H. and Meijer, G. (1978) 'The importance of nomothetic geography for school geography' in Graves, N. (ed) *Geographical Education: Curriculum Problems in Certain European Countries with Special Reference to the 16–19 Age Group*. London: IGUCGE/University of London Institute of Education, pp. 41–69.

5135 Vekilska, P. and Kantchev, D. (1984) 'The training of geography teachers in the People's Republic of Bulgaria' in Marsden, W. E. (ed) *Teacher Education Models in Geography: An International Comparison.* London: IGUCGE/University of London Institute of Education, pp. 5–11.

5136 Verduin-Muller, H. (1978) 'A conceptual model for curriculum planning in geography' in Graves, N. (ed) *Geographical Education: Curriculum Problems in Certain European Countries with Special Reference to the 16–19 Age Group.* London: IGUCGE/University of London Institute of Education, pp. 6–40.

5137 Verduin-Muller, H. (1980) 'Geographical education in the Dutch Republic (1579–1795)' in Marsden, W. E. *Historical Perspectives on Geographical Education.* London: IGUCGE/University of London Institute of Education, pp. 18–31.

5138 Verduin-Muller, H. (1988) 'Information theory and geography education' in Haubrich, H. (ed) *Perception of People and Places through Media, Volume 2.* Freiburg: IGUCGE/Pädagogische Hochschule Freiburg, pp. 208–219, 468–488.

5139 Waterman, S. (1979) 'Developments in geographical education in Ireland', *Geographical Viewpoint*, 8, pp. 60–66.

5140 Weinbrenner, U. (1996) 'Education towards European solidarity by means of geography school textbooks' in van der Zijpp, T., van der Schee, J. and Trimp, H. (eds) *Innovation in Geographical Education: Proceedings of the 28th International Geographical Congress Commission on Geographical Education.* Amsterdam: IGUCGE/Centrum voor Educatieve Geografie Vrije Universiteit Amsterdam, pp. 41–45.

5141 Wolforth, J. (1982) 'Changes in secondary school geography in the Federal Republic of Germany', *Canadian Geographer*, 26, 3, pp. 225–242.

# 2. Australia and New Zealand

5142 Australian Geography Teachers' Association (1988) 'Geography in secondary education', *Geographical Education*, 5, 4, pp. 5–13.

5143 Ballantyne, R. (1996) 'Factors affecting student choice of geography as a senior secondary school subject in Queensland', *IRGEE*, 5, 3, pp. 172–185.

5144 Ballantyne, R., Lidstone, J. and Packer, J. (1993) 'A critically reflective pre-service geography teacher education course: attitude and practice changes among graduates', *IRGEE*, 2, 1, pp. 41–50.

5145 Bartlett, L. and Cox, B. (1982) *Learning to Teach Geography: Practical Workshops in Geographical Education.* Brisbane: Wiles.

5146 Biddle, D. S. (1973) 'Geographical education in the 1970s' in Biddle, D. S. and Deer, C. E. (eds) *Readings in Geographical Education: Selections from Australian and New Zealand Sources, Volume 2: 1966–1972.* Sydney: Whitcombe and Tombs/Australian Geography Teachers' Association, pp. 1–18.

5147 Biddle, D. S. (1976) 'Paradigms in geography: some implications for curriculum development', *Geographical Education*, 2, 4, pp. 403–419.

5148 Biddle, D. S. (1980) 'Paradigms and geography curricula in England and Wales, 1882–1972' in Boardman, D. (ed) (1985) *New Directions in Geographical Education.* London: Falmer Press, pp. 11–33.

5149    Biddle, D. S. (1982) 'Course planning in geography' in Graves, N. (ed) *New UNESCO Source Book for Geography Teaching*. Harlow/Paris: Longman/UNESCO Press, pp. 272–312.

5150    Biddle, D. S. (1982) 'Geographical education in Australia' in Haubrich, H. (ed) *International Focus on Geographical Education*. Brunswick: Georg Eckert Institute for International Textbook Research, pp. 17–27.

5151    Biddle, D. S. (1992) 'An Australian example: a case study of curriculum change' in Naish, M. (ed) *Geography and Education: National and International Perspectives*. London: University of London Institute of Education, pp. 247–261.

5152    Biddle, D. S. (1996) 'Theories and practices in the development of curriculums in geography' in Gerber, R. and Lidstone, J. (eds) *Developments and Directions in Geographical Education*. Clevedon: Channel View Publications, pp. 15–35.

5153    Biddle, D. S. and Deer, C. E. (eds) (1972) *Readings in Geographical Education: Selections from Australian and New Zealand Sources, Volume 1: 1954–1966*. Sydney: Whitcombe and Tombs/Australian Geography Teachers' Association.

5154    Biddle, D. S. and Deer, C. E. (eds) (1973) *Readings in Geographical Education: Selections from Australian and New Zealand Sources, Volume 2: 1966–1972*. Sydney: Whitcombe and Tombs/Australian Geography Teachers' Association.

5155    Blachford, K. R. (1971) 'Why is geography in the curriculum?', *Geographical Education*, 1, 3, pp. 216–222.

5156    Bryant, L. (1980) 'Geography curriculum, teaching methods and teaching materials in Victoria 1850–1910', *Geographical Education*, 3, 4, pp. 559–576.

5157    Butler, D. and Simpson, J. (1996) 'Geography in the South Australian school curriculum', *Geographical Education*, 9, 1, pp. 28–30.

5158    Codrington, S. (1996) 'Developing a new geography course for the International Baccalaureate' in van der Zijpp, T., van der Schee, J. and Trimp, H. (eds) *Innovation in Geographical Education: Proceedings of the 28th International Geographical Congress Commission on Geographical Education*. Amsterdam: IGUCGE/Centrum voor Educatieve Geografie Vrije Universiteit Amsterdam, pp. 14–19.

5159    Conolly, G. (1996) 'Learning about society and environment: the role of geographical education in New South Wales', *Geographical Education*, 9, 1, pp. 18–25.

5160    Cordwell, K. A. (1972) 'Educational rationale in school geography', *Geographical Education*, 1, 4, pp. 361–374.

5161    Courtenay, P. P. (1995) 'Geography, development and an uncertain world', *Geographical Education*, 8, 3, pp. 27–30 and 63.

5162    Cox, B. (1973) 'Textbooks for secondary school geography' in Biddle, D. S. and Deer, C. E. (eds) *Readings in Geographical Education: Selections from Australian and New Zealand Sources, Volume 2: 1966–1972*. Sydney: Whitcombe and Tombs/Australian Geography Teachers' Association, pp. 206- 211.

5163    Cox, B. (1997) 'Teaching meaningful geography', *Geographical Education*, 10, pp. 50–52.

5164    Davey, C. (1979) 'Intercultural education and the geography teacher', *Geographical Education*, 3, 3, pp. 365–375.

5165    Davey, C. (1995) 'Looking forward: the secondary geography curriculum', *Geographical Education*, 8, 3, pp. 39–45.

5166    Davey, C. (1996) 'Advancing education through geography' in Gerber, R. and Lidstone, J. (eds) *Developments and Directions in Geographical Education*. Clevedon: Channel View Publications, pp. 93–115.

5167    Davidson, C. F. (1987) 'The changing topography of school geography', *New Zealand Journal of Geography*, 84, pp. 20–22.

5168    Deer, C. E. (1976) 'Elaboration in curriculum change in geography: the Australian experience', *New Era*, 57, pp. 152–156.

5169    Emery, J. S. (1976) 'Trends in environmental education in Australia: some implications for geography', *Geographical Education*, 2, 4, pp. 455–472.

5170    Fien, J. (1979) 'Towards a humanistic perspective in geographical education', *Geographical Education*, 3, 4, pp. 407–421.

5171    Fien, J. (1980) 'Operationalizing the humanistic perspective in geographical education', *Geographical Education*, 3, 4, pp. 477–487.

5172    Fien, J. (1983) '"Par for the course": a case study in urban environmental education', *Geographical Education*, 4, 2, pp. 107–115.

5173    Fien, J. (1984) 'Structural silence: aborigines in Australian geography textbooks', *Contemporary Issues in Geography and Education*, 1, 2, pp. 22–25.

5174    Fien, J. (1988) 'The Australian environment: visions, imperatives and classroom reality', *Geographical Education*, 5, 4, pp. 20–27.

5175    Fien, J. (1993) *Education for the Environment: Critical Curriculum Thinking and Environmental Education*. Geelong: Deakin University Press.

5176    Fien, J. (ed) (1993) *Environmental Education: A Pathway to Sustainability*. Geelong: Deakin University Press.

5177    Fien, J. (1996) 'Teaching to care: a case for commitment in teaching environmental values' in Gerber, R. and Lidstone, J. (eds) *Developments and Directions in Geographical Education*. Clevedon: Channel View Publications, pp. 77–91.

5178    Fien, J. and Ferreira, J.-A. (1997) 'Environmental education in Australia: a review', *IRGEE*, 6, 3, pp. 234–239.

5179    Fien, J. and Gerber, R. (eds) (1988) *Teaching Geography for a Better World*. Edinburgh: Oliver and Boyd.

5180    Fien, J., Gerber, R. and Wilson, P. (eds) (1984) *The Geography Teacher's Guide to the Classroom*. Melbourne: Macmillan.

5181    Fien, J., Hodgkinson, J. and Herschel, R. (1984) 'Using games and simulations in the geography classroom' in Fien, J., Gerber, R. and Wilson, P. (eds) *The Geography Teacher's Guide to the Classroom*. Melbourne: Macmillan, pp. 111–122.

5182    Fien, J. and Slater, F. (1981) 'Four strategies for values education', *Geographical Education*, 4, 1, pp. 39–52.

5183    Fien, J. and Wilson, P. (1997) 'Teaching about studies of Asia: a mirror on practice', *Geographical Education*, 10, pp. 45–49.

5184    Forer, P. (1984) 'Computers in the geography classroom' in Fien, J., Gerber, R. and Wilson, P. (eds) *The Geography Teacher's Guide to the Classroom*. Melbourne: Macmillan, pp. 172–184.

5185    Forer, P. and Tan, F. B. (1996) 'Geographic information technology in environmental education: an Auckland perspective on changing praxis', *IRGEE*, 5, 3, pp. 213–216.

5186    Gerber, R. (1977) 'Audiovisuals in geography teaching', *Geographical Education*, 3, 1, pp. 25–42.

5187    Gerber, R. (1981) 'Young children and their understanding of the elements of maps', *Teaching Geography*, 6, 3, pp. 128–133.

5188    Gerber, R. (1984) 'The diagnosis of student learning in geography' in Fien, J., Gerber, R. and Wilson, P. (eds) *The Geography Teacher's Guide to the Classroom*. Melbourne: Macmillan, pp. 185–196.

5189    Gerber, R. (1984) 'Teacher education for Australian geography teachers' in Marsden, W. E. (ed) *Teacher Education Models in Geography: An International Comparison*. Kalamazoo, MI: IGUCGE/Western Michigan University, pp. 67–80.

5190    Gerber, R. (1985) 'Competence and performance in cartographic language' in Boardman, D. (ed) *New Directions in Geographical Education*. London: Falmer Press, pp. 153–170.

5191    Gerber, R. (1985) 'Designing graphics for effective learning', *Geographical Education*, 5, 1, pp. 27–33.

5192    Gerber, R. (1989) 'Are geography educators skilful?', *Journal of Geography in Higher Education*, 13, 2, pp. 204–206.

5193    Gerber, R. (1991) 'Geography's contribution to technological education', *Geographical Education*, 6, 3, pp. 19–23.

5194    Gerber, R. (1992) 'Is mapping in schools reflecting development in cartography and geographical information?' in Naish, M. (ed) *Geography and Education: National and International Perspectives*. London: University of London Institute of Education, pp. 194–211.

5195    Gerber, R. (1992) 'Technology education: an emerging component in geographical education' in Hill, A. D. (ed) *International Perspectives on Geographical Education*. Boulder, CO/Skokie, IL: IGUCGE/Rand, McNally and Co., pp. 283–298.

5196    Gerber, R. (1994) 'The role of qualitative research in geographical education' in Haubrich, H. (ed) *Europe and the World in Geographical Education (Geographiedidaktische Forschungen, Band 22)*. Nuremberg: IGUCGE, pp. 367–381.

5197    Gerber, R. (1994) 'Variations in the experience of geography by pre-service geographical educators', *Geographical Education*, 7, 2, pp. 26–33.

5198    Gerber, R. (1995) 'A geographical education for life based on technological and graphic literacy', *Geographical Education*, 8, 3, pp. 50–56, 64.

5199    Gerber, R. (1996) 'Directions for research in geographical education: the maturity of qualitative research' in Gerber, R. and Lidstone, J. (eds) *Developments and Directions in Geographical Education*, Clevedon: Channel View Publications, pp. 131–150.

5200    Gerber, R. (1996) 'Environmental learning: knowing, experiencing and acting for the environment' in van der Zijpp, T., van der Schee, J. and Trimp, H. (eds) *Innovation in Geographical Education: Proceedings of the 28th International Geographical Congress Commission on Geographical Education*. Amsterdam: IGUCGE/Centrum voor Educatieve Geografie Vrije Universiteit Amsterdam, pp. 102–106.

5201    Gerber, R. (1997) 'Geography, work and lifelong learning', *Geographical Education*, 10, pp. 38–44.

5202    Gerber, R. (1997) 'Lifelong learning and the relevance of geography for work' in Convey, A. and Nolzen, H. (eds) *Geography and Education (Münchner Studien zur Didaktik der Geographie, Band 10)*. Munich: Lehrstuhl für Didaktik der Geographie der Universität München, pp. 101–110.

5203    Gerber, R. (1997) 'Valuing the concept of work in geographical education' in Naish, M. (ed) *Values in Geography Education: Proceedings*, London: IGUCGE/University of London Institute of Education.

5204    Gerber, R. and Lidstone, J. (eds) (1988) *Developing Skills in Geographical Education*. Brisbane: IGUCGE/Jacaranda Press.

5205    Gerber, R. and Lidstone, J. (eds) (1996) *Developments and Directions in Geographical Education*. Clevedon: Channel View Publications.

5206    Gerber, R. and Lidstone, J. (1996) 'Reflecting on developments and directions in geographical education' in Gerber, R. and Lidstone, J. (eds) *Developments and Directions in Geographical Education*. Clevedon: Channel View Publications, pp. 1–11.

5207    Gerber, R., Lidstone, J. and Nason, R. (1992) 'Expertise in understanding maps', *IRGEE*, 1, 1, pp. 31–43.

5208    Gerber, R. and Stewart-Dore, N. (1994) 'Strategies for improving reading and learning in geography lessons', *Teaching Geography*, 9, 5, pp. 216–221.

5209    Gerber, R. and Williams, M. (1992) *Distance Education and Geography Teaching*. Swansea: IGUCGE/University of Wales Swansea.

5210    Gerber, R. and Williams, M. (1996) 'Introduction to qualitative research in geographical education', in Gerber, R. and Williams, M. (eds) *Qualitative Research in Geographical Education*. Armidale, NSW: IGUCGE/University of New England Press, pp. 1–5.

5211    Gerber, R., Williams, M. and Biilmann, O. (1996) 'Geographical educators' understanding of the concept of qualitative research' in Gerber, R. and Williams, M. (eds) *Qualitative Research in Geographical Education*. Armidale, NSW: IGUCGE/University of New England Press, pp. 21–32.

5212    Gerber, R. and Wilson, P. (1979) 'Spatial reference systems and mapping with eleven-year-olds', *Geographical Education*, 3, 3, pp. 387–397.

5213    Gerber, R. and Wilson, P. (1984) 'Maps in the geography classroom' in Fien, J., Gerber, R. and Wilson, P. (eds) *The Geography Teacher's Guide to the Classroom*. Melbourne: Macmillan, pp. 185–196.

5214    Gilbert, R. (1979) 'Image, experience and personal geography: some implications for education', *Geographical Education*, 3, 3, pp. 399–406.

5215    Gilbert, R. (1988) 'Curriculum contradictions and the social purposes of geography teaching', *New Zealand Journal of Geography*, 85, pp. 12–16.

5216    Gilbert, R. and Singh, M. (1992) 'Geography teaching and social justice', *Geographical Education*, 6, 4, pp. 7–12.

5217    Gough, A. (1997) 'Evaluation of Australian government literature on the environment', *Journal of Environmental Education*, 28, 4, pp. 18–25.

5218    Gough, A. (1997) 'Founders of environmental education: narrations of the Australian environmental education movement', *Environmental Education Research*, 3, 1, pp. 43–57.

5219 Greenall, A. (1981) 'Environmental education: a case study in national curriculum action', *Environmental Education and Information*, 1, 4, pp. 285–294.

5220 Greenall, A. (1986) Searching for a meaning: what is environmental education?', *Geographical Education*, 5, 2, pp. 9–12.

5221 Greenall Gough, A. (1993) *Founders in Environmental Education*. Geelong: Deakin University Press.

5222 Greenall Gough, A. and Robottom, I. (1993) 'Towards a socially critical environmental education: water quality studies in a coastal school', *Journal of Curriculum Studies*, 23, 4, pp. 301–316.

5223 Halloway, W. (1984) 'Planning a school based assessment program' in Fien, J., Gerber, R. and Wilson, P. (eds) *The Geography Teacher's Guide to the Classroom*. Melbourne: Macmillan, pp. 278–293.

5224 Hobbs, P. G. (1978) 'Geography in primary schools', *Geographical Education*, 3, 2, pp. 219–235.

5225 Johnston, W. B. (1982) 'The numbers game: geography in relation to other subjects in New Zealand's secondary schools', *New Zealand Journal of Geography*, 72, pp. 2–10.

5226 Jones, A. (1979) 'Curriculum research in geography in New Zealand', *Geographical Education*, 3, 3, pp. 299–318.

5227 Jones, A. (1980) 'How New Zealand students see the USSR and India' in Slater, F. and Spicer, B. (eds) *Perception and Preference Studies at the International Level*. Tokyo: IGUCGE/AIP, pp. 138–146.

5228 Keown, P. (1996) 'Standards-based assessment and secondary school geography in New Zealand' in van der Zijpp, T., van der Schee, J. and Trimp, H. (eds) *Innovation in Geographical Education: Proceedings of the 28th International Geographical Congress Commission on Geographical Education*. Amsterdam: IGUCGE/Centrum voor Educatieve Geografie Vrije Universiteit Amsterdam, pp. 278–282.

5229 Keown, P. (1997) 'The role of geographical education in the study of society and environment: the New Zealand education service', *Geographical Education*, 10, pp. 29–37.

5230 Knight, C. (1976) 'Pupils' perceptions of the pedagogical process: New Zealand' in Stoltman, J. (ed) *International Research in Geographical Education*. Kalamazoo, MI: IGUCGE/Western Michigan University, pp. 127–143.

5231 Kwan, T. Yim-lin (1994) 'A reflective report on action research towards understanding conceptions of action research held by geography teachers' in Haubrich, H. (ed) *Europe and the World in Geographical Education (Geographiedidaktische Forschungen, Band 22)*. Nuremberg: IGUCGE, pp. 387–406.

5232 Kwan, T. Yim-lin (1996) 'Children and mapping: their intuitive experience in a familiar environment' in van der Zijpp, T., van der Schee, J. and Trimp, H. (eds) *Innovation in Geographical Education: Proceedings of the 28th International Geographical Congress Commission on Geographical Education*. Amsterdam: IGUCGE/Centrum voor Educatieve Geografie Vrije Universiteit Amsterdam, pp. 64–68.

5233 Kwan, T. Yim-lin (1996) 'Multiple case study on children's understanding and experience of maps before formal map teaching takes place in schools' in Gerber, R. and Williams, M. (eds) *Qualitative Research in Geographical Education*. Armidale, NSW: IGUCGE/University of New England Press, pp. 95–106.

5234    Kwan, T. Yim-lin (1996) 'Understanding children's intuitive experience of maps before formal map teaching takes place in schools' in Gerber, R. and Lidstone, J. (eds) *Developments and Directions in Geographical Education*. Clevedon: Channel View Publications, pp. 197–224.

5235    Kwan, T. Yim-lin (1996) 'The use of interactive journal writing as an effective strategy in the training of geography teachers' in van der Zijpp, T., van der Schee, J. and Trimp, H. (eds) *Innovation in Geographical Education: Proceedings of the 28th International Geographical Congress Commission on Geographical Education*. Amsterdam: IGUCGE/Centrum voor Educatieve Geografie Vrije Universiteit Amsterdam, pp. 204–208.

5236    Laws, K. (1977) 'Geographical education in the primary school', *Geographical Education*, 3, 1, pp. 85–91.

5237    Laws, K. (1984) 'Learning geography through fieldwork' in Fien, J., Gerber, R. and Wilson, P. (eds) *The Geography Teacher's Guide to the Classroom*. Melbourne: Macmillan, pp. 134–145.

5238    Lergessner, D. A. (1972) 'Fundamental research and school geography', *Geographical Education*, 1, 4, pp. 375–391.

5239    Lidstone, J. (1984) 'Teaching geography in the mixed ability classroom' in Fien, J., Gerber, R. and Wilson, P. (eds) *The Geography Teacher's Guide to the Classroom*. Melbourne: Macmillan, pp. 197–207.

5240    Lidstone, J. (1985) 'Introduction: textbooks in geography teaching', *Geographical Education*, 5, 1, p. 2.

5241    Lidstone, J. (1988) 'Research in geographical education' in Gerber, R. and Lidstone, J. (eds) *Developing Skills in Geographical Education*. Brisbane: IGUCGE/Jacaranda Press, pp. 273–352.

5242    Lidstone, J. (1992) 'In defence of textbooks' in Naish, M. (ed) *Geography and Education National and International Perspectives*. London: University of London Institute of Education, pp. 177–193.

5243    Lidstone, J. (1992) 'Natural disasters: promoting international perspectives through geographical education' in Hill, A. D. (ed) *International Perspectives on Geographical Education*. Boulder, CO/Skokie, IL: IGUCGE/Rand, McNally and Co., pp. 209–220.

5244    Lidstone, J. (1994) 'Using a conventional geography textbook' in Murray, L. (ed) *Lesson Planning in Geography*. Southsea: LDJ Educational, pp. 54–70.

5245    Lidstone, J. (1995) 'Global education, global change and disaster education' in Lidstone, J., Romanova, E., and Kondakov, A. (eds) *Global Change and Geographical Education*. Brisbane/Moscow: IGUCGE/Queensland University of Technology/Moscow State University, pp. 13–30.

5246    Lidstone, J. (1996) 'The essence of geographical education: an essential issue to address' in Convey, A. and Nolzen, H. (eds) *Geography and Education (Münchner Studien zur Didaktik der Geographie, Band 10)*. Munich: Lehrstuhl für Didaktik der Geographie der Universität München, pp. 169–187.

5247    Lidstone, J. (1996) 'Professionalism in geographical education' in Gerber, R. and Lidstone, J. (eds) *Developments and Directions in Geographical Education*. Clevedon: Channel View Publications, pp. 151–162.

5248    Lidstone, J. and Wiber, M. (1996) 'Preparing for the twenty-first century: geography education in Australia', *International Journal of Social Education*, 10, 2, pp. 27–41.

5249   McCauley, J. (1984) 'Teacher education in geography: the New Zealand model' in Marsden, W. E. (ed) *Teacher Education Models in Geography: An International Comparison*. Kalamazoo, MI: IGUCGE/Western Michigan University, pp. 45–55.

5250   McCulloch, G. (1992) 'Defining and defending subjects: the case of the New Zealand Geographical Society' in McCulloch, G. (ed) *The School Curriculum in New Zealand: History, Theory, Policy and Practice*. Palmerston North, NZ: Dunmore Press.

5251   McDonald, G. T. (1995) 'Environment and society in a spatial context: future directions in geography', *Geographical Education*, 8, 3, pp. 17–21.

5252   McElroy, B. (1984) 'Models and reality: integrating practical work and fieldwork in geography' in Fien, J., Gerber, R. and Wilson, P. (eds) *The Geography Teacher's Guide to the Classroom*. Melbourne: Macmillan, pp. 123–133.

5253   McElroy, B. (1984) 'Evaluating your geography courses' in Fien, J., Gerber, R. and Wilson, P. (eds) *The Geography Teacher's Guide to the Classroom*. Melbourne: Macmillan, pp. 294–305.

5254   McGee, C. (1982) 'Children's perception of symbols on maps and aerial photographs', *Geographical Education*, 4, 2, pp. 51–59.

5255   Marsh, C. J. (1987) 'The development of a senior school geography curriculum in Western Australia 1964–1984' in Goodson, I. F. (ed) *International Perspectives in Curriculum History*. London: Croom Helm, pp. 179–208.

5256   O'Malley, M. P. (1977) 'Viewpoints on geographical education: a decade of change', *New Zealand Journal of Geography*, 63, pp. 1–8.

5257   Paterson, J. L. (1991) 'Putting pop into place: using popular music in the teaching of geography', *New Zealand Journal of Geography*, 92, pp. 18–19.

5258   Rea, J. (1995) 'Educating for our environment: an Australian experience', *Environmentalist*, 15, 4, pp. 246–251.

5259   Renner, J. M. (1972) 'Geography in New Zealand schools', *Geographical Education*, 1, 4, pp. 351–360.

5260   Richardson, D. M. (1986) 'The social studies survey and geography', *New Zealand Journal of Geography*, 81, pp. 2–6.

5261   Robertson, M. (1994) 'The influence of place on adolescents' responses to environmental stimuli', *IRGEE*, 3, 2, pp. 3–21.

5262   Robertson, M. (1995) 'Adolescents, place experience and visual intelligence: implications for educators', *IRGEE*, 4, 2, pp. 65–84.

5263   Robertson, M. (1996) 'Geographical education in Tasmania: a moving target or what's in a name?', *Geographical Education*, 9, 2, pp. 131–133.

5264   Robottom, I. (ed) (1987) *Environmental Education: Practice and Possibility*. Geelong: Deakin University Press.

5265   Robottom, I. (1993) 'The role of ecology in education: an Australian perspective' in Hale, M. (ed) *Ecology in Education*. Cambridge: Cambridge University Press.

5266   Robottom, I. and Hart, P. (1993) *Research in Environmental Education: Engaging the Debate*. Geelong: Deakin University Press.

5267   Romey, W. and Elberty, W. (1984) 'On being a geography teacher in the 1980s and beyond' in Fien, J., Gerber, R. and Wilson, P. (eds) *The Geography Teacher's Guide to the Classroom*. Melbourne: Macmillan, pp. 306–316.

5268 **Shortle, D.** (1975) 'Geography as a discipline of knowledge: some curriculum implications', *Geographical Education*, 2, 3, pp. 281–303.

5269 **Singh, M.** (1991) 'Geography's contribution to multi-cultural education', *Geographical Education*, 6, 3, pp. 9–13.

5270 **Slater, F.** (1980) 'The preference patterns of New Zealand students' in Slater, F. and Spicer, B. (eds) *Perception and Preference Studies at the International Level*. Tokyo: IGUCGE/AIP, pp. 124–137.

5271 **Slater, F.** (1982) 'Geography in the New Zealand educational system and the process of curriculum change' in Haubrich, H. (ed) *International Focus on Geographical Education*. Brunswick: Georg Eckert Institute for International Textbook Research, pp. 215–236.

5272 **Slater, F.** (1983) 'The mishmash curriculum', *New Zealand Journal of Geography*, 75, pp. 7–9.

5273 **Smith, J. H.** (1997) 'The national professional development program for environmental education in Australia', *IRGEE*, 6, 3, pp. 244–246.

5274 **Spicer, B.** (1980) 'The view from down under: Australian students' residential and holiday preferences' in Slater, F. and Spicer, B. (eds) *Perception and Preference Studies at the International Level*. Tokyo: IGUCGE/AIP, pp. 63–76.

5275 **Walker, R. J.** (1980) 'Map using abilities of five to nine year old children', *Geographical Education*, 3, 4, pp. 545–554.

5276 **Wendt, N.** (1988) 'Environmental education in the South Pacific' in Gerber, R. and Lidstone, J. (eds) *Skills in Geographical Education Symposium '88, Volume 1*. Brisbane: IGUCGE/Brisbane College of Advanced Education, pp. 214–226.

5277 **Willcocks, R.** (1997) 'Electronic environmental education in Australia', *IRGEE*, 6, 3, pp. 256–260.

5278 **Wilson, P., Gerber, R.** and **Fien, J.** (eds) (1981) *Research in Geographical Education*. Brisbane: Australian Geographical Education Research Association.

# 3. North America

5279 **Altman, I.** and **Wohwill, J. F.** (eds) (1978) *Children and the Environment*, New York: Plenum Publishers.

5280 **Anderson, J.** (1985) 'Teaching map skills: an inductive approach' (parts 1–4), *Journal of Geography*, 84, 1, pp. 25–32; 84, 2, pp. 72–78; 84, 3, pp. 117–122; 84, 4, pp. 169–176.

5281 **Andrews, S. K., Otis-Witborn, A.** and **Young, T. M.** (1991) *Beyond Seeing and Hearing: Teaching Geography to Sensory Impaired Children*. Indiana, PA: National Council for Geographic Education.

5282 **Atkins, C. L.** (1981) 'Introducing basic map and globe concepts to young children', *Journal of Geography*, 80, 6, pp. 228–233.

5283 **Bacon, P.** (ed) (1970) *Focus on Geography: Key Concepts and Teaching Strategies*. Washington, DC: National Council for the Social Studies.

5284 **Bakshi, T. S.** and **Naveh, Z.** (1980) *Environmental Education: Principles, Methods and Applications*. New York: Plenum Press.

5285    Ball, J., Steinbrink, J. and Stoltman, J. (1971) *The Social Sciences and Geographic Education: A Reader.* New York: John Wiley and Sons.

5286    Barrs, D. (1988) 'School geography in the USA', *Teaching Geography*, 13, 1, pp. 4–6.

5287    Bartz, B. S. (1970) 'Maps in the classroom', *Journal of Geography*, 69, 1, pp. 18–24.

5288    Bednarz, R. S. and Bednarz, S. W. (1992) 'School geography in the United States: lessons learned and relearned' in Hill, A. D. (ed) *International Perspectives on Geographical Education.* Boulder, CO/Skokie, IL: IGUCGE/Rand, McNally and Co., pp. 139–154.

5289    Bednarz, R. S. and Peterson, J. F. (eds) (1994) *A Decade of Reform in Geographic Education: Inventory and Prospect.* Indiana, PA: National Council for Geographic Education.

5290    Bednarz, S. W. (1989) 'What's good about alliances?', *Professional Geographer*, 41, 4, pp. 484–488.

5291    Bednarz, S. W. (1995) 'Using mnemonics to learn place geography', *Journal of Geography*, 94, 1, pp. 330–338.

5292    Bednarz, S. W. (1996) 'The effects of the National Geography Standards on high school geography' in van der Zijpp, T., van der Schee, J. and Trimp, H. (eds) *Innovation in Geographical Education: Proceedings of the 28th International Geographical Congress Commission on Geographical Education.* Amsterdam: IGUCGE/Centrum voor Educatieve Geografie Vrije Universiteit Amsterdam, pp. 252–256.

5293    Bednarz, S. W. (1996) 'The variable meaning of curricula: a Texas case study', *IRGEE*, 5, 2, pp. 98–106.

5294    Bednarz, S. W. (1997) 'Research on geography textbooks in the United States', *IRGEE*, 6, 1, pp. 63–67.

5295    Bettis, N. C. (1996) 'The renaissance in geography education in the United States 1974–1994', *International Journal of Social Education*, 10, 2, pp. 61–72.

5296    Blaut, J. M. (1997) 'The mapping abilities of young children: children can', *Annals of the Association of American Geographers*, 87, 1, pp. 152–158.

5297    Blaut, J. M. (1997) 'Piagetian pessimism and the mapping abilities of young children: a rejoinder to Liben and Downs', *Annals of the Association of American Geographers*, 87, 1, pp. 168–177.

5298    Blaut, J. M., McCleary, G. S. and Blaut, A. S. (1970) 'Environmental mapping in young children', *Environment and Behaviour*, 2, pp. 335–49.

5299    Blaut, J. M. and Stea, D. (1971) 'Studies in geographic learning', *Annals of the Association of American Geographers*, 61, 2, pp. 387–393.

5300    Blaut, J. M. and Stea, D. (1974) 'Mapping at the age of three', *Journal of Geography*, 73, 7, pp. 5–9.

5301    Boehm, R. G., Brierley, J. and Sharma, M. (1994) 'The *bête noir* of geographic education: teacher training programs' in Bednarz, R. S. and Peterson, J. F. (eds) *A Decade of Reform in Geographic Education: Inventory and Prospect.* Indiana, PA: National Council for Geographic Education, pp. 89–98.

5302    Boehm, R. G. and Peterson, J. F. (1987) 'Teaching place names and locations in grades 4–8: map of errors', *Journal of Geography*, 86, 4, pp. 167–170.

5303    Boehm, R. G. and Peterson, J. F. (1997) *The First Assessment: Research in Geographical Education*. San Marcos, TX: Gilbert M. Grosvenor Center for Geographic Education, South West Texas State University.

5304    Bowers, C. A. (1993) *Education, Cultural Myths, and the Ecological Crisis*. Albany, NY: State University of New York Press.

5305    Buggey, J.-A. and Kracht, J. (1986) 'Geographic learning' in Atwood, V. A. (ed) *Elementary School Social Studies: Research as a Guide to Practice*. Washington, DC: National Council for the Social Studies, pp. 55–67.

5306    Castner, H. W. (1987) 'Education through mapping: a new role for school atlases?', *Cartographica*, 24, 1, pp. 82–100.

5307    Castner, H. W. (1990) *Seeking New Horizons: A Perceptual Approach to Geographic Education*. Montreal/Kingston: McGill/Queen's University Press.

5308    Castner, H. W. (1992) 'Geography's potential contributions to general education' in Hill, A. D. (ed) *International Perspectives on Geographical Education*. Boulder, CO/Skokie, IL: IGUCGE/Rand, McNally and Co., pp. 169–178.

5309    Castner, H. W. (1995) *Discerning New Horizons: A Perceptual Approach to Geographic Education*. Indiana, PA: National Council for Geographic Education.

5310    Castner, H. W. and Wheate, R. (1979) 'Re-assessing the role played by shaded relief in topographic scale maps', *Cartographic Journal*, 16, 2, pp. 77–85.

5311    Chakravarti, A. K. and Tiwari, R. C. (1990) 'A basic research paradigm in geography', *Journal of Geography*, 89, 2, pp. 53–57.

5312    Childress, R. B. (1978) 'Public school environmental education curricula: a national profile', *Journal of Environmental Education*, 9, 3, pp. 2–11.

5313    Choquette, R., Wolforth, J. and Villenure, M. (1980) *Canadian Geographical Education*. Ottawa: Canadian Association of Geographers/University of Ottawa Press.

5314    Cirrincione, J. M. and Decaroli, J. (1977) 'Developing curriculum for geographic education' in Manson, G. A. and Ridd, M. K. (eds) *New Perspectives on Geographic Education: Putting Theory into Practice*. Dubuque, IA: Kendall Hunt Publishing Co., pp. 39–54.

5315    Cogan, J. and Nakayama, S. (1985) 'The role of geography in developing international understanding', *Social Education*, 49, 1, pp. 48–51.

5316    Cohen, S. B. (1988) 'Geography: public awareness and the public arena', *Social Education*, 52, 4, pp. 248–250.

5317    Corcoran, P. B. (1996) 'Environmental education in North America: alternative perspectives', *IRGEE*, 5, 2, pp. 117–131.

5318    Crisp, W. (1975) *Development and Use of the Outdoor Classroom: An Annotated Bibliography*. Metuchen, NJ: Scarecrow Press.

5319    Downs, R. M. (1990) 'Reply: surveying the landscape of developmental geography (a dialogue with Howard Gardner)', *Annals of the Association of American Geographers*, 80, 1, pp. 124–128.

5320    Downs, R. M. (1994) 'Being and becoming a geographer: an agenda for geographical education', *Annals of the Association of American Geographers*, 84, 2, pp. 175–191.

5321    Downs, R. M. (1994) 'The need for research in geographic education: it would be nice to have some data' in Bednarz, R. S. and Peterson, J. F. (eds) *A Decade of Reform in Geographic Education: Inventory and Prospect*. Indiana, PA: National Council for Geographic Education, pp. 127–133.

5322    Downs, R. M. and Liben, L. S. (1997) 'The mapping abilities of young children: the final submission: the defense rests', *Annals of the Association of American Geographers*, 87, 1, pp. 178–180.

5323    Downs, R. M., Liben, L. S. and Daggs, D. G. (1988) 'On education and geographers: the role of cognitive developmental theory in geographical education', *Annals of the Association of American Geographers*, 78, 4, pp. 680–700.

5324    Downs, R. M. and Stea, D. (eds) (1973) *Image and Environment: Cognitive Mapping and Spatial Behavior*. Chicago, IL: Aldine.

5325    Downs, R. M. and Stea, D. (eds) (1977) *Maps in Minds: Reflections on Cognitive Mapping*. New York: Harper and Row.

5326    Drake, C. (1983) 'Teaching about Third World women', *Journal of Geography*, 82, 4, pp. 163–169.

5327    Drake, C. (1987) 'Education for responsible global citizenship', *Journal of Geography*, 86, 6, pp. 300–306.

5328    Eliot, J. (1972) 'Some research possibilities', *Journal of Geography*, 71, 4, pp. 201–214.

5329    Farrell, R. T. and Cirrincione, J. M. (1988) 'Teachers assess the five fundamental themes of geography' in Natoli, S. J. (ed) *Strengthening Geography in the Social Studies*. Washington, DC: National Council for the Social Studies, pp. 119–122.

5330    Farrell, R. T. and Cirrincione, J. M. (1989) 'The content of the geography curriculum: a teacher's perspective', *Social Education*, 53, 2, pp. 105–108.

5331    Flaim, M. L. and Chiodo, J. J. (1994) 'A novel approach to geographic education: using literature in the social studies', *Social Studies*, 85, 5, pp. 225–227.

5332    Fleming, D. (1981) 'The impact of nationalism on world geography textbooks in the United States', *International Journal of Political Education*, 4, 4, pp. 373–381.

5333    Ford, L. R. (1984) 'A core of geography: what geographers do best', *Journal of Geography*, 83, 3, pp. 102–106.

5334    Forsyth, A. S. (1992) 'Successfully integrating geography: the front door approach and the back door approach', *Social Education*, 56, 6, pp. 323–327.

5335    Forsyth, A. S. (1995) *Learning Geography: An Annotated Bibliography of Research Paths*. Indiana, PA: National Council for Geographic Education.

5336    Forsyth, A. S. (1995) 'Research in geographic education: where do the paths lead?', *IRGEE*, 4, 2, pp. 1–2.

5337    Forsyth, A. S. (1996) 'An analysis of US research on geography learning in relation to the National Geography Standards' in van der Zijpp, T., van der Schee, J. and Trimp, H. (eds) *Innovation in Geographical Education: Proceedings of the 28th International Geographical Congress Commission on Geographical Education*. Amsterdam: IGUCGE/Centrum voor Educatieve Geografie Vrije Universiteit Amsterdam, pp. 265–269.

5338  Frazier, J. W. (1994) 'Geography in the workplace: a personal assessment with a look to the future', in Bednarz, R. S. and Peterson, J. F. (eds) *A Decade of Reform in Geographic Education: Inventory and Prospect*. Indiana, PA: National Council for Geographic Education, pp. 67–79.

5339  Fredrich, B. and Fuller, K. (1996) 'Linking geography and art: Inness *The Lackawanna Valley*', *Journal of Geography*, 95, 6, pp. 254–262.

5340  Fuller, G. (1989) 'Why geographic alliances won't work', *Professional Geographer*, 41, 4, pp. 480–484.

5341  Gardner, D. P. (1986) 'Geography in the school curriculum', *Annals of the Association of American Geographers*, 76, 1, pp. 1–4.

5342  Gay, S. M. (1995) 'Making the connections: infusing the National Geography Standards into the classroom', *Journal of Geography*, 94, 4, pp. 459–461.

5343  Geography Education Standards Project (1994) *Geography for Life*. Washington, DC: National Geographic Society.

5344  Gersmehl, P. J. (1992) 'Themes and counterpoints in geographic education', *Journal of Geography*, 91, 3, pp. 119–123.

5345  Gersmehl, P. J. and Young, J. E. (1992) 'Images, analysis and evaluation: a linguistic basis for a regional geography course' in Hill, A. D. (ed) *International Perspectives on Geographical Education*. Boulder, CO/Skokie, IL: IGUCGE/Rand, McNally and Co., pp. 229–240.

5346  Gigliotti, L. M. (1990) 'Environmental education: what went wrong? what can be done?', *Journal of Environmental Education*, 22, 1, pp. 9–12.

5347  Gigliotti, L. M. (1992) 'Environmental attitudes: 20 years of change', *Journal of Environmental Education*, 24, 1, pp. 15–26.

5348  Gilmartin, P. P. and Patton, J. C. (1984) 'Comparing the sexes on spatial abilities: map-use skills', *Annals of the Association of American Geographers*, 74, 4, pp. 605–619.

5349  Green, J. L. (1984) 'Does geography have a sound curriculum theory?', *Social Studies*, 75, 4, pp. 145–148.

5350  Gregg, M. and Leinhardt, G. (1993) 'Geography in history: what is the where?', *Journal of Geography*, 92, 2, pp. 56–63.

5351  Gregg, M. and Leinhardt, G. (1994) 'Mapping out geography: an example of epistemology and education', *Review of Educational Research*, 64, 2, pp. 311–361.

5352  Gregg, M., Stainton, C. and Leinhardt, G. (1997) 'Strategies for geographic memory: oh, what a state we're in!', *IRGEE*, 6, 1, pp. 41–59.

5353  Grosvenor, G. M. (1995) 'In sight of the tunnel: the renaissance of geography education', *Annals of the Association of American Geographers*, 85, 3, pp. 409–420.

5354  Haddock, K. C. (1993) 'Teaching geography of the aged: a suggested resource', *Journal of Geography*, 92, 3, pp. 118–120.

5355  Haddock, K. C. and Mulvihili, J. L. (1981) 'Assessing the locational attributes of housing for the elderly through classroom and field studies', *Journal of Geography*, 80, 4, pp. 136–141.

5356  Han, S. H. and Sewing, D. R. (1987/88) 'Barriers to environmental education', *Journal of Environmental Education*, 19, 2, pp. 25–33.

5357    Hardwich, S. W. (1995) 'Looking toward the future: a concepts, themes and standards approach to preservice teacher education', *Journal of Geography*, 94, 5, pp. 513–518.

5358    Harper, R. A. (1982) 'Geography in general education: the need to focus on the geography of the field', *Journal of Geography*, 81, 4, pp. 122–139.

5359    Harper, R. A. (1990) 'The new school geography: a critique', *Journal of Geography*, 89, 1, pp. 27–30.

5360    Harrah, D. F. and Harrah, B. K. (1975) *Conservation/Ecology: Resources for Environmental Education.* Metuchen, NJ: Scarecrow Press.

5361    Harris, L. D. (1977) 'Lecturing from the atlas: an experiment in teaching', *Journal of Geography*, 76, 6, pp. 211–214.

5362    Hart, R. (1979) *Children's Experience of Place.* New York: Irvington Publishers.

5363    Helburn, N. (1991) 'The geographical perspective: geography's role in citizenship education' in Gross, R. E. and Dynneson, T. L. (eds) *Social Science Perspectives on Citizenship Education.* New York: Teachers College Press, pp. 116–140.

5364    Hewes, D. W. (1982) 'Pre-school geography: developing a sense of self in time and space', *Journal of Geography*, 81, 3, pp. 94–97.

5365    Hickey, M. and Bein, F. L. (1996) 'Students' learning difficulties in geography and teachers' interventions: teaching cases from K-12 classrooms', *Journal of Geography*, 95, 3, pp. 118–125.

5366    Hill, A. D. (1981) 'A survey of the global understanding of American college students: a report to geographers', *Professional Geographer*, 33, 2, pp. 237–245.

5367    Hill, A. D. (1989) 'Geography and education: North America', *Progress in Human Geography*, 13, 4, pp. 589–98.

5368    Hill, A. D. (1992) 'Geography and education: North America', *Progress in Human Geography*, 16, 2, pp. 232–242.

5369    Hill, A. D. (ed) (1992) *International Perspectives on Geographical Education.* Boulder, CO/Skokie, IL: IGUCGE/Rand, McNally and Co.

5370    Hill, A. D. (1994) 'Geography and education: North America', *Progress in Human Geography*, 18, 1, pp. 65–73.

5371    Hill, A. D. (1995) 'Geography standards, instruction and competencies for the new world of work', *Geographical Education*, 8, 3, pp. 47–49, 63.

5372    Hill, A. D. (1996) 'Geographic Inquiry into Global Issues (GIGI)' in van der Zijpp, T., van der Schee, J. and Trimp, H. (eds) *Innovation in Geographical Education: Proceedings of the 28th International Geographical Congress Commission on Geographical Education.* Amsterdam: IGUCGE/Centrum voor Educatieve Geografie Vrije Universiteit Amsterdam, pp. 270–272.

5373    Hill, A. D., Dorsey, B., Dunn, J. M. and Klein, P. (1992) 'The Geographic Inquiry into Global Issues project: rationale, development and evaluation' in Hill, A. D. (ed) *International Perspectives on Geographical Education.* Boulder, CO/Skokie, IL: IGUCGE/Rand, McNally and Co., pp. 241–253.

5374    Hill, A. D. and La Prarie, I. A. (1989) 'Geography in American education' in Gaile, G. L. and Willmott, C. J. (eds) *Geography in America.* Columbus, OH: Merrill, pp. 1–26.

5375    Holcomb, B. and Tiefenbacher, J. (1989) 'National Geography Awareness Week 1987: an assessment', *Journal of Geography in Higher Education*, 13, 2, pp. 159–164.

5376  Imperatore, W. (1971) 'Geography at the kindergarten level: report of a study', *Journal of Geography*, 70, 5, pp. 296–302.

5377  Jackson, R. H. (1976) 'The persistence of outmoded ideas in high school geography texts', *Journal of Geography*, 75, 7, pp. 199–208.

5378  James, P. E. (1971) 'The significance of geography in American education' in Ball, J., Steinbrink, J. and Stoltman, J. (eds) *The Social Sciences and Geographic Education: A Reader.* New York: John Wiley and Sons, pp. 3–19.

5379  Jenks, G. F., Steinke, T., Buchert, B. and Armstrong, L. (1971) 'Illustrating the concepts of the contour symbol, interval, and spacing via 3D maps', *Journal of Geography*, 70, 8, pp. 280–282.

5380  Jennings, S. A. (1996) 'An evaluation of the influence of travel on the geographic knowledge of geography students', *IRGEE*, 5, 1, pp. 45–54.

5381  Johnson, P. C. and Gondesen, M. E. (1991) 'Teaching longitude and latitude in the upper elementary grades', *Journal of Geography*, 90, 2, pp. 73–78.

5382  Joint Committee on Geographic Education (1984) *Guidelines for Geographic Education: Elementary and Secondary Schools.* Washington, DC: National Council for Geographic Education/Association of American Geographers.

5383  Jumper, S. R. (1991) 'National geographic education: an interview with Gilbert M. Grosvenor', *Journal of Geography in Higher Education*, 15, 2, pp. 101–112.

5384  Kincheloe, J. L. (1984) 'The trouble with geography', *Social Studies*, 75, 4, pp. 141–144.

5385  Kirman, J. M. (1988) 'Integrating geography with other school subjects: a view from an education faculty member', *Journal of Geography*, 87, 3, pp. 104–106.

5386  Klein, P. (1996) 'A model for creating a "quality inquiry learning experience"' in van der Zijpp, T., van der Schee, J. and Trimp, H. (eds) *Innovation in Geographical Education: Proceedings of the 28th International Geographical Congress Commission on Geographical Education.* Amsterdam: IGUCGE/Centrum voor Educatieve Geografie Vrije Universiteit Amsterdam, pp. 283–287.

5387  Kohn, C. (1982) 'Real problem-solving' in Graves, N. (ed) *New UNESCO Source Book for Geography Teaching.* Harlow/Paris: Longman/UNESCO Press, pp. 114–140.

5388  Kravitz, B. (1984) 'Results of recent research in elementary and secondary geographic education', *Social Studies Review*, 24, 1, pp. 3–7.

5389  Kurfman, D. G. (ed) (1971) *Evaluation in Geographic Education.* Belmont, CA: Fearon.

5390  Larimore, A. E. (1978) 'Humanizing the writing in cultural geography textbooks', *Journal of Geography*, 77, 5, pp. 183–185.

5391  Lee, R. (1983) 'Teaching geography: the dialectic of structure and agency', *Journal of Geography*, 82, 3, pp. 102–109.

5392  Le Sourd, S. J. (1993) 'Selected children's representations of people in five countries', *Theory and Research in Social Education*, 21, 4, pp. 316–340.

5393  Le Vasseur, M. (1993) *Finding a Way: Encouraging Underrepresented Groups in Geography: An Annotated Bibliography.* Indiana, PA: National Council for Geographic Education.

5394  Libbee, M. (1988) 'World geography and international understanding', *Journal of Geography*, 87, 1, pp. 5–12.

5395    Liben, L. S. and Downs, R. M. (1997) 'The mapping abilities of young children: can-ism and can'tianism: a straw child', *Annals of the Association of American Geographers*, 87, 1, pp. 159–167.

5396    Loyd, B. and Rengert, A. (eds) (1978) 'Women in geographic curricula', *Journal of Geography*, 77, 5, pp. 164–191.

5397    Lyman, L. and Foyle, H. (1991) 'Teaching geography using cooperative learning', *Journal of Geography*, 90, 5, pp. 223–226.

5398    McGee, M. G. (1979) *Spatial Abilities: Sources of Sex Differences*. New York: Praeger.

5399    Manson, G. (1973) 'Classroom questioning for geography teachers', *Journal of Geography*, 72, 4, pp. 24–30.

5400    Manson, G. (1981) 'Notes on the status of geography in American schools', *Journal of Geography*, 80, 7, pp. 244–248.

5401    Manson, G. and Ridd, M. K. (1977) *New Perspectives on Geographic Education: Putting Theory into Practice*. Dubuque, IA: Kendall Hunt Publishing Co.

5402    Marran, J. (1994) 'Discovering innovative curricular models for school geography' in Bednarz, R. S. and Peterson, J. F. (eds) *A Decade of Reform in Geographic Education: Inventory and Prospect*. Indiana, PA: National Council for Geographic Education, pp. 23–29.

5403    Marran, J. and Ziegler, D. (1996) 'The US National Geography Standards: blueprint for reform and prospectus for research' in van der Zijpp, T., van der Schee, J. and Trimp, H. (eds) *Innovation in Geographical Education: Proceedings of the 28th International Geographical Congress Commission on Geographical Education*. Amsterdam: IGUCGE/Centrum voor Educatieve Geografie Vrije Universiteit Amsterdam, pp. 302–306.

5404    Martin, G. J. (1987) *A Contribution to the History of Geography in the United States of America 1892–1925*, unpublished PhD thesis. University of London.

5405    Martin, K. D. (1989) 'Creating an interactive globe', *Journal of Geography*, 88, 4, pp. 140–142.

5406    Massey, D. (1986) 'Inside a textbook', *Journal of Geography*, 85, 3, pp. 116–119.

5407    Mayer, T. (1989) 'Consensus and invisibility: the representation of women in human geography textbooks', *Professional Geographer*, 41, 4, pp. 397–409.

5408    Mayer, V. J. (1997) 'Global science literacy: an earth system view', *Journal of Research in Science Teaching*, 24, 2, pp. 101–105.

5409    Merrett, C. D. (1997) 'Research and teaching in political geography: national standards and the resurgence of the "wayward child"', *Journal of Geography*, 96, 2, pp. 50–54.

5410    Meyer, J. M. W. (1973) 'Map skills instruction and the child's developing cognitive abilities', *Journal of Geography*, 72, 6, pp. 27–35.

5411    Milburn, D. (1984) 'Geography and teacher training in Canada' in Marsden, W. E. (ed) *Teacher Education Models in Geography: An International Comparison*. Kalamazoo, MI: IGUCGE/Western Michigan University, pp. 23–33.

5412    Miller, J. W. (1972) 'A content/operations/product/time model for research in geographic learning', *Journal of Geography*, 71, 4, pp. 233–237.

5413    Miller, J. W. (1985) 'Teaching map skills: theory, research, practice', *Social Education*, 49, 1, pp. 30–33.

5414    Miller, J. W., Bartz, B. S., Eliot, J. and Towler, J. (1972) 'Research in geographic learning: a special task force report to the National Council for Geographic Education', *Journal of Geography*, 71, 4, pp. 199–240.

5415    Monk, J. (1971) 'Preparing tests to measure course objectives', *Journal of Geography*, 70, 3, pp. 157–162.

5416    Monk, J. (1983) 'Integrating women into the geography curriculum', *Journal of Geography*, 82, 6, pp. 271–273.

5417    Monk, J. (1984) 'The responsibility of geography', *Annals of the Association of American Geographers*, 74, 1, pp. 1–8.

5418    Monk, J. (1986) 'The Association of American Geographers' role in educational leadership: an interview with Sam Natoli', *Journal of Geography in Higher Education*, 10, 2, pp. 113–131.

5419    Monk, J. (1987) 'Geography meeting its mission', *Journal of Geography*, 86, 4, pp. 143–146.

5420    Monk, J. (1994) 'Place matters: comparative international perspectives on feminist geography', *Professional Geographer*, 46, 3, pp. 277–288.

5421    Monk, J. and Hanson, S. (1982) 'On not excluding half of the human in human geography', *Professional Geographer*, 34, 1, pp. 11–23.

5422    Muessig, R. H. (1985) 'Building higher-level geographic skills with topographic maps', *Social Education*, 49, 1, pp. 34–37.

5423    Muessig, R. H. (1987) 'An analysis of developments in geographic education', *Elementary School Journal*, 87, 5, pp. 519–530.

5424    Muir, S. P. (1985) 'Understanding and improving students' map reading skills', *Elementary School Journal*, 86, 2, pp. 207–216.

5425    Muir, S. P. and Cheek, H. N. (1991) 'Assessing spatial development: implications for map skill instruction', *Social Education*, 55, 5, pp. 316–319.

5426    Muir, S. P. and Frazee, B. (1986) 'Teaching map reading skills: a developmental perspective', *Social Education*, 50, 3, pp. 199–203.

5427    Nagy, J. N. and Baird, J. C. (1978) 'Children as environmental planners' in Altman, I. and Wohwill, J. F. (eds) *Children and the Environment*. New York: Plenum Press, pp. 259–294.

5428    Natoli, S. J. (1986) 'The evolving nature of geography' in Wronski, S. P. and Bragaw, D. H. (eds) *Social Studies and Social Sciences: A Fifty-year Perspective*. Washington, DC: National Council for the Social Studies, pp. 28–42.

5429    Natoli, S. J. (ed) (1988) *Strengthening Geography in the Social Studies*. Washington, DC: National Council for the Social Studies.

5430    Natoli, S. J. (1994) 'Guidelines for geographic education and the fundamental themes of geography' in Bednarz, R. S. and Peterson, J. F. (eds) *A Decade of Reform in Geographic Education: Inventory and Prospect*. Indiana, PA: National Council for Geographic Education, pp. 13–22.

5431    Natoli, S. J. and Ritter, F. A. (1979) 'The revision of the High School Geography Project', *Journal of Geography in Higher Education*, 3, 2, pp. 102–105.

5432    Oden, P. (1989) 'Geography is everywhere in children's literature', *Journal of Geography*, 88, 3, pp. 151–158.

5433    Orr, D. W. (1992) *Ecological Literacy: Education and the Transition to a Postmodern World*. Albany, NY: State University of New York Press.

5434    Orr, D. W. (1994) *Earth in Mind: On Education, Environment and the Human Prospect*. Washington, DC: Island Press.

5435    Petersen, J. F. (1994) 'The guidelines for geographic education: a ten-year retrospective', *Social Education*, 58, 4, pp. 206–210.

5436    Peterson, G. A. (1987) 'The future of the geography education program of the National Geographic Society', *Journal of Geography*, 86, 5, pp. 233–235.

5437    Phipps, W. E. (1987) 'Cartographic ethnocentricity', *Social Studies*, 78, 6, pp. 260–263.

5438    Prakash, M. S. (1995) 'Ecological literacy for moral virtue: Orr on (moral) education for postmodern sustainability', *Journal of Moral Education*, 24, 1, pp. 3–18.

5439    Rallis, D. N. and Rallis, H. (1995) 'Changing the image of geography', *Social Studies*, 86, 4, pp. 167–168.

5440    Rand, D., Towler, J. and Price, D. (1976) 'Geographic knowledge as measure by Piaget's spatial stages' in Stoltman, J. (ed) *International Research in Geographical Education*. Kalamazoo, MI: IGUCGE/Western Michigan University, pp. 61–78.

5441    Rawling, E. (1993) 'Crossing the Atlantic for lessons in geography', *Teaching Geography*, 18, 1, p. 33.

5442    RBP (1972) 'High School Geography Project: geography in an urban age', *Social Education*, 36, 7, pp. 750–752.

5443    Robert, B. (1997) 'The ecosystem approach to the development of a school atlas', *IRGEE*, 6, 1, pp. 68–71.

5444    Roberts, K. M. (1997) 'Getting a grip on geography', *Social Education*, 61, 2, pp. 80–82.

5445    Ruff, T. and Hansen, J. M. (1992) 'Teaching geography: the world really is getting smaller', *Social Studies Review*, 32, 1, pp. 39–47.

5446    Rushdoony, H. A. (1971) 'The geographer, the teacher, and the child's perception of maps and mapping', *Journal of Geography*, 70, 7, pp. 429–433.

5447    Sale, L. L. and Lee, E. W. (1972) *Environmental Education in the Elementary School*. New York: Holt Rinehart and Winston.

5448    Salter, C. L. (1986) 'Geography and California's educational reform: an approach to a common core', *Annals of the Association of American Geographers*, 76, 1, pp. 5–17.

5449    Salter, C. L. (1987) 'The nature and potential of a geographic alliance', *Journal of Geography*, 86, 5, pp. 211–215.

5450    Salter, C. L. (1991) 'Geographic alliances: be moved, but not alarmed', *Professional Geographer*, 43, 1, pp. 102–104.

5451    Salter, C. L. (1992) 'The US Geography Consensus Project: dynamics and outcome' in Hill, A. D. (ed) *International Perspectives on Geographical Education*. Boulder, CO/Skokie, IL: IGUCGE/Rand, McNally and Co., pp. 155–166.

5452    Salter, C. L. (1995) 'The geographic imperative', *Journal of Geography*, 94, 4, pp. 471–477.

5453    Salter, K. and Salter, C. L. (1995) 'Significant new materials for the geography classroom', *Journal of Geography*, 94, 4, pp. 444–452.

5454    Sauve, L. and Boutard, A. (1991) 'Environmental education in Quebec: time for concerted action', *European Journal of Education*, 26, 4, pp. 347–355.

5455  Saveland, R. N. (1983) 'Map skills around the world: how to test and diagnose place vocabulary capabilities', *Social Education*, 47, 3, pp. 206–211.

5456  Saveland, R. N. and Pannell, C. W. (1978) 'Some aspects of the study and teaching of geography in the United States: a review of current research 1965–1975' in Naish, M. (ed) *Teaching Geography Occasional Papers, No. 30*. Sheffield: Geographical Association.

5457  Schoenfeld, C. (1970) 'Toward a national strategy for environmental education', *Journal of Educational Research*, 64, 1, pp. 5–11.

5458  Scott, R. C. (1984) 'Trends in introductory physical geography college textbooks', *Journal of Geography*, 83, 6, pp. 269–272.

5459  Scriven, M. (1970) 'Environmental education' in Johnson, H. D. (ed) *No Deposit – No Return: Man and his Environment: A View toward Survival*. Reading, MA: Addison-Wesley Publishing Co., pp. 242–249.

5460  Senathirajah, N. and Weiss, J. (1971) *Evaluation in Geography: A Resource Book for Teachers*. Toronto: Ontario Institute for Studies in Education.

5461  Stapp, W. (1974) 'Historical setting of environmental education' in Swan, J. and Stapp, W. (eds) *Environmental Education: Strategies Toward a More Livable Future*. New York: Sage Publications, pp. 42–49.

5462  Steinberg, P. E. (1997) 'Political geography and the environment', *Journal of Geography*, 96, 2, pp. 113–118.

5463  Steinbrink, J. (1976) 'Researching instructional style and classroom environments' in Stoltman, J. (ed) *International Research in Geographical Education*. Kalamazoo, MI: IGUCGE/Western Michigan University, pp. 89–114.

5464  Stevenson, R. B. (1993) 'Becoming compatible: curriculum and environmental thought', *Journal of Environmental Education*, 24, 2, pp. 4–9.

5465  Stillman, C. W. (1974) 'Reflections on environmental education', *Teachers College Record*, 74, 2, pp. 195–200.

5466  Stoltman, J. (1976) 'Territorial concept development: a review of the literature' in Stoltman, J. (ed) *International Research in Geographical Education*. Kalamazoo, MI: IGUCGE/Western Michigan University, pp. 1–15.

5467  Stoltman, J. (1976) 'Student perception of teacher style: the effects of the High School Geography Project' in Stoltman, J. (ed) *International Research in Geographical Education*. Kalamazoo, MI: IGUCGE/Western Michigan University, pp. 89–114.

5468  Stoltman, J. (1976) 'An international perspective on teacher classroom style' in Stoltman, J. (ed) *International Research in Geographical Education*. Kalamazoo, MI: IGUCGE/Western Michigan University, pp. 225–240.

5469  Stoltman, J. (1977) 'Children's conceptions of space and territorial relationships', *Social Education*, 41, 2, pp. 142–145.

5470  Stoltman, J. (1980) 'Perception of residential and holiday places by United States pupils' in Slater, F. and Spicer, B. (eds) *Perception and Preference Studies at the International Level*. Tokyo: IGUCGE/AIP, pp. 198–206.

5471  Stoltman, J. (1980) 'Round one for HSGP: a report on acceptance and diffusion', *Professional Geographer*, 32, 2, pp. 209–215.

5472    Stoltman, J. (1982) 'Geographical education in the United States since 1960' in Haubrich, H. (ed) *International Focus on Geographical Education*. Brunswick: Georg Eckert Institute for International Textbook Research, pp. 284–288.

5473    Stoltman, J. (1986) 'Geographical education and society: changing perspectives on school geography in the United States' in Hernando, A. (ed) *Geographical Education and Society*. Barcelona: IGUCGE, pp. 1–15.

5474    Stoltman, J. (1988) 'The effects of self-directed atlas study upon student learning in geography' in Gerber, R. and Lidstone, J. (eds) *Skills in Geographical Education Symposium '88, Volume. 2*. Brisbane: IGUCGE/Brisbane College of Advanced Education, pp. 675–684.

5475    Stoltman, J. (1990) 'Geography's role in general education in the United States', *GeoJournal*, 20, 1, pp. 7–14.

5476    Stoltman, J. (1991) 'Research on geography teaching' in Shaver, J. P. (ed) *Handbook of Research in Social Studies Teaching and Learning*. New York: Macmillan, pp. 437–447.

5477    Stoltman, J. (1992) 'Geographic education in the United States: the renaissance of the 1980s' in Naish, M. (ed) *Geography and Education: National and International Perspectives*. London: University of London Institute of Education, pp. 262–275.

5478    Stoltman, J. (1995) 'The national geography content standards: implications for initial teacher training', *New Era*, 76, 1, pp. 19, 22–24.

5479    Stoltman, J. (ed) (1996) *International Developments in Geographical Education: Preparing for the Twenty-first Century (International Journal of Social Education*, 10, 2; special edition). Muncie, IN: Ball State University.

5480    Stoltman, J. (1996) 'Reform in geographical education in the United States' in van der Zijpp, T., van der Schee, J. and Trimp, H. (eds) *Innovation in Geographical Education: Proceedings of the 28th International Geographical Congress Commission on Geographical Education*. Amsterdam: IGUCGE/Centrum voor Educatieve Geografie Vrije Universiteit Amsterdam, pp. 326–330.

5481    Stoltman, J. (1997) 'International cooperation and understanding in geography curricula: stepping into the 21st century' in Convey, A. and Nolzen, H. (eds) *Geography and Education (Münchner Studien zur Didaktik der Geographie, Band 10)*. Munich: Lehrstuhl für Didaktik der Geographie der Universität München, pp. 263–272.

5482    Stoltman, J. and Freye, R. (1988) 'School atlases in the United States: an analysis of characteristics' in Gerber, R. and Lidstone, J. (eds) *Developing Skills in Geographical Education*. Brisbane: IGUCGE/Jacaranda Press, pp. 350–352.

5483    Stoltman, J. and Libbee, M. (1988) 'Geography in the social studies: scope and sequence' in Natoli, S. J. *Strengthening Geography in the Social Studies*. Washington, DC: National Council for the Social Studies, pp. 43–51.

5484    Stoltman, J. and Wardley, S. (1996) 'Geographic education in the United States: systematic reforms leading to national standards and assessment' in van der Schee, J., Schoenmaker, G., Trimp, H. and van Westrhenen, H. (eds) *Innovation in Geographical Education (Netherlands Geographical Studies, 208)*. Utrecht/Amsterdam: IGUCGE/Centrum voor Educatieve Geografie Vrije Universiteit Amsterdam, pp. 259–271.

5485    Stoltman, J. and Wardley, S. (1997) 'Geographic education in the United States: a decade of change', *Geographical Education*, 10, pp. 15–21.

5486   Stutz, F. P. (1985) 'Enhancing high school geography at the local level', *Professional Geographer*, 37, 4, pp. 391–395.

5487   Sunal-Szymanski, C. (1987) 'Mapping for the young child', *Social Studies*, 78, 4, pp. 178–182.

5488   Swan, J. (1971) 'The challenge of environmental education' in Ball, J., Steinbrink, J. and Stoltman, J. (eds) *The Social Sciences and Geographical Education: A Reader*. New York: John Wiley and Sons, pp. 318–323.

5489   Swan, J. (1971) 'Environmental education: one approach to resolving the environmental crisis', *Environment and Behavior*, 3, 3, pp. 223–229.

5490   Swan, J. and Stapp, W. (eds) (1974) *Environmental Education: Strategies toward a More Livable Future*. New York: Sage Publications.

5491   Terry, M. (1971) *Teaching for Survival*. New York: Friends of the Earth/Ballantine.

5492   Thomas, P. F. (1992) 'Some critical structural factors in the institutional context of Canadian school geography' in Hill, A. D. (ed) *International Perspectives on Geographical Education*. Boulder, CO/Skokie, IL: IGUCGE/Rand, McNally and Co., pp. 119–129.

5493   Thomas, P. F. (1994) 'The great misinformation machine and the promulgation of naive school geography: implications for Canadian sovereignty' in Haubrich, H. (ed) *Europe and the World in Geography Education (Geographiedidaktische Forschungen, Band 22)*. Nuremberg: IGUCGE, pp. 187–196.

5494   Thomas, P. F. (1996) 'The looming impact of the new American school-geography standards on the Canadian situation' in van der Zijpp, T., van der Schee, J. and Trimp, H. (eds) *Innovation in Geographical Education: Proceedings of the 28th International Geographical Congress Commission on Geographical Education*. Amsterdam: IGUCGE/Centrum voor Educatieve Geografie Vrije Universiteit Amsterdam, pp. 341–345.

5495   Thornton, S. J. and Wenger, R. N. (1990) 'Geography curriculum and instruction in three fourth-grade classrooms', *Elementary School Journal*, 90, 5, pp. 515–531.

5496   Towler, J. (1970) 'The elementary school child's concept of reference systems', *Journal of Geography*, 69, pp. 89–93.

5497   Towler, J. and Price, D. (1976) 'The development of nationality and spatial relationship concepts in children: Canada' in Stoltman, J. (ed) *International Research in Geographical Education*. Kalamazoo, MI: IGUCGE/Western Michigan University, pp. 79–88.

5498   Troost, C. J. and Altman, H. (1972) *Environmental Education: A Sourcebook*. New York: John Wiley and Sons.

5499   Unwin, T. (1992) 'Geography in the secondary curriculum in North America' in Unwin, T. *The Place of Geography*. Harlow: Longman, pp. 8–11.

5500   Vining, J. W. (1990) *The National Council for Geographic Education: The First Seventy-five Years and Beyond*. Indiana, PA: National Council for Geographic Education.

5501   Vivian, V. E. (1973) *Sourcebook for Environmental Education*. Saint Louis, MO: The C. V. Mosby Company.

5502   Wheeler, J. O. (1985) 'Creating local field trips: seeing geographical principles through empirical eyes', *Journal of Geography*, 84, 5, pp. 217–219.

5503   White, G. F. (1971) 'Geography in liberal education' in Ball, J., Steinbrink, J., and Stoltman, J. (eds) *The Social Sciences and Geographic Education: A Reader.* New York: John Wiley and Sons, pp. 209–217.

5504   Wilbanks, T. J. (1994) 'Geographic education in a national context' in Bednarz, R. S. and Peterson, J. F. (eds) *A Decade of Reform in Geographic Education: Inventory and Prospect.* Indiana, PA: National Council for Geographic Education, pp. 116–120.

5505   Wilson, R. A. (1993) 'Education for earth: a guide for early childhood instruction', *Journal of Environmental Education*, 24, 2, pp. 15–21.

5506   Winston, B. (1984) 'Teacher education in geography in the United States' in Marsden, W. E. (ed) *Teacher Education Models in Geography: An International Comparison.* Kalamazoo, MI: IGUCGE/Western Michigan University, pp. 133–150.

5507   Winston, B. (1986) 'Teaching and learning in geography' in Wronski, S. P. and Bragaw, D. H. (eds) *Social Studies and Social Sciences: A Fifty-year Perspective.* Washington, DC: National Council for the Social Studies, pp. 43–58.

5508   Wolforth, J. (1976) 'The new geography – and after?', *Geography*, 61, 3, pp. 143–149.

5509   Wolforth, J. (1980) 'Canadian students' preferences among countries as places in which to live or vacation' in Slater, F. and Spicer, B. (eds) *Perception and Preference Studies at the International Level.* Tokyo: IGUCGE/AIP, pp. 87–102.

5510   Wolforth, J. (1980) 'Research in geographical education' in Choquette, R., Wolforth, J., and Villenure, M. *Canadian Geographical Education.* Ottawa: Canadian Association of Geographers/University of Ottawa Press.

5511   Wolforth, J. (1982) 'Geographical education in Canada' in Haubrich, H. (ed) *International Focus on Geographical Education.* Brunswick: Georg Eckert Institute for International Textbook Research, pp. 55–58.

5512   Wolforth, J. (1986) 'School geography: alive and well in Canada', *Annals of the Association of American Geographers*, 76, 1, pp. 17–24.

5513   Woodring, P. (1984) 'Geography's place in basic education', *Journal of Geography*, 83, 3, pp. 143–144.

5514   Wright, D. (1986) 'Whose outline of American geography?: an exercise in textbook research', *Social Studies*, 77, 1, pp. 44–46.

## 4. Latin America and the Caribbean

5515   Bynoe, P. and Hale, W. (1997) 'An analysis of environmental education provision in a sample of Caribbean National Environment Action Plans (NEAPs)', *Environmental Education Research*, 3, 1, pp. 59–68.

5516   Carneiro, S. M. (1988) 'Objectives for fieldwork and laboratory studies in geography at primary and secondary schools' in Gerber, R. and Lidstone, J. (eds) *Developing Skills in Geographical Education.* Brisbane: IGUCGE/Jacaranda Press, pp. 212–214.

5517   Dutton, R. (1980) 'Environmental education: a suggested strategy for Jamaica', *Caribbean Journal of Education*, 7, 1, pp. 43–63.

5518   Eyre, L. A. (1985) 'Biblical symbolism and the role of fantasy geography among the Rastafarians of Jamaica', *Journal of Geography*, 84, 4, pp. 144–148.

5519 Francis, G. (1989) 'Tertiary environmental education in its second decade', *Caribbean Journal of Education*, 16, 1/2, pp. 67–80.

5520 Glasgow, J. (1984) 'Report on the subregional workshop on teacher training in environmental education for the Caribbean', *Caribbean Journal of Education*, 11, 1, pp. 48–69.

5521 Glasgow, J. (1989) 'Environmental education: global concern, Caribbean focus', *Caribbean Journal of Education*, 16, 1/2, pp. 1–12.

5522 Glean, C. (1979) 'Social studies teacher education: rationale and process for the eastern Caribbean', *Caribbean Journal of Education*, 6, 3, pp. 221–241.

5523 Howell, C. A. (1989) 'Emerging trends in environmental education in the English-speaking Caribbean', *Convergence*, 22, 4, pp. 45–53.

5524 Howell, C. A. (1995) 'Educating for sustainable development: an overview of environmental education programs in the Caribbean', *Environmental Education and Information*, 14, 4, pp. 419–432.

5525 Hudson, B. (1994) 'Geography in colonial schools: the classroom experience in West Indian literature', *Geography*, 79, 4, pp. 322–329.

5526 Lockledge, A. (1992) 'Street festivals in the Caribbean: geography lessons for elementary teachers', *Social Studies*, 83, 1, pp. 17–20.

5527 Miller, B. A. and Howell, C. A. (1989) 'Environmental education in the English-speaking Caribbean: a report', *Caribbean Journal of Education*, 16, 1/2, pp. 105–116.

5528 Morrissey, M. (1980) 'International preferences of a Jamaican sample' in Slater, F. and Spicer, B. (eds) *Perception and Preference Studies at the International Level*. Tokyo: IGUCGE/AIP, pp. 114–124.

5529 Morrissey, M. (1983) 'Country preferences of school children in seven Caribbean territories', *Caribbean Quarterly*, 29, 3/4, pp. 1–20.

5530 Morrissey, M. (1984) 'Place recognition by Jamaican children' in Haubrich, H. (ed) *Perception of People and Places through Media, Volume 1*. Freiburg: IGUCGE/Pädagogische Hochschule Freiburg, pp. 292–309.

5531 Morrissey, M. (1984) 'Teacher participation in a curriculum development project in a Third World country', *Caribbean Journal of Education*, 11, 2/3, pp. 143–157.

5532 Morrissey, M. (1986) 'Mapping educational disparities in the Caribbean', *Teaching Geography*, 10, 2, pp. 56–60.

5533 Morrissey, M. (1987) 'Trends in school geography in the post-colonial Commonwealth Caribbean' in Haubrich, H. (ed) *International Trends in Geographical Education*. Freiburg: IGUCGE, pp. 61–71.

5534 Morrissey, M. (1988) 'Stimulating endogenous textbook development in the Caribbean micro-states' in Gerber, R. and Lidstone, J. (eds) *Developing Skills in Geographical Education*. Brisbane: IGUCGE/Jacaranda Press, pp. 222–227.

5535 Morrissey, M. (ed) (1990) *Curriculum Reform in the Third World: The Case of School Geography*. Mona, Jamaica: Institute of Social and Economic Studies, University of the West Indies.

5536 Mucciolo, M. (1984) 'Brazilian children's geographic perceptions' in Haubrich, H. (ed) *Perception of People and Places through Media, Volume 1*. Freiburg: IGUCGE/Pädagogische Hochschule Freiburg, pp. 285–292.

5537   Mucciolo, M. (1988) 'Styles of teaching in a developing country: Brazil' in Gerber, R. and Lidstone, J. (eds) *Developing Skills in Geographical Education*. Brisbane: IGUCGE/Jacaranda Press, pp. 60–62.

5538   Oliveira, L. (1972) 'Geography in modern education' in Adams, W. P. and Helleiner, F. M. (eds) *International Geography 1972*. Montreal: IGUCGE/University of Toronto Press, pp. 1057–1058.

5539   Oliveira, L. (1976) 'The concept of territorial decentration in Brazilian school children' in Stoltman, J. (ed) *International Research in Geographical Education*. Kalamazoo, MI: IGUCGE/University of Western Michigan, pp. 17–38.

5540   Oliveira, L. (1980) 'A place to live, a place to visit: Brazilian preferences' in Slater, F. and Spicer, B. (eds) *Perception and Preference Studies at the International Level*. Tokyo: IGUCGE/AIP, pp. 77–86.

5541   Oliveira, L. (1984) 'Three Brazilian cognitive studies on geographical education' in Graves, N. (ed) *Research and Research Methods in Geographical Education*. London: IGUCGE/University of London Institute of Education, pp. 165–178.

5542   Ostuni, J. (1994) 'The thematic map: learning a procedure: description' in Haubrich, H. (ed) *Europe and the World in Geographical Education (Geographiedidaktische Forschungen, Band 22)*. Nuremberg: IGUCGE, pp. 255–264.

5543   Ostuni, J. (1996) 'The decision mechanism: contribution to meaningful learning' in van der Zijpp, T., van der Schee, J. and Trimp, H. (eds) *Innovation in Geographical Education: Proceedings of the 28th International Geographical Congress Commission on Geographical Education*. Amsterdam: IGUCGE/Centrum voor Educatieve Geografie Vrije Universiteit Amsterdam, pp. 312–316.

5544   Schneider, H. J. (1974) 'Chile: geographers and the "road towards socialism"' in Brockie, W., Le Heron, R. and Stokes, E. (eds) *Proceedings of the IGU Regional Conference and Eighth New Zealand Geography Conference*. Palmerston North: New Zealand Geographical Society, pp. 377–380.

5545   Villalobos, N. S. and Igor, M. O. (1996) 'Dendroenergy of native forests in the south of Chile: a contribution of geography to environmental education' in van der Zijpp, T., van der Schee, J. and Trimp, H. (eds) *Innovation in Geographical Education: Proceedings of the 28th International Geographical Congress Commission on Geographical Education*. Amsterdam: IGUCGE/Centrum voor Educatieve Geografie Vrije Universiteit Amsterdam, pp. 165–167.

5546   Webb, G. (1986) 'Resources and practices in A-level geography education in Jamaica and England', *Caribbean Geography*, 2, 2, pp. 100–109.

5547   Webb, G. (1987) 'Factors affecting achievement in the University of Cambridge GCE A level geography examination in Jamaica', *Research in Education*, 38, pp. 17–26.

5548   Webb, G. and Brissett, B. (1986) 'The mental maps of Jamaican children: a case study', *Caribbean Journal of Education*, 13, 3, pp. 181–204.

5549   Zamorano de Montiel, G. L. (1994) 'The selection and fitness of curriculum geographical contents in the 21st century' in Haubrich, H. (ed) *Europe and the World in Geography Education (Geographiedidaktische Forschungen, Band 22)*. Nuremberg: IGUCGE, pp. 145–154.

5550   Zamorano de Montiel, G. L. (1996) 'The geography curriculum and its contents: preparing for the twenty-first century in Argentina geography education', *International Journal of Social Education*, 10, 2, pp. 53–60.

# 5. Africa

5551    Abba, S. B. (1988) *Some Aspects of the Dynamics of Curriculum Change in Geography with Special Reference to the Secondary School Geography in Borno State, Nigeria*, unpublished PhD thesis. University of Southampton.

5552    Abdel, K. (1984) *A Critical Account of Teaching Practice in Geography in Egypt*, unpublished PhD thesis. University of Durham.

5553    Acar, C. (1993) 'Environmental education in the primary school science curriculum in Uganda' in Hale, M. (ed) *Ecology in Education*. Cambridge: Cambridge University Press, pp. 1–9.

5554    Adara, O. A. (1996) 'Strategies of environmental education in social studies in Nigeria by the year 2000', *Environmental Education Research*, 2, 2, pp. 237–246.

5555    Adeyoyin, F. A. (1978) 'The threat of social studies to geography: real or imagined?', *Nigerian Geographical Journal*, 21, 2, pp. 179–185.

5556    Adejujigbe, O. (1970) 'Re-shaping high school geography in Nigeria', *Nigerian Geographical Journal*, 13, 1, pp. 89–94.

5557    Adjimoko, I. O. (1978) 'Geography in relation to other school subjects in Nigeria' in Okunrotifa, P. O. and Ola, D. K. (eds) *Commission on Geography in Education*. Ibadan: IGUCGE/University of Ibadan, pp. 118–127.

5558    Aiyepeku, W. O. (1973) 'Geographers as bibliographers', *Nigerian Geographical Journal*, 16, 2, pp. 177–181.

5559    Akande, M. O. (1982) 'Withdrawal from the geography class: a case study of the "push" and "pull" factors', *Nigerian Geographical Journal*, 25, 1/2, pp. 105–118.

5560    Akimbole, A. and Balogun, O. Y. (1980) 'Concept operationalization in high school geography: a challenge for effective teaching', *Nigerian Geographical Journal*, 23, 1/2, pp. 177–186.

5561    Anikweze, C. M. (1985/86) 'Teacher effectiveness: a necessary tool for improving the study of geography', *Nigerian Geographical Journal*, 28/29, 1/2, pp. 201–207.

5562    Areola, O. (1973) 'The teaching of aerial photography in secondary schools', *Nigerian Geographical Journal*, 16, 1, pp. 77–90.

5563    Areola, O. (1979) 'The importance of fieldwork in geographic education in Nigerian schools', *Nigerian Geographical Journal*, 22, 1, pp. 89–96.

5564    Ayoade, J. O. (1977) 'On the school weather station and the teaching of climatology in Nigeria high schools', *Nigerian Geographical Journal*, 20, 1, pp. 91–97.

5565    Ballantyne, R. (1982) 'Geography curriculum development: the need for school-based research', *South African Geographer*, 10, 1, pp. 73–76.

5566    Ballantyne, R. (1987/88) 'Graves' typology and geography in South Africa', *South African Geographer*, 15, 1/2, pp. 109–115.

5567    Ballantyne, R. and Oelofse, C. G. (1989) 'Implementing environmental education policy in South African schools', *South African Journal of Education*, 9, 1, pp. 7–12.

5568    Ballantyne, R. and Sparks, R. (1988) 'Assessment skills: the training of raters in geography education' in Gerber, R. and Lidstone, J. (eds) *Skills in Geographical Education Symposium '88, Volume 2*. Brisbane: IGUCGE/Jacaranda Press, pp. 355–363.

5569    Balogun, A. E. O. (1982) *The Dynamics of Geography Education: An Investigation into the Changing Concepts of Geography and the Implications for Geography Curriculum Planning in Nigerian Secondary Schools*, unpublished PhD thesis. University of Wales Cardiff.

5570    Baloucif, A. (1991) *A Survey of Geography Teaching in Algerian Secondary Education*, unpublished MLitt thesis. University of Glasgow.

5571    Dally, A. M. (1978) 'Sociological factors affecting geographic education in Nigeria' in Okunrotifa, P. O. and Ola, D. K. (eds) *Commission on Geography in Education*. Ibadan: IGUCGE/University of Ibadan, pp. 156–169.

5572    De Villiers, P. M. (1979) *A Comparative Study of the Development of Geography Teaching in Lesotho and Malawi*, unpublished MEd dissertation. University of Leeds.

5573    El Zubeir, Z. (1992) 'Intermediate level environmental education in Sudan: a proposal for a new programme', *Environmental Education and Information*, 11, 2, pp. 93–110.

5574    Fadare, J. A. (1984) 'Field excursions in the teaching of geography', *Nigerian Geographical Journal*, 27, 1/2, pp. 172–176.

5575    Fisher, W. B. (1971) 'Geography in contemporary education', *South African Geographical Journal*, 53, 1, pp. 10–17.

5576    Fitzgerald, M. (1990) 'Education for sustainable development: decision-making for environmental education in Ethiopia', *International Journal of Educational Development*, 10, 4, pp. 289–300.

5577    Henning, J. (1984) 'The curriculum and geography', *South African Geographical Journal,* 66, 1, pp. 3–15.

5578    High, C. and Richards, P. (1970) 'Some dynamic hardware models for teaching geography', *Nigerian Geographical Journal*, 13, 2, pp. 201–210.

5579    Kyagulanyi, E. (1988) 'The development of abilities and skills through the integrated geography syllabus in Uganda' in Gerber, R. and Lidstone, J. (eds) *Developing Skills in Geographical Education*. Brisbane: IGUCGE/Jacaranda Press, pp. 109–118.

5580    Kyagulanyi, E. (1988) 'In-service geographical education: the Ugandan experience' in Gerber, R. and Lidstone, J. (eds) *Skills in Geographical Education Symposium '88, Volume 2*. Brisbane: IGUCGE, pp. 398–409.

5581    Lincoln, D. (1979) 'Ideology and South African development geography', *South African Geographical Journal*, 61, 2, pp. 99–110.

5582    Lwanga-Lukwago, J. (1979) *An Investigation into the Development and Organisation of the Geographical Education and Training Curricula for Secondary School Geography Teachers in Nigeria*, unpublished MSc (Ed) dissertation. University of Southampton.

5583    Lwanga-Lukwago, J. (1982) *The Development of Territorial Decentration in Children: A Study of Piaget's Spatial Stages in Relation to the School Geography Curriculum in Kenya*, unpublished PhD thesis. University of Southampton.

5584    Mucunguzi, P. (1995) 'Environmental education in the formal section of education in Uganda', *Environmental Education Research*, 1, 2, pp. 233–240.

5585    Mucunguzi, P. (1995) 'A review of non-formal environmental education in Uganda', *Environmental Education Research*, 1, 3, pp. 337–344.

5586    Nicol, I. G. (1974) 'Geography teaching in the seventies', *South African Geographical Journal*, 56, 2, pp. 105–110.

5587    Oduaran, A. B. (1989) 'Education against environmental pollution in Nigeria', *Convergence*, 22, 4, pp. 55–62.

5588    Ogundana, B. (1978) 'The growth and contribution of the Nigerian Geographical Association', *Nigerian Geographical Journal*, 21, 1, pp. 25–30.

5589    Okoro, P. A. (1978) 'The teaching of geography in Nigerian primary schools' in Okunrotifa, P. O. and Ola, D. K. (eds) *Commission on Geography in Education*. Ibadan: IGUCGE/University of Ibadan, pp. 102–108.

5590    Okpala, J. (1980) 'Nigerian students' perception of and preference for forty countries of the world' in Slater, F. and Spicer, B. (eds) *Perception and Preference Studies at the International Level*. Tokyo: IGUCGE/AIP, pp. 147–159.

5591    Okpala, J. (1981) 'Academic ability of School Certificate geography students', *Nigerian Geographical Journal*, 24, 1/2, pp. 167–174.

5592    Okpala, J. (1984) 'Geography teacher education programmes in Nigerian universities and implications for secondary school geography' in Marsden, W. E. (ed) *Teacher Education Models in Geography: An International Comparison*. Kalamazoo, MI: IGUCGE/Western Michigan University, pp. 81–97.

5593    Okpala, J. (1988) 'Strategies employed in introducing "contour" in teaching situations and textbooks' in Gerber, R. and Lidstone, J. (eds) *Skills in Geographical Education Symposium '88, Volume 2*. Brisbane: IGUCGE, pp. 581–591.

5594    Okpala, J. (1988) 'Teaching styles in reading and interpreting topographical maps: the Nigerian experience' in Gerber, R. and Lidstone, J. (eds) *Developing Skills in Geographical Education*. Brisbane: IGUCGE/Jacaranda Press, pp. 31–38.

5595    Okpala, J. (1988) 'Research in geographical education in Nigeria from 1981 to 1986' in Gerber, R. and Lidstone, J. (eds) *Developing Skills in Geographical Education*. Brisbane: IGUCGE/Jacaranda Press pp. 298–308.

5596    Okpala, J. (1992) 'Geography education beyond the western world: a case study of Nigeria' in Naish, M. (ed) *Geography and Education: National and International Perspectives*. London: University of London Institute of Education, pp. 276–290.

5597    Okpala, J. (1996) 'Concept mapping in geographical education in Nigeria: from theory into practice' in van der Schee, J., Schoenmaker, G., Trimp, H. and van Westrhenen, H. (eds) *Innovation in Geographical Education (Netherlands Geographical Studies, 208)*. Utrecht/Amsterdam: IGUCGE/Centrum voor Educatieve Geografie Vrije Universiteit Amsterdam, pp. 103–110.

5598    Okpala, J. (1996) 'Perceptions of appropriate geography curriculum for the twenty-first century Nigerian citizen', *International Journal of Social Education*, 10, 2, pp. 86–94.

5599    Okpala, J., Nwagu, E., Ezeudu, A. and Ugwuda, S. (1996) 'Effect of concept mapping on academic achievement and attitude in geography' in van der Zijpp, T., van der Schee, J. and Trimp, H. (eds) *Innovation in Geographical Education: Proceedings of the 28th International Geographical Congress Commission on Geographical Education*. Amsterdam: IGUCGE/Centrum voor Educatieve Geografie Vrije Universiteit Amsterdam, pp. 69–73.

5600    Okpalanma, L. O. (1978) 'Training teachers for geography in Nigeria' in Okunrotifa, P. O. and Ola, D. K. (eds) *Commission on Geography in Education*. Ibadan: IGUCGE, pp. 139–149.

5601    Okunrotifa, P. O. (1971) 'The aims and objectives of geographical education', *Nigerian Geographical Journal*, 14, 2, pp. 221–230.

5602  Okunrotifa, P. O. (1974) 'The performance of Nigerian pupils in a programmed unit in geography', *African Journal of Educational Research*, 74, pp. 43–52.

5603  Okunrotifa, P. O. (1974) 'A study of geography teaching in some Welsh secondary schools', *Nigerian Geographical Journal*, 17, 2, pp. 165–174.

5604  Okunrotifa, P. O. (1976) 'Student perception of teacher style: Nigeria' in Stoltman, J. (ed) *International Research in Geographical Education*. Kalamazoo, MI: IGUCGE/University of Western Michigan, pp. 181–193.

5605  Okunrotifa, P. O. (1978) 'A review of geographic education in Nigerian schools' in Okunrotifa, P. O. and Ola, D. K. (eds) *Commission on Geography in Education*. Ibadan: IGUCGE/University of Ibadan, pp. 26–37.

5606  Okunrotifa, P. O. (1982) 'Gathering information' in Graves, N. (ed) *New UNESCO Source Book for Geography Teaching*. Harlow/Paris: Longman/UNESCO Press, pp. 141–168.

5607  Okunrotifa, P. O. (1982) 'Processing information' in Graves, N. (ed) *New UNESCO Source Book for Geography Teaching*. Harlow/Paris: Longman/UNESCO Press, pp. 169–205.

5608  Onasanya, K. (1987/88) 'Improving the quality of instruction through mastery learning strategy: an example of geography teaching', *Nigerian Geographical Journal*, 30/31, 1/2, pp. 159–168.

5609  Phiri, F. (1988) 'Geography, decision making and socio-economic development issues in Zambia' in Gerber, R. and Lidstone, J. (eds) *Developing Skills in Geographic Education*. Brisbane: IGUCGE/Jacaranda Press, pp. 172–178.

5610  Preston-Whyte, R. A. (1983) 'Environmentalism in geography: the missing link', *South African Geographical Journal*, 65, 1, pp. 2–12.

5611  Ramutsindela, M. F. (1995) 'Global scale challenges in the teaching of geography' in Lidstone, J., Romanova, E., and Kondakov, A. (eds) *Global Change and Geographical Education*. Brisbane/Moscow: IGUCGE/Queensland University of Technology/Moscow State University, pp. 37–44.

5612  Renshaw, P. H. (1979) *The Perception of Atlas Maps: A Preliminary Investigation among Secondary School Pupils in Botswana*, unpublished MSc (Ed) dissertation. University of Southampton.

5613  Sada, P. O. (1983) 'Geography in Nigeria: perspective and prospects: a presidential address', *Nigerian Geographical Journal*, 26, 1/2, pp. 1–14.

5614  Sarpong, E. (1994) 'Some aspects of geography education in Transkei', *Geographical Education*, 7, 2, pp. 47–51.

5615  Smit, M. J. (1994) 'Geography education in the school curriculum for a new South Africa: a country in transition' in Haubrich, H. (ed) *Europe and the World in Geography Education (Geographiedidaktische Forschungen, Band 22)*. Nuremberg: IGUCGE, pp. 171–178.

5616  Smit, T. (1994) 'School geography in a new South Africa' in Haubrich, H. (ed) *Europe and the World in Geography Education (Geographiedidaktische Forschungen, Band 22)*. Nuremberg: IGUCGE, pp. 179–186.

5617  Smit, T. (1994) 'Topographical maps as teaching aid: an elementary approach at secondary level' in Haubrich, H. (ed) *Europe and the World in Geography Education (Geographiedidaktische Forschungen, Band 22)*. Nuremberg: IGUCGE, pp. 247–254.

5618    Smith, K. (1993) 'Creating a climate for conservation in West Africa' in Hale, M. (ed) *Ecology in Education*. Cambridge: Cambridge University Press, pp. 179–188.

5619    Spicer, B. (1980) 'The view of the countries in which South African students would most prefer to live and to holiday' in Slater, F. and Spicer, B. (eds) *Perception and Preference Studies at the International Level*. Tokyo: IGUCGE/AIP, pp. 174–183.

5620    Stander, E. (1970) 'South African geography: trends and prospects', *South African Geographical Journal*, 52, 1, pp. 3–12.

5621    Tait, N. (1994) 'Perceptual differences of geographical concepts by schoolchildren' in Haubrich, H. (ed) *Europe and the World in Geography Education (Geographiedidaktische Forschungen, Band 22)*. Nuremberg: IGUCGE, pp. 207–216.

5622    Tait, N. (1996) 'Geography education in a post-apartheid society', *International Journal of Social Education*, 10, 2, pp. 73–85.

5623    van Hermelen, U. and Irwin, P. (1995) 'Challenging geography: a South African perspective', *Geographical Education*, 8, 3, pp. 35–38.

5624    Wellings, P. (1983) 'Penetrating the frontiers: the geography of Third World education', *South African Geographical Journal*, 65, 2, pp. 87–110.

5625    Wilkinson, H. (1971) 'Some problems of teaching geography in the Zambian bush', *Geography*, 56, 4, pp. 311–314.

5626    Willatts, R. M. (1975) 'Educational aspects of geographical fieldwork in Kenya', *Geography*, 60, 1, pp. 59–62.

# 6. Asia

5627    Aggarval, U. (1988) 'Planning a geography curriculum for Indian schools' in Gerber, R. and Lidstone, J. (eds) *Skills in Geographical Education Symposium '88, Volume 2*. Brisbane: IGUCGE, pp. 469–476.

5628    Albarracin, N. B. (1975) 'Geography and its relevance to educational programs and economic development', *Philippines Geographical Journal*, 19, 4, pp. 175–185.

5629    Ang, S. H. (1985) *Curriculum Development in Geographical Education in England and Singapore*, unpublished MA (Ed) dissertation. University of Southampton.

5630    Anonymous (1988) 'Proposed bill to Congress re geography teaching as a separate subject in the primary and secondary schools', *Philippines Geographical Journal*, 32, 1, pp. 42–43.

5631    Asakura, R. (1984) 'Research methods in geographical education in Japan' in Graves, N. (ed) *Research and Research Methods in Geographical Education*. London: IGUCGE/University of London Institute of Education, pp. 215–221.

5632    Bar-Gal, Y. (1984) '"There are no butterflies here": an inter-cultural experiment in landscape perception' in Haubrich, H. (ed) *Perception of People and Places through Media, Volume 1*. Freiburg: IGUCGE/Pädagogische Hochschule Freiburg, pp. 386–400.

5633    Bar-Gal, Y. (1984) 'Writing textbooks of regional geography' in Haubrich, H. (ed) *Perception of People and Places through Media, Volume 2*. Freiburg: IGUCGE/Pädagogische Hochschule Freiburg, pp. 594–614.

5634    Bar-Gal, Y. (1993) 'Geographical teaching in Israel: a retrospective view', *Journal of Geography*, 92, 2, pp. 64–68.

5635    Bar-Gal, Y. (1994) 'The image of the "Palestinian" in geography textbooks in Israel', *Journal of Geography*, 93, 5, pp. 224–233.

5636    Bar-Gal, Y. (1996) 'Ideological propaganda in maps and geographical education' in van der Schee, J., Schoenmaker, G., Trimp, H. and van Westrhenen, H. (eds) *Innovation in Geographical Education (Netherlands Geographical Studies, 208)*. Utrecht/Amsterdam: IGUCGE/Centrum voor Educatieve Geografie Vrije Universiteit Amsterdam, pp. 67–78.

5637    Chan Ka-ki (1997) 'Geography teachers in Hong Kong: trends, contexts and dilemmas', *Geographical Education*, 10, pp. 22–28.

5638    Chao Chen (1988) 'School map compilation in China' in Gerber, R. and Lidstone, J. (eds) *Skills in Geographical Education Symposium '88*. Brisbane: IGUCGE, pp. 605–608.

5639    Chengdu, C. (1990) 'Environmental education in China', *Environmental Education and Information*, 9, 2, pp. 73–78.

5640    Chu, S. K. (1976) 'Hong Kong students' perceptions of secondary geography teachers' classroom style' in Stoltman, J. (ed) *International Research in Geographical Education*. Kalamazoo, MI: IGUCGE/University of Western Michigan, pp. 195–210.

5641    Das, H. P. (1972) 'Teaching geography as a science subject in schools', *Geographical Review of India*, 34, 1, pp. 93–96.

5642    Dasgupta, N. and Ghosh, S. (1988) 'The curriculum and textbooks on economic geography', *Geographical Review of India*, 50, 2, pp. 81–82.

5643    Fien, J. and Corcoran, P. B. (1996) 'Learning for a sustainable environment: professional development and teacher education in environmental education in the Asia–Pacific region', *Environmental Education Research*, 2, 2, pp. 227–237.

5644    Fung Yee-wang (1988) 'Civic education through geography' in Gerber, R. and Lidstone, J. (eds) *Developing Skills in Geographical Education*. Brisbane: IGUCGE/Jacaranda Press, pp. 156–163.

5645    Fung Yee-wang (1992) 'The development of geographical education in Hong Kong and China (1949–1988): a comparative study' in Hill, A. D. (ed) *International Perspectives on Geographical Education*. Boulder, CO/Skokie, IL: IGUCGE/Rand, McNally and Co., pp. 51–62.

5646    Garsole, S. G. (1984) 'The impact of British geographical writings on school textbooks in Marathi: Maharashtra (India)' in Haubrich, H. (ed) *Perception of People and Places through Media, Volume 2*. Freiburg: IGUCGE/Pädagogische Hochschule Freiburg, pp. 644–655.

5647    Gonzales, J. X. (1973) 'The great outdoors is the laboratory in the study of geography', *Philippines Geographical Journal*, 17, 3/4, pp. 77–82.

5648    Gough, S. (1995) 'Environmental education in a region of rapid economic development: the case of Sarawak', *Environmental Education Research*, 1, 3, pp. 327–336.

5649    Gunterman, B. and van Meegan, J. (1996) 'Geography for a better world: experiencing schools in Turkey' in van der Zijpp, T., van der Schee, J. and Trimp, H. (eds) *Innovation in Geographical Education: Proceedings of the 28th International Geographical Congress Commission on Geographical Education*. Amsterdam: IGUCGE/Centrum voor Educatieve Geografie Vrije Universiteit Amsterdam, pp. 24–26.

5650 Hellens, R. (1979) 'Teaching geography in Japanese schools', *Teaching Geography*, 5, 2, pp. 88–90.

5651 Hwang, M. (1992) 'Geography teacher education in Korea: curricula in geography education departments' in Hill, A. D. (ed) *International Perspectives on Geographical Education*. Boulder, CO/Skokie, IL: IGUCGE/Rand, McNally and Co., pp. 77–82.

5652 Imahori, K. (1984) 'Environmental education in Japan', *Environmental Education and Information*, 3, 1, pp. 61–72.

5653 Kwan, T. Yim-lin (1996) 'Children and mapping: their intuitive experience in a familiar environment' in van der Zijpp, T., van der Schee, J. and Trimp, H. (eds) *Innovation in Geographical Education: Proceedings of the 28th International Geographical Congress Commission on Geographical Education*. Amsterdam: IGUCGE/Centrum voor Educatieve Geografie Vrije Universiteit Amsterdam, pp. 64–68.

5654 Kwan, T. Yim-lin and Lee, J. Chi-kin (1994) 'A reflective report on an action research towards understanding conceptions of action research held by geography teachers' in Haubrich, H. (ed) *Europe and the World in Geography Education (Geographiedidaktische Forschungen, Band 22)*. Nuremberg: IGUCGE, pp. 387–406.

5655 Lai Kwok-chan (1996) 'Revisiting fieldwork: difference between intention and practice', *Geographical Education*, 9, 1996, pp. 44–48.

5656 Lai Kwok-chan (1996) 'Understanding student teachers' experiences of geographical fieldwork' in van der Zijpp, T., van der Schee, J. and Trimp, H. (eds) *Innovation in Geographical Education: Proceedings of the 28th International Geographical Congress Commission on Geographical Education*. Amsterdam: IGUCGE/Centrum voor Educatieve Geografie Vrije Universiteit Amsterdam, pp. 136–140.

5657 Lam Chi-chung (1988) 'Problems of new town development: using values in geography lessons' in Gerber, R. and Lidstone, J. (eds) *Developing Skills in Geographical Education*. Brisbane: IGUCGE/Jacaranda Press, pp. 27–30.

5658 Lam Chi-chung (1996) 'The new junior secondary school geography curriculum in Hong Kong: the impact of 1997' in van der Zijpp, T., van der Schee, J. and Trimp, H. (eds) *Innovation in Geographical Education: Proceedings of the 28th International Geographical Congress Commission on Geographical Education*. Amsterdam: IGUCGE/Centrum voor Educatieve Geografie Vrije Universiteit Amsterdam, pp. 292–296.

5659 Lee, C. Kim-eng (1996) 'Using cooperative learning with computers in geography classrooms' in van der Schee, J., Schoenmaker, G., Trimp, H. and van Westrhenen, H. (eds) *Innovation in Geographical Education (Netherlands Geographical Studies, 208)*. Utrecht/Amsterdam: IGUCGE/Centrum voor Educatieve Geografie Vrije Universiteit Amsterdam, pp. 137–143.

5660 Lee, J. Chi-kin (1993) 'Geography teaching in England and Hong Kong: contributions towards environmental education', *IRGEE*, 2, 1, pp. 25–40.

5661 Lee, J. Chi-kin (1994) 'Environmental education through geography in Hong Kong', *Geographical Education*, 7, 2, pp. 34–41.

5662 Lee, J. Chi-kin (1996) 'Geography teachers' receptivity to environmental education in Hong Kong' in van der Zijpp, T., van der Schee, J. and Trimp, H. (eds) *Innovation in Geographical Education: Proceedings of the 28th International Geographical Congress Commission on Geographical Education*. Amsterdam: IGUCGE/Centrum voor Educatieve Geografie Vrije Universiteit Amsterdam, pp. 141–145.

5663    Lee, J. Chi-kin (1996) 'A study of environmental attitudes and concepts of geography student teachers: implications for teacher education', *IRGEE*, 5, 3, pp. 154–171.

5664    Lee, R. (1983) 'Why do a geography degree?: the choice of geography in higher education', *Philippines Geographical Journal*, 27, 1/2, pp. 1–36.

5665    Liaw, B. T. (1988) 'Effects of practical experience and sequential skills in map reading' in Gerber, R. and Lidstone, J. (eds) *Developing Skills in Geographical Education*. Brisbane: IGUCGE/Jacaranda Press, pp. 80–83.

5666    Lu, J. L. (1992) 'China's geographic education' in Hill, A. D. (ed) *International Perspectives on Geographical Education*. Boulder, CO/Skokie, IL: IGUCGE/Rand, McNally and Co., pp. 63–76.

5667    Nakayama, S. (1988) 'The current state of in-service training of geography teachers in Hiroshima prefecture, Japan' in Gerber, R. and Lidstone, J. (eds) *Developing Skills in Geographical Education*. Brisbane: IGUCGE/Jacaranda Press, pp. 253–255.

5668    Nakayama, S. (1996) 'The development of teaching materials of geography: an experience in the US–Japan joint project' in van der Zijpp, T., van der Schee, J. and Trimp, H. (eds) *Innovation in Geographical Education: Proceedings of the 28th International Geographical Congress Commission on Geographical Education*. Amsterdam: IGUCGE/Centrum voor Educatieve Geografie Vrije Universiteit Amsterdam, pp. 26–30.

5669    Nakayama, S. (1996) 'The new era of geography education in Japan', *International Journal of Social Education*, 10, 2, pp. 22–26.

5670    Nakayama, S. (1997) 'Problems and prospects of pre-service training of geography teachers in Japan' in Convey, A. and Nolzen, H. (eds) *Geography and Education (Münchner Studien zur Didaktik der Geographie, Band 10)*. Munich: Lehrstuhl für Didaktik der Geographie der Universität München, pp. 209–220.

5671    Nakayama, S., Wada, F. and the **Hiroshima Geographic Alliance** (1992) 'Geographic education in Japan: a new perspective' in Hill, A. D. (ed) *International Perspectives on Geographical Education*. Boulder, CO/Skokie, IL: IGUCGE/Rand, McNally and Co., pp. 83–88.

5672    Nam, S.-J. (1995) 'Environmental education in primary and secondary schools in Korea: current developments and future agendas', *Environmental Education Research*, 1, 1, pp. 109–122.

5673    Oi, E. W. M. and **Stimpson, P.** (1994) 'Teaching styles of Hong Kong's environmental educators in secondary schools', *Research in Education*, 52, pp. 1–12.

5674    Salita, D. C. (1976) 'Geography: the core of environmental education', *Philippines Geographical Journal*, 20, 3, pp. 87–93.

5675    Salita, D. C. (1979) 'Geography and environmental education', *Philippines Geographical Journal*, 23, 3, pp. 89–94.

5676    Salita, D. C. (1983) 'Geographic education in relation to map making and map reading', *Philippines Geographical Journal*, 27, 1/2, pp. 41–43.

5677    Salita, D. C. (1990) 'Why geography should be taught as a separate subject', *Philippines Geographical Journal*, 34, 3, pp. 135–140.

5678    Seong, K. T. (1996) 'Interactive multimedia and GIS applications for teaching school geography', *IRGEE*, 5, 3, pp. 205–212.

5679 **Shen, J.** (1994) 'Ideological management in textbooks: a study of the changing image of the United States in China's geography textbooks', *Theory and Research in Social Education*, 22, 2, pp. 194–213.

5680 **Singh, C. P.** (1982) 'Managing resources for learning' in Graves, N. (ed) *New UNESCO Source Book for Geography Teaching*. Harlow/Paris: Longman/UNESCO Press, pp. 255–271.

5681 **Soerjani, M.** (1993) 'Ecological concepts as a basis for environmental education in Indonesia' in Hale, M. (ed) *Ecology in Education*. Cambridge: Cambridge University Press, pp. 145–160.

5682 **Speak, C.** (1984) 'Textbook types and their impact' in Haubrich, H. (ed) *Perception of People and Places through Media, Volume 2*. Freiburg: IGUCGE/Pädagogische Hochschule Freiburg, pp. 615–619.

5683 **Speak, C.** (1988) 'Children's conceptual development through their drawings' in Gerber, R. and Lidstone, J. (eds) *Skills in Geographical Education Symposium '88, Volume 1*. Brisbane: IGUCGE, pp. 112–125.

5684 **Spicer, B.** (1980) 'The Singaporeans' view of the world' in Slater, F. and Spicer, B. (eds) *Perception and Preference Studies at the International Level*. Tokyo: IGUCGE/AIP, pp. 160–173.

5685 **Stimpson, P.** (1986) 'The development of computer assisted learning (CAL) in Hong Kong' in Kent, A. (ed) *The Use of Computers in the Teaching of Geography*. London: IGUCGE/University of London Institute of Education, pp. 193–210.

5686 **Stimpson, P.** (1988) 'Assessment-led curriculum development in geography: a case study from Hong Kong' in Gerber, R. and Lidstone, J. (eds) *Skills in Geographical Education Symposium '88, Volume 1*. Brisbane: IGUCGE, pp. 205–213.

5687 **Stimpson, P.** (1988) 'Questionnaire surveys in geography education research: some problems and possible solutions' in Gerber, R. and Lidstone, J. (eds) *Developing Skills in Geographical Education*. Brisbane: IGUCGE/Jacaranda Press, pp. 339–343.

5688 **Stimpson, P.** (1994) 'The relationship between the intended and the implemented curriculum and the issue of teaching style' in Haubrich, H. (ed) *Europe and the World in Geography Education (Geographiedidaktische Forschungen, Band 22)*. Nuremberg: IGUCGE, pp. 331–338.

5689 **Stimpson, P.** (1997) 'Environmental education in Hong Kong and Guangzhou: one purpose, two systems', *Compare*, 27, 1, pp. 63–74.

5690 **Sun Da-wen** (1988) 'A personal view of the designing of geography curriculum plans in middle school' in Gerber, R. and Lidstone, J. (eds) *Skills in Geographical Education Symposium, Volume 2*. Brisbane: IGUCGE, pp. 537–550.

5691 **Tilbury, D.** (1997) 'Teaching geography about and for sustainable development in Hong Kong', *Geographical Education*, 10, pp. 53–56.

5692 **Velazco, G.** (1996) 'Effects of environmental values education on environmental orientation of children' in van der Zijpp, T., van der Schee, J. and Trimp, H. (eds) *Innovation in Geographical Education: Proceedings of the 28th International Geographical Congress Commission on Geographical Education*. Amsterdam: IGUCGE/Centrum voor Educatieve Geografie Vrije Universiteit Amsterdam, pp. 160–164.

5693    Wang Liang-huew (1978) 'Some thoughts on the teaching of urban economic geography in developing countries', *Philippines Geographical Journal*, 22, 4, pp. 186–196.

5694    Wong, J. Yuk-yong (1996) 'Geographic Information Systems education in the Asia-Pacific area', *IRGEE*, 5, 3, pp. 196–198.

5695    Wong, J. Yuk-yong (1996) 'Will Geographic Information Systems (GIS) have a greater impact on geography education in Singapore, Malaysia and Thailand in the future?', *IRGEE*, 5, 3, pp. 220–224.

5696    Xie Kun-qing (1996) 'GIS education in China', *IRGEE*, 5, 3, pp. 217–219.

5697    Xuan, S. (1994) 'Linguistic–symbolic study and geographical education' in Haubrich, H. (ed) *Europe and the World in Geography Education (Geographiedidaktische Forschungen, Band 22)*. Nuremberg: IGUCGE, pp. 265–284.

5698    Xuan, S. (1996) 'Human geography: the focus of the innovation in geographical education in the People's Republic of China' in van der Zijpp, T., van der Schee, J. and Trimp, H. (eds) *Innovation in Geographical Education: Proceedings of the 28th International Geographical Congress Commission on Geographical Education*. Amsterdam: IGUCGE/Centrum voor Educatieve Geografie Vrije Universiteit Amsterdam, pp. 361–364.

5699    Xuan, S. (1996) 'Meaningful learning in geographical education' in van der Schee, J., Schoenmaker, G., Trimp, H. and van Westrhenen, H. (eds) *Innovation in Geographical Education (Netherlands Geographical Studies, 208)*. Utrecht/Amsterdam: IGUCGE/Centrum voor Educatieve Geografie Vrije Universiteit Amsterdam, pp. 79–90.

5700    Yau, B. and Fung Yee-wang (1988) 'An analysis of geography questions in the Hong Kong Certificate of Education examinations since 1970' in Gerber, R. and Lidstone, J. (eds) *Skills in Geographical Education Symposium '88, Volume 1*. Brisbane: IGUCGE, pp. 341–351.

5701    Yee Sze-onn (1988) 'Continuing education of geography teachers: the Singapore experience' in Gerber, R. and Lidstone, J. (eds) *Skills in Geographical Education Symposium '88, Volume 2*. Brisbane: IGUCGE, pp. 454–466.

5702    Yee Sze-onn (1997) 'Make a joyful noise: teaching geography through songs', *Geographical Education*, 10, pp. 57–60.

5703    Yeung, S. Pui-ming (1995) 'Environmental consciousness and geography teaching in Hong Kong: an empirical study', *International Journal of Environmental Education and Information*, 14, 2, pp. 171–194.

5704    Yeung, S. Pui-ming (1996) 'Teaching environmental issues in school geography: the Hong Kong experience', *IRGEE*, 5, 2, pp. 117–130.

5705    Yoshida, M. (1993) 'The present status of environmental education in Japan' in Hale, M. (ed) *Ecology in Education*. Cambridge: Cambridge University Press, pp. 161–166.

5706    Zhang, L.-S. and Huang, Y. (1997) 'The development of the research in geographical education in China' in Convey, A. and Nolzen, H. (eds) *Geography and Education (Münchner Studien zur Didaktik der Geographie, Band 10)*. Munich: Lehrstuhl für Didaktik der Geographie der Universität München, pp. 303–309.

5707    Zhang Ya-nam (1996) 'Geography standards for China: new dimensions for geography teaching', *International Journal of Social Education*, 10, 2, pp. 95–105.

5708   Zhu Di-chen (1996) 'Combine the teaching of the course of geography with the geographical condition in the locality' in van der Zijpp, T., van der Schee, J. and Trimp, H. (eds) *Innovation in Geographical Education: Proceedings of the 28th International Geographical Congress Commission on Geographical Education.* Amsterdam: IGUCGE/Centrum voor Educatieve Geografie Vrije Universiteit Amsterdam, pp. 257–259.

# INDEX OF AUTHORS' NAMES

Abba, S. B.  5551

Abbett, J.  3175

Abdel, K.  5552

Abler, R.  3058

Acar, C.  5553

Acheson, D. A.  3526

Acredolo, L. P.  2480

Adamczyk, P.  4004

Adams, A.  3949

Adams, E.  4992, 4993, 4994, 4995, 4996

Adams, J. S.  3058

Adams, K.  3382

Adara, O. A.  5554

Adejujigbe, O.  5556

Adeyoyin, F. A.  5555

Adjimoko, I. O.  5557

Aerni, K.  5026

Agar, N.  4997

Aggarval, U.  5627

Agyeman, J.  4582

Ahier, J.  2145, 3527, 4583

Ahmad, A.  2117

Aho, L.  4584

Aiyepeku, W. O.  5558

Akande, M. O.  5559

Akimbole, A.  5560

Albarracin, N. B.  5628

Albrecht, V.  5027, 5028

Aldrich-Moodie, B.  4585

Alen, J.  2912

Alexopoulos, I.  5055

Al-Ghasm, A. M. A.  4327

Allchin, A.  3009, 3010

Allen, G. L.  2458

Altman, H.  4877, 5498

Altman, I.  4586, 5279

Ambrose, L.  2860

Ambrose, P. J.  2146

Amlund, J. T.  2457

Andain, I.  3950

Andersen, H. P.  5029

Anderson, J.  3447, 5280

Anderson, S.  4587

Andrew, J.  4588

Andrews, R.  4589

Andrews, S. K.  2506, 2815, 5281

Ang, S. H.  5629

Angier, N. Q.  2598

Anikweze, C. M.  5561

Anonymous  5630

Anooshian, L. J.  2599, 2600

Anson, R.  4460

Archer, J. E.  4028

Areola, O.  5562, 5563

Armstrong, L.  5379

Arnfield, S. B.  4590

Arnold, P.  2601

Arnold, R.  3383

Aron, R. H.  2602, 2663

Asakura, R.  5631

Ash, S.  3121

Aspinall, S.  4029

Astles, A.  3011

Atkins, C. L.  5282

Atkinson, J.  3528, 4158

Audigier, F.  4219

Audley, R. J.  2553

Australian Geography Teachers' Association  5142

Awolola, M. D.  4552

Ayoade, J. O.  5564

Bachiorri, A.  4591

Bacon, P.  5283

Baczala, K.  4592

Baez, A. V.  4593

Bailey, P.  2000, 2001, 2147, 2148, 2301, 2302, 2303, 2342, 2343, 2344, 2345, 2459, 2782, 2861, 2949, 2950, 2951, 3269, 3286, 3287, 3620, 3717, 3722, 3841, 3951, 3952, 3953, 4030, 4031, 4033, 4053, 4054, 4055, 4056, 4082, 4461

Bainbridge, K.  3725

Baines, J.  4903

Baird, J. C.  4785, 5427

Bak, N.  4594

Baker, E.  4728

Baker, R. R.  2603

Bakshi, T. S.  4595, 5284

Balchin, W.  2149, 2460, 3448

Balderstone, D.  2604, 3726

Bale, J.  2002, 2003, 2346, 2755, 2913, 3357, 4124, 4125, 4159, 4328, 4398, 4462, 4502

Ball, J.  3954, 5285

Ballantyne, R.  3727, 4596, 4597, 4598, 4599, 5143, 5144, 5565, 5566, 5567, 5568

Balling, J. D.  3308

Balogun, A. E. O.  5569

Balogun, O. Y.  5560

Baloucif, A.  5570

Bamber, C.  2897, 3384

Banks, J. A.  2862

Banks, V.  2713, 3337, 3955

Bar, V.  2605

Barber, J. A. H.  3649

Barber, L.  3288

Barff, R.  3059

Bar-Gal, Y.  5632, 5633, 5634, 5635, 5636

Barker, E.  2004

Barnett, M.  3650, 3651, 3652

Barnett, S. 3956, 4998

Barratt, R. 3385

Barrell, G. V. 3410

Barret, M. 4244, 4278

Barrett, H. 4137

Barron, A. 4543

Barrs, D. 4100, 4329, 4384, 4904, 5286

Barth, J. 5030

Bartlett, L. 5145

Bartz, B. S. 3621, 5287, 5414

Bassnett, J. 3728

Batchelor, R. J. 2606

Bateman, D. 3894, 3957

Batterham, D. 2607, 4600

Battersby, J. 2005, 2783, 2952, 3122

Baxter, J. 2067

Bayliss, D. G. 3436

Beal, W. K. 4601

Beasley, K. 4220

Beatty, W. W. 2608, 4160

Beddis, R. 2150, 3123, 3124, 3270, 3510

Bednarz, R. S. 5288, 5289

Bednarz, S. W. 5288, 5290, 5291, 5292, 5293, 5294

Bein, F. L. 2839, 5365

Bell, G. H. 3511, 4221, 4222, 4223, 4224

Bell, S. 4896

Bellamy, M. P. 3895

Belonso, B. 5031

Benayas, J. 5032

Bennett, J. 5033

Bennett, S. 3529

Bennetts, T. 2304, 2347, 2348, 2349, 2784, 2785, 2786, 2787, 2953

Benneworth, L. 3587

Bentley, J. 3289, 3449, 3797

Benwell, J. F. N. 2914, 2954

Berkowitz, A. R. 4602

Bernadin, J.-M. 5034

Berry, D. 3290

Bettis, N. C. 5295

Beveridge, S. 2859

Biddle, D. S. 2151, 3729, 5146, 5147, 5148, 5149, 5150, 5151, 5152, 5153, 5154

Biddulph, M. 4079

Biilmann, O. 2068, 4225, 4279, 4321, 5035, 5036, 5211

Bilham-Boult, A. 3291, 3653

Billett, S. 2461

Billimore, B. 4603

Bilski, R. 3125

Binns, J. A. 4280

Binns, T. 2152, 2153, 2154, 2155, 2156, 2303, 2333, 4004, 4330, 4399

Birchall, P. 4463

Birkenhauer, J. 5037, 5038

Birkill, S. 3126

Birmingham Development Education Centre 4101, 4331

Bisard, W. J. 2602

Blachford, K. R. 2863, 2864, 4905, 5155

Black, H. D. 3730

Black, S. 4503

Blackwell, M. 4226

Blades, M. 2462, 2463, 2464, 2465, 2466, 2467, 2468, 2469, 2470, 2471, 2472, 2473, 2474, 2475, 2520, 2568, 2569, 2687, 2688, 3411, 3423

Bland, K. 2350, 2609, 3292

Blatch, Baroness 2351

Blaut, A. S. 2478, 5298

Blaut, J. M. 2476, 2477, 2478, 2479, 2610, 5296, 5297, 5298, 5299, 5300

Bleasdale, S. 2746, 3114

Bloomer, G. 4543

Bloomfield, P. 3358, 3450, 3482, 3483, 3484, 3485, 3486

Bluestein, N. 2480

Blyth, A. 2006, 2007, 2352, 2915, 3221, 3222, 3223, 3224, 3225, 3226, 3519, 3798, 3799, 3958, 3959, 3960

Blyth, J. 2008

Board, C. 2481

Boardman, D. 2009, 2010, 2157, 2158, 2159, 2160, 2161, 2305, 2353, 2482, 2483, 2484, 2485, 2756, 2816, 2817, 2818, 2955, 3127, 3128, 3129, 3130, 3131, 3271, 3272, 3293, 3451, 3622, 3623, 3624, 3625, 3896, 4005, 4162, 4177, 4906

Boden, P. 2011, 2956, 3530, 3531, 4400

Boehm, R. G. 5301, 5302, 5303

Bogdin, D. F. R. 2611

Bohn, D. 3532, 5039

Bolam, D. W. 3961

Bolscho, D. 5040

Bolton, T. 3294

Bolwell, L. H. 4604, 4605, 4764

Bondi, L. 2101, 2102, 2103, 3060

Böök, A. 2499, 2629

Booth, M. 2819

Booth, R. 4606

Boots, B. 3061

Boschhuizen, R. 4607

Boutard, A. 5454

Bowden, D. 3359, 3491

Bowen, P. 3533, 4332, 4333

Bowers, C. A. 4608, 5304

Bowlby, S. 4161, 4609

Bowler, I. 3897

Bowles, R. 2012, 2788, 2916, 2917, 3295, 3360, 3452, 3492, 3520, 3800

Boyes, E. 2607, 2612, 2613, 2614, 2615, 2634, 2670, 4600, 4610, 4611, 4612, 4613, 4700, 4828, 4831

Bradbeer, J. 3062

Bradford, M. 2104, 2105, 2106, 2107, 2108, 2109, 2110, 2138, 3012, 3013, 3063, 3898

Brady, B. M. 5041

Braham, M. 4614

Brainerd, J. W. 4615

Bramley, W. 3064, 4057

Bramwell, J. 4163

Brenchley, D. L. 4979

Brenchley, S. 3132

Brennan, A. 4616

Briceno, S. 4617

Bridges, D. 4401

Brierley, J. 5301

Briggs, K. 3296, 4087

Brijker, M. 5042

Brinkman, F. G. 4607, 4618

Brissett, B. 5548

Brock, C. 2111

Bromley, R. D. 3065

Brook, D. L. 2162

Brook, G. A. 2162

Brooker-Gross, S. R. 3058, 4126, 4138, 4164

Brough, E. 3962

Brown, A. 4004

Brown, B. 3066, 4058

Brown, C. 2306

Brown, E. H. 3067

Brown, L. 4619

Brown, M. 3963

Brown, M. R. 4620, 4621

Brown, P. 4776, 5101

Brown, P. J. B. 2112

Brown, R. H. 3014

Brown, S. 2957, 3654

Brunn, S. D. 4059

Brunsden, D. 3297, 4907

Bryan, P. E. 2163

Bryant, L. 5156

Bryson, J. 3068

Buchert, B. 5379

Buckingham-Hatfield, S. 3069

Buggey, J.-A. 5305

Bull, G. B. G. 3298, 4032

Bull, P. 2721, 3075, 4468

Bull, R. 3512

Bunce, V. 2307, 2958, 3964

Burden, J. 2354, 3176

Burdett, F. 2109, 2110, 2113

Burgess, H. 3385

Burke, M. 4060

Burkill, S. 3655

Burnley, J. 4385

Burt, T. 4006

Burtenshaw, D. 3015, 3899, 3900

Burton, M. St J. W. 3626

Butler, D. 5157

Butt, G. 2355, 2356, 2357, 2616, 2714, 2715, 2716, 2757, 2865, 2959, 3016, 3017, 3018, 3019, 3534, 3554, 3588, 3731, 3732, 3775, 3815, 3816, 3817, 3818, 3819, 3842, 3901, 3902, 3903, 3904, 3905, 4102, 4194, 4464, 4465, 4504, 4530

Button, J. 4334

Bynoe, P. 5515

Caduto, M. 4622, 4623

Cambers, G. 4061

Cambier, A. 3518

Camino, E. 3513

Campbell, R. 4227

Campion, K. 4062

Carhart, J. 3843

Carlstein, T. 2617

Carneiro, S. M. 5516

Carnie, J. 4281, 4282

Carpenter, J. R. 3324

Carr, R. D. 3656

Carson, S. McB. 4624

Carswell, R. J. B. 2618

Carter, D. 3589, 4139

Carter, R. 2358, 2717, 2789, 2866, 2918, 3020, 4033, 4062, 4195, 4196, 4466

Cass, D. 3385

Castner, H. W. 2619, 2620, 2621, 3627, 5306, 5307, 5308, 5309, 5310

Caswell, P. 4467

Catford, R. A. G. 3733

Catling, S. 2164, 2165, 2166, 2167, 2277, 2294, 2308, 2309, 2310, 2359, 2360, 2361, 2362, 2363, 2364, 2365, 2486, 2487, 2488, 2489, 2718, 2820, 2821, 2867, 2919, 2920, 2921, 3361, 3430,

3435, 3453, 3454, 3455, 3456, 3457, 3458, 3459, 3460, 3461, 3462, 3463, 3487, 3500, 4034, 4402, 4908

Cave, B. 4625

Central Bureau for Educational Visits and Exchanges 4228, 4229

Centre for Educational Research and Innovation 4626, 4627

Cerovsky, J. 4628

Cervera-March, S. 4691

Chadwick, J. 2868

Chakravarti, A. K. 5311

Chalkley, B. 3734, 3796, 3946

Chambers, B. 2013, 3292, 3437, 3493, 3801, 4909, 4910, 4911

Chambers, G. 2719, 3965

Chan Ka-ki 5637

Chandler, S. 2649

Chao Chen 5638

Chapman, D. 4553

Chapman, J. 3362, 4315

Chapman, K. 3070, 3071, 3072, 3073

Charles, C. 4629

Charlton, W. A. 3449

Charman, D. J. 3074

Cheek, H. N. 2557, 5425

Chell, K. 3386

Chengdu, C. 5639

Chidley, L. 4630

Childress, R. B. 4631, 5312

Chilton, J. S. 2490

Chiodo, J. J. 3969, 5331

Chippendale, F. 5023

Choquette, R. 5313

Christian, C. M. 2114

Chu, S. K. 5640

Church, A. 2721, 3075, 4468

Ciesla, M. J. 2822

Cirrincione, J. M. 5314, 5329, 5330

Clare, P. H. 2622, 4007

Clare, R. 3363, 3535

Clark, C. 4554

Clark, G. 2720

Clark, J. 3021, 3906

Clark, L. 2311

Clark, M. 3177

Clarke, J. 2852, 3966, 4632

Clarke, K. 2366

Clary, M. 4227, 4633

Claval, P. 5043

Cleverley, P. 2168, 2220, 4035

Cleves, P. 3327

Closs, H.-M. 5044

Clough, N. 3981, 4751

Coates, B. E. 2115, 2312, 4127

Codrington, S. 5158

Cogan, J. 4455, 5315

Cohen, R. 2491

Cohen, S. B. 5316

Cole, J. P. 3488

Cole, R. 2869

Coleman, B. I. 2116

Coley, J. A. 2169

Collins, J. D. 4634

Collis, M. 4635

Colwell, T. 4636

Conkey, L. 3058

Conley, F. 4103

Conner, C. 2922

Connolly, J. 4165, 4166

Conolly, G. 5159

Convey, A. 2014, 2722, 3024, 3907, 4227, 4230, 4231, 4232, 4233, 4234, 4235, 4236, 4237, 4238, 4239, 4637

Convey, F. M. 2722

Cook, A. 3022, 3023, 3178

Cook, I. 4104

Cook, J. 3336, 3364

Cooper, C. 3387

Cooper, G. 3299, 4638, 4858

Cooper, K. 2006, 3225, 3226, 3227, 3960

Cooper, P. J. 3410

Copeland, T. 4999

Copland, W. O. 4639

Coppock, J. T. 4912

Corcoran, P. B. 5317, 5643

Cordwell, K. A. 5160

Cornell, E. H. 3412

Corney, G. 2823, 2824, 3076, 3179, 3180, 3236, 3237, 3238, 3239, 3240, 3241, 3242, 3243, 3244, 3245, 3246, 3247, 4197, 4198, 4199, 4200, 4201, 4202, 4203, 4505, 4506, 4640, 4641, 4913

Cortés, C. E. 5045, 5046

Couldridge, E. 2367

Council for Environmental Education 4642, 4643

Council of Europe 3514, 4240, 4644, 5047

Courtenay, P. P. 4335, 5161

Cowie, P. M. 2870, 2871

Cowley, J. W. 3077

Cox, B. 3536, 4403, 5145, 5162, 5163

Cox, D. J. 3300

Cox, M. 4914

Cracknell, J. R. 2313, 3657, 4063

Cracknell, R. 2314, 4036

Crane, C. R. 4336

Cranfield, J. 3638

Creighton, C. 4404

Crew, J. 4337

Cribb, M. 4915

Crick, B. 4105

Crisp, W. 5318

Croft, R. 3382

Crookes, C. 3639

Cross, J. A. 2623

Cross, S. 4004

Crouch, N. 3844

Crowley, S. 3248

Cummings, R. 2723, 3658

Curran, D. 5048

Curriculum and Assessment Authority for Wales 2368, 3820, 3821

Curriculum Council for Wales 2369, 2370, 2371, 2372, 2923, 4204, 4645

Currie, S. 3133

Curson, C. 3494


Daggs, D. G. 2626, 5323

Dale, P. F. 2492

Dally, A. M. 5571

Dalton, T. H. 2960, 3134, 3640, 4064

Daniel, P. A. 3735

Darvizeh, Z. 2570, 2571, 2572, 2574, 2689, 2690, 3424

Das, H. P. 5641

Dasgupta, N. 5642

Daugherty, R. 2054, 2170, 2315, 2316, 2373, 2374, 2375, 2376, 2790, 2961, 3736, 3737, 3738, 3739, 3822, 3823, 3830, 3845, 3846, 3908, 3909, 4037

Davey, C. 4919, 5164, 5165, 5166

Davey, J. 4491

David, D. W. 3464

Davidson, C. F. 5167

Davidson, G. 4469

Davidson, J. 3078, 3659, 3660, 3661, 3662

Davies, B. 3137

Davies, F. 3537

Davies, P. 2872, 3135, 3136, 3137, 3740, 4205, 4215

Davies, S. 2377

Dawson, M. 3011

Day, A. 2171

de Blas, P. 5032

De Jong, R. 5042

de Lucio, J. V. 5032

De Villiers, M. 2019, 2020, 2021, 2022, 2023

De Villiers, P. M. 5572

Decaroli, J. 5314

Deer, C. E. 5153, 5154, 5168

Delaney, E. J. 2728, 3088

Denver, D. 2873, 3025

Flogaitis, E. 5055

Fogelman, K. 4085

Foley, M. 2024, 2928, 3366, 3465, 3521, 3802

Ford, L. R. 5333

Ford, P. 3310, 4675

Forer, P. 3667, 5184, 5185

Forge, K. 4728

Forrest, M. 3981, 4751

Forsyth, A. S. 5334, 5335, 5336, 5337

Foskett, N. 2970, 3220, 3311, 3383, 4509

Foskett, R. 3668, 3718

Foster, I. 3090

Fowler, G. 4474

Fox, M. 3080, 3081

Fox, P. 2001, 2951, 3620, 3669, 3694, 4056, 4475

Foyle, H. 2764, 5397

Frampton, S. 3027, 3028

Francek, M. A. 2602, 2663

Frances, L. 3745

Franchi, N. M. 4167, 4284

Francis, C. 2670, 4828

Francis, G. 4676, 5519

Fraser, B. 2697

Fraser, M. 4560

Frazee, B. 5426

Frazier, J. W. 5338

Frederiksen, R. 5056

Fredrich, B. 3970, 5339

Freeman, D. 3670, 3671, 3672, 3673, 3674

Freeman, P. 4245

Freundschuh, S. 2498

Frew, J. 2791, 3312

Frey, A. 3913, 3914

Freye, R. 5482

Fry, P. 2386, 2971, 4107, 4285

Fuchs, F. 3253, 5057

Fuller, G. 5340

Fuller, K. 3970, 5339

Fullerton, H. 3074

Fung Yee-wang 5644, 5645, 5700

Fyfe, E. 2077, 3915

Fyson, A. 5024

Gadsden, A. 3501

Gaffney, J. 2457

Gale, N. 2628, 2632

Gale, P. 4246

Gant, R. 4185, 4186

Garcia-Ramon, M. D. 5058

Gardner, D. 3675

Gardner, D. P. 5341

Garlic, J. 3640

Gärling, T. 2499, 2629

Garratt, D. 4832

Garsole, S. G. 5646

Gass, M. 3313

Gatward, Y. 2929

Gay, S. M. 5342

Gayford, C. 2387, 4677, 4678, 4679, 4680, 4681, 4682, 4683, 4684, 4685

Geipel, R. 2119, 3254, 3255, 5059

Geographical Association 2317, 2388, 2389, 2390, 2391, 3029, 3314, 3315, 3916, 4476, 4923 Environmental Education Working Group 4924 Sixth Form and University Working Group 3917

Geography Education Standards Project 4561, 5343

Georgas, S. 3161

George, B. 3390

Gerber, R. 2068, 2070, 2500, 2501, 2502, 2503, 2504, 2505, 2630, 2724, 3628, 3676, 4407, 4510, 4562, 4563, 4564, 4565, 4566, 4686, 4925, 4926, 4927, 5179, 5180, 5186, 5187, 5188, 5189, 5190, 5191, 5192, 5193, 5194, 5195, 5196, 5197, 5198, 5199, 5200, 5201, 5202, 5203, 5204, 5205, 5206, 5207, 5208, 5209, 5210, 5211, 5212, 5213, 5278

Gersmehl, P. J. 2506, 2725, 5344, 5345

Ghaye, A. 2071, 2631

Ghosh, S. 5642

Giddings, G. J. 3341

Gigliotti, L. M. 4687, 4688, 5346, 5347

Gilbert, E. W. 2025

Gilbert, R. 3538, 3539, 4086, 4128, 5214, 5215, 5216

Gilchrist, G. 2758

Gilchrist, G. E. 2176

Gill, D. 3138, 3139, 3971, 4140, 4141, 4142, 4143, 4286

Gill, M. E. 4663

Gillmore, D. A. 5060

Gilmartin, P. P. 2507, 5348

Giolitto, P. 5061

Girkin, K. G. 4008

Glasgow, J. 4689, 4690, 5520, 5521

Glean, C. 5522

Glendinning, H. 3439

Goble, T. 3677

Goffin, L. 5062

Gold, J. R. 3082, 4066

Goldberg, J. 2508

Goldschmidt, C. 4409

Goldschneider, L. 3594

Golledge, R. G. 2520, 2628, 2632, 2633, 2660, 4178

Gomez-Granell, C. 4691

Gondesen, M. E. 5381

Gonzales, J. X. 5647

Gonzalez, B. 4144

Gonzalez, E. 4144

Goodall, S. 4692

Goodenough, R. A. 3449

Goodey, B. 4693

Goodman, P. 4694

Goodson, F. 4247

Goodson, I. F. 2177, 2178, 2179, 2180, 4009, 4695, 4696, 4697, 4928, 4929

Goodwin, M. 2711

Gopal, S. 4178

Gorbanyov, V. 5063

Gordon, P. 3972

Gough, A. 5217, 5218
*see also* Greenall, A.;
Greenall Gough, A.

Gough, N. 4698

Gough, S. 5648

Gould, P. 2509, 3083

Gould, W. T. S. 2120, 2121, 2122, 2123, 2124

Gowing, D. 2181, 3289

Grady, A. D. 2182

Graham, I. M. 3273

Grant, A. T. 3746

Grant, R. 4567

Graves, N. 2003, 2026, 2027, 2028, 2029, 2030, 2031, 2032, 2042, 2072, 2073, 2074, 2075, 2183, 2184, 2185, 2186, 2187, 2188, 2189, 2190, 2191, 2192, 2193, 2194, 2195, 2196, 2197, 2198, 2199, 2200, 2201, 2318, 2392, 2393, 2972, 2973, 2974, 2975, 3030, 3274, 3275, 3540, 3541, 3747, 3748, 3749, 3750, 3751, 3752, 3849, 3918, 3919, 4410, 4411, 4477, 4511, 4512, 4513, 4699, 5064

Gray, F. 4568

Greasley, B. 3140, 3316, 3965, 4238

Greaves, E. 2634, 4700

Green, D. 3673, 3674

Green, J. L. 5349

Green, S. 4237

Greenall, A. 4701, 4702, 5219, 5220
*see also* Gough, A.;
Greenall Gough, A.

Greenall Gough, A. 4703, 4704, 5221, 5222

Gregg, M. 5350, 5351, 5352

Gregory, S. 3925

Greig, S. 4705, 4706

Grenyer, N. 2202, 2835, 2836, 3920

Griffin, E. 3058

Griffin, T. L. C. 2510

Grimshaw, P. M. 4087

Grimwade, K. 2976, 3407, 3753, 3827

Gronemeyer, M. 4569

Grosvenor, G. M. 5353

Grove, R. H. 4707

Grubb, A. 3431

Gruffudd, P. 4708

Grummit, S. 3678

Grun, M. 4709

Gunn, A. M. 3256

Gunterman, B. 5065, 5649

Gwilliam, P. 2319, 2930, 3367, 4010

Hacking, E. 2033, 2977, 3141, 4145, 4514, 4515

Hackman, S. 2713, 3955

Haddock, K. C. 4187, 4188, 5354, 5355

Haddon, J. 3317

Haggett, P. 2290

Haigh, M. J. 3084

Haines-Young, R. H. 3085

Hale, M. 4710, 4711, 4712, 4713, 4714, 4715, 4716, 4760

Hale, W. 5515

Halfyard, C. H. R. 3257

Hall, D. 2034, 2203, 2204, 2205, 2394, 2395, 2635, 2978, 3031, 3032, 3276, 3679, 3850, 3921, 3922, 3923, 4516, 4544

Hall, G. 4129

Hall, P. 3182

Hall, R. 4388, 5004, 5005

Hallinen, M. 5066, 5067

Halloway, W. 3754, 5223

Halocha, J. 4248

Ham, S. H. 4849

Hamill, A. 3391

Hamilton, J. 2726

Hammersley, A. 4818

Hammond, R. 4130

Han, S. H. 4717, 5356

Hanley, G. 2521

Hannon, B. 2895, 4792

Hansen, J. M. 5445

Hanson, J. 3542

Hanson, S. 5421

Harber, C. 4339

Hardie, J. 4716

Hardwich, S. W. 5357

Hardwick, J. 3220

Hare, R. T. 3386

Harlen, W. 4660

Harn, R. 4321

Harnapp, V. 2511

Harnett, P. 3981, 4751

Harper, R. A. 5358, 5359

Harper, S. 4189

Harrah, B. K. 4718, 5360

Harrah, D. F. 4718, 5360

Harris, C. 4067, 4719

Harris, G. 3440

Harris, L. D. 2759, 5361

Harris, M. 3466

Harris, P. L. 2702

Harrison, D. A. 2512

Harrison, M. E. 3086

Harrison, N. 2574

Harrison, P. 3467, 3468

Harrison, R. 4720

Harrison, S. 3467, 3468

Hart, C. 2878, 3044, 3183, 3184, 3185, 3186, 3187, 3188, 3189, 3210, 3392, 3393, 3642, 3924, 4478, 4479, 4480, 4481

Hart, P. 4835, 5266

Hart, R. 2636, 5362

Hartland, D. 2637

Hartley, R. M. 2879

Hartman, S. R. 2599

Hartoonian, H. M. 4412

Harvey, B. 4570

Harvey, J. 2638

Harvey, P. 3333, 3398

Harvey, P. K. 3394

Harwood, D. 2639, 2640, 2837, 2838, 3469, 4108, 4389, 4413, 4414

Haslam, J. 2641

Hassell, D. 3673, 3674, 3680, 3681

Hatcher, B. 2513

Iozzi, L. A. 4743

Irwin, H. S. 4744

Irwin, P. 5623

Jackson, P. 2639, 4148

Jackson, R. H. 3548, 5377

Jacobson, S. K. 4745

Jakle, J. A. 2114

James, C. V. 4251

James, P. E. 5378

Janikoun, J. 2024, 2928, 3366, 3465, 3521, 3802, 3803

Jarrett, B. 3975

Jarvis, H. 4429

Jaus, H. H. 4746

Jay, L. J. 2037, 2078, 2215

Jefferys, S. A. 3682

Jeffrey, T. 2554

Jenkins, A. 2729, 3082, 3094, 3095, 3096, 3097, 3098, 3099, 3396, 4066, 4487

Jenkins, S. 2321

Jenks, G. F. 5379

Jenness, R. 3351

Jennings, J. 5008

Jennings, S. A. 5380

Jewson, T. 3442, 3507, 3508

Jickling, B. 4588

Job, D. 3321, 4935, 4936

John, A. 2886, 3852, 4089

John, M. E. 2216

Johnson, J. P. 3549

Johnson, P. C. 5381

Johnson, S. 3950, 3976

Johnson, S. P. 2217

Johnson, T. 3977

Johnston, R. J. 3100, 3925, 3978, 4488, 4521

Johnston, W. B. 5225

Joicey, H. B. 5009

Joint Committee on Geographic Education 5382

Jones, A. 3760, 5226, 5227

Jones, A. I. 3034

Jones, B. 3146, 3829, 3853, 4347

Jones, D. 4040

Jones, D. I. 2218

Jones, E. B. 4090

Jones, F. A. 2642

Jones, J. F. 4747

Jones, K. 4818

Jones, M. 2518, 3142, 3143, 3761, 3854, 3915

Jones, N. 4090, 4722

Jones, P. F. 3926, 3927, 3928, 4014

Jones, S. 2219, 2220, 3163, 3164, 3855, 3856

Jones, W. H. 2643, 2730

Jordan, J. 2842

Joseph, C. 3762, 3857

Joseph, K. 2322

Jowitt, R. G. 3035, 3194

Jumper, S. R. 5383

Jungkunz, T. 4298

Kakela, P. 3101

Kaminske, V. 2644, 5082

Kantchev, D. 5135

Keane, P. 5010

Keates, J. S. 3470

Keighley, P. W. S. 3322, 4748

Keliher, V. 4749

Keller, V. 3979

Kelly, C. R. M. 2760

Kelly, J. 3250, 4207

Kelly, P. 3980

Kelly, P. A. 2887

Kelly, P. J. 4750

Kelly, V. 4937

Kemp, R. 2793, 2843, 2844, 3489, 3858, 4208

Kendrick, C. F. W. 4348

Kent, A. 2032, 2038, 2039, 2075, 2221, 2392, 2393, 2761, 2932, 2980, 2981, 3042, 3175, 3193, 3207, 3208, 3323, 3495, 3550, 3650, 3651, 3679, 3683, 3684, 3685, 3686, 3687, 3688, 4068, 4069, 4299, 4300, 4938

Kenyon, J. 4015

Keown, P. 5228, 5229

Kern, E. L. 3324

Kerr, D. 4091

Kerr, R. A. 3689

Khalid, K. 4218

Kilburn, E. B. 2645

Kimber, D. 3981, 4751

Kincheloe, J. L. 5384

King, D. 2511

King, R. 2222, 4349

King, R. L. 3763, 3764, 3765, 3766

King, S. 3859

Kington, C. 3551, 3552

Kinnear, P. R. 2519

Kirasic, K. C. 2458

Kirby, A. 2223

Kirby, J. R. 2646

Kirman, J. M. 2508, 5385

Kirsch, I. S. 2543

Kirschberg, G. 4252, 5083

Kitchin, R. M. 2520

Klein, P. 5373, 5386

Knamiller, G. W. 4350, 4593, 4752

Knapp, C. 4753

Kneale, P. 3102

Knight, C. 5230

Knight, P. 2040, 2224, 4017, 5011

Kniveton, B. H. 2128

Knox, P. 4131

Kohn, C. 5387

Kon, J. H. 2594

Kondakov, A. 4433, 4944

Kosonen, O. 5084

Kracht, J. 5305

Krause, J. 2007, 2915, 2942, 3502, 3519, 3662, 3799, 4062

Kravitz, B. 5388

Kromer, M. K. 2600

Kuehn, C. 2691

Kuhn, M. W. 4948

Kuhnlova, H. 5085

Kulhavy, R. W. 2457

Kunaver, J. 5086

Kurfman, D. G. 3767, 5389

Kwan, T. Yim-lin  5231, 5232, 5233, 5234, 5235, 5653, 5654

Kwong, J.  4585

Kyagulanyi, E.  5579, 5580

La Prarie, I. A.  5374

Lacey, C.  4754, 4755

Lacey, P. J.  3629

Lai Kwok-chan  5655, 5656

Lam Chi-chung  5657, 5658

Lambert, D.  2039, 2075, 2095, 2223, 2376, 2392, 2393, 2400, 2401, 2888, 2959, 2966, 3019, 3036, 3534, 3553, 3554, 3598, 3726, 3732, 3739, 3768, 3769, 3770, 3771, 3772, 3773, 3774, 3775, 3776, 3817, 3818, 3819, 3825, 3830, 3860, 4132, 4209, 4301, 4302, 4522, 4533

Lambert, S.  4430

Lancastle, T.  3397

Lane, J. A.  3165

Langridge, D.  5087

Larimore, A. E.  3555, 5390

Larsen, B.  3861, 4168, 4169

Latham, J.  3387

Lavanchy, S.  4756

Lawes, B.  3413

Lawler, C. D.  3325, 3690

Lawless, J. V.  2845

Lawrence, S.  4322

Laws, G.  4189

Laws, K.  2762, 2846, 3326, 5236, 5237

Laws, S.  4491

Le Sourd, S. J.  5392

Le Vasseur, M.  5393

Leal Filho, W.  4757, 4758, 4759, 4760, 4761, 5088, 5089, 5090

Leang, M. J.  2731

Leat, D.  2647, 2648, 2649, 4523

Leather, A. D.  2650

Lee, A.  2079

Lee, C. Kim-eng  5659

Lee, E. W.  4840, 5447

Lee, J. Chi-kin  4939, 4940, 4941, 4942, 5654, 5660, 5661, 5662, 5663

Lee, M. C. E.  2889

Lee, R.  3082, 3929, 4066, 4133, 4253, 4524, 5391, 5664

Leigh, M.  4303

Leinhardt, G.  5350, 5351, 5352

Lenegran, D. A.  2676, 2997

Lenon, B.  3327

Leonard, P.  3691

Lergessner, D. A.  2080, 5238

Lester, A.  2732

Lester, A. J.  3556

Levine, M.  2521

Lewis, D.  2733, 2890, 3930, 4776, 5101

Lewis, E.  3368, 3441, 3503

Lewis, R.  4762

Lewis, S.  3599

Liaw, B. T.  5665

Libbee, M.  5394, 5483

Liben, L. S.  2477, 2494, 2522, 2626, 2651, 5322, 5323, 5395

Lidstone, J.  2652, 2763, 3328, 3557, 3558, 3559, 3560, 4431, 4432, 4433, 4943, 4944, 5144, 5204, 5205, 5206, 5207, 5239, 5240, 5241, 5242, 5243, 5244, 5245, 5246, 5247, 5248

Liepe, J.  4763

Liiber, U.  5091

Lillis, K.  3284

Lillo, J.  2653

Lincoln, D.  5581

Lindberg, E.  2499, 2629

Lindsay, M.  4572

Lines, C. J.  4605, 4764

Lines, D.  2095, 4351

Linke, R. D.  4765, 4766

Lisowski, M.  3332

Livingstone, I.  3090

Lloyd, K.  2402

Lloyd, R.  2523

Lob, R. E.  4767, 5092, 5093, 5094

Lockledge, A.  5526

Long, M.  2041, 2225, 3561

Lowe, J.  4254

Lowe, M.  4609

Lowenthal, D.  4768

Loyd, B.  4170, 5396

Lu, J. L.  5666

Lucas, A. M.  4769

Lucas, I.  3692

Lucas, R.  3329

Lugg, S.  4322

Lukehurst, C. T.  2042

Luker, K.  3721, 4070

Lwanga-Lukwago, J.  5582, 5583

Lyle, S.  2654

Lyman, L.  2764, 5397

Lyons, T. S.  4459

Macaro, E.  4237

McArthur, J. L.  4945

MacCabe, C. L.  2524

McCauley, J.  5249

McCleary, G. S.  2478, 5298

McCormick, V.  2858

McCulloch, G.  5250

MacDermott, F.  4761, 5090

Macdonald, A.  3600

McDonald, A.  3037, 3195, 3931

MacDonald, B.  3147, 3278

McDonald, G. T.  4946, 5251

McDowell, L.  3103

McDuff, M. D.  4745

MacEachren, A. M.  2525, 2526, 2527, 2528

McElroy, B.  3330, 3777, 4117, 5252, 5253

McElroy, B. I.  3196

McEwen, N.  2982

McFarlane, C.  4434, 4435

McGahan, H.  2698

McGee, C.  2529, 5254

McGee, M. G.  5398

McGeorge, C.  2530

McGivney, V.  4247

McGloin, P.  5095

Machon, P.  2226, 2450, 3004, 4092, 4116, 4118

Mackenzie, A. A.  3331

McKenzie, G. D.  3332

McKenzie, J.  2734

McKenzie, V.  2735

McKeown-Ice, R.  4947

MacKewan, N.  2227

Mackintosh, M.  2678, 2933, 3438

Mackle, A.  3471

Maclean, K.  2228

McMorrow, J.  3601

McMullen, K.  2847

McNeill, C.  3414

McPartland, M.  2158, 2159, 2160, 2161, 3272, 3333, 3398, 4502, 4525, 4526, 5012

McShane, J.  2640

McSorley, F.  3038, 3197

Maddrell, A. M. C.  4083, 4093

Maddrell, M. C.  2229

Magson, Y.  4004

Maher, M.  4770

Maitland, S.  2909, 4378

Maksakovsky, V. P.  5096, 5097

Malindine, D.  3602

Mansell, J.  3148

Mansell, J. E.  3334

Manshard, W.  4436

Manson, G.  5399, 5400, 5401

Marbeau, L.  2081, 5098, 5099, 5100

Marchant, E. C.  2043, 4255, 4489

Marchant, J.  4663

Marchon, I.  2521

Mares, C.  3510, 4771

Marran, J.  5402, 5403

Marriott, A.  3039, 4171, 4573, 4772

Marsden, W. E.  2044, 2045, 2046, 2082, 2083, 2084, 2085, 2129, 2130, 2131, 2132, 2133, 2134, 2135, 2136, 2137, 2230, 2231, 2232, 2233, 2234, 2235, 2236, 2237, 2238, 2239, 2240, 2241, 2242, 2243, 2244, 2323, 2324,

2403, 2404, 2736, 2794, 2891, 2931, 2983, 2984, 2985, 3259, 3260, 3515, 3523, 3562, 3563, 3778, 3779, 3780, 3781, 3804, 3982, 4099, 4149, 4190, 4256, 4257, 4304, 4305, 4306, 4437, 4438, 4527, 4528, 4545, 4773, 4774, 4775, 5038

Marsh, C. J.  5255

Marshall, L. D.  4352

Marshall, S. P.  2633

Martin, E. S.  4776, 5101

Martin, F.  2047, 2795, 3496, 3693, 3722, 3805, 3862

Martin, G. C.  4777

Martin, G. J.  5404

Martin, K. D.  5405

Martin, L.  4094

Martin, P.  4778

Martinez, M.  3335

Martland, J. R.  2531, 2532, 3414, 3415, 3416, 3417, 3418, 3419, 3420, 3421, 3422, 3425, 3426, 3427, 3428, 3429

Martorella, P. H.  2892

Marvell, A.  4119, 4490

Mason, P.  4353

Mason, P. F.  4948

Massey, D.  3564, 5406

Masterton, T. H.  2245, 3788, 4779

Mathias, P.  3983

Matless, D.  4095

Maton, J. C.  2796

Matthews, H.  3090

Matthews, J.  4808

Matthews, M. H.  2103, 2533, 2534, 2535, 2536, 2537, 2538, 2539, 2655, 2656, 4172, 4173, 4174, 4780

Matusiak, C.  2461

Maund, D.  3279

May, S.  3336, 3337, 3353, 3364, 3369

May, T.  2657

Maye, B.  2893

Mayer, T.  5407

Mayer, V. J.  5408

Mays, P.  2658, 4781

Mead, W. R.  3067

Medd, A.  3154

Mee, K.  3806

Megarry, A.  3932

Meijer, G.  5134

Meijer, H.  3565, 4439, 5102

Mellor, J.  4237

Mellor, V. A.  3104

Menter, I.  3981, 4751

Mercer, J. J.  5013

Mercier, J.  3058

Merenne-Schoumaker, B.  5103

Merrett, C. D.  5409

Metz, H. M.  2540

Meux, M.  2868

Meyer, J. M. W.  2541, 5410

Middleton, N.  3076, 4641, 4913

Midgely, H.  3694

Mikkelson, K.  5104

Milburn, D.  2737, 5411

Milford, S.  5018

Millar, J. B.  3566

Millard, J.  3105

Miller, B. A.  5527

Miller, C. R.  3984

Miller, J. W.  5412, 5413, 5414

Mills, C.  4150

Mills, D.  2048, 2325, 2326, 2738, 4041

Milne, A. K.  4919, 4949

Milne, P.  4491

Milner, A.  2934, 2935

Milton, M.  2797, 3650, 3651, 3652, 3860, 3933, 4491

Minshull, R.  3640

Mische, P. M.  4782

Misra, R. P.  2118

Mitchell, D. J.  4354

Mitchell, S.  2575, 4855

Mobbs, D.  3121

Mohan, J.  3106

Moline, N.  3058

Molyneux, F. 2049, 2659, 2765, 2986

Monk, J. 3082, 4066, 4175, 4176, 5415, 5416, 5417, 5418, 5419, 5420, 5421

Monmonier, M. 2542

Montefiore, H. 4783

Montford, S. 4722, 5014

Moon, A. 3132

Moore, G. T. 2660

Moore, R. 2661

Moore, T. 2318

Morgan, J. 2246, 2247, 4784

Morgan, W. 2327, 2405, 2406, 2407, 2408, 2409, 2936, 2937, 2938, 2939

Morris, J. S. 2410, 3149, 4120

Morris, J. W. 2328

Morrish, M. 4355

Morrissey, M. 5528, 5529, 5530, 5531, 5532, 5533, 5534, 5535

Morron, M. 3370

Morsley, K. 2569, 2688

Morten, A. 3863

Morton, C. A. 2798

Mosenthal, P. B. 2543

Moss, B. 4587

Moss, R. W. 3150

Mossa, J. 3107

Mottershead, D. 3078, 4016, 4950

Moulden, M. 2138

Mucciolo, M. 5536, 5537

Mucunguzi, P. 5584, 5585

Muessig, R. H. 5422, 5423

Muir, S. P. 2556, 2557, 5424, 5425, 5426

Mulvihili, J. L. 4188, 5355

Murphy, Z. 4761, 5090

Murray, D. 2544

Murray, K. P. 3782

Murray, L. 2987

Nagy, J. N. 4785, 5427

Nairn, K. 2766

Naish, M. 2032, 2039, 2050, 2075, 2086, 2087, 2088, 2089, 2248, 2249, 2250, 2251, 2252, 2253, 2329, 2393, 2411, 2412, 2413, 2414, 2662, 2767, 2894, 2988, 2989, 2990, 2991, 3040, 3041, 3042, 3043, 3044, 3108, 3198, 3199, 3200, 3201, 3202, 3203, 3204, 3205, 3206, 3207, 3208, 3209, 3210, 3752, 3934, 4042, 4071, 4072, 4529, 4546, 4951

Naish, S. 4546

Nakayama, S. 5315, 5667, 5668, 5669, 5670, 5671

Nam, S.-J. 5672

Namafe, C. 4786

Nash, C. 4096

Nash, P. 3831

Nason, R. 5207

National Council for Educational Technology 3695, 3696

National Curriculum Council 2415, 2416, 2417, 2418, 4210, 4787

National Institute for Adult Continuing Education 4574

Natoli, S. J. 3261, 5428, 5429, 5430, 5431

Naveh, Z. 4595, 5284

Neal, P. 4788, 4807, 5015

Nelder, G. 3437

Nelson, B. D. 2602, 2663

Newbury, P. A. 3294

Newby, P. T. 2254

Newcombe, N. 2651

Newman, E. 3981, 4751

Newman, P. W. G. 4789

Newman, R. J. 3603

Newsham, P. A. 3604

Nicholas, H. 4245

Nicholas, J. 4790

Nicholls, A. C. 2831, 2848

Nicholls, A. D. 2255, 4791

Nichols, G. 3338

Nicholson, H. N. 2051, 3504, 3505, 3985

Nicol, E. 4258

Nicol, I. G. 5586

Niemz, G. 5105

Nilsson, T. 2629

Nisbet, J. 3251

Nishi, M. 3986

Noble, P. 3339

Nolzen, H. 2014, 3262, 5106

Norton, B. G. 2895, 4792

Norton, D. E. 2739, 3987

Novak, J. D. 2665

Noyes, E. 2553

Noyes, L. 2545, 2546

Numata, M. 4793

Nussbaum, J. 2664, 2665

Nuttall, D. 3793

Nuttall, S. E. 3045

Nwagu, E. 5599

Oden, P. 3988, 5432

Oduaran, A. B. 5587

Oelofse, C. G. 5567

Oettle, R. E. 3046

Office for Standards in Education 2992, 3807

Ogundana, B. 5588

O'Hear, A. 4794

Oi, E. W. M. 5673

Ojala, J. 4795

Okoro, P. A. 5589

Okpala, J. 5590, 5591, 5592, 5593, 5594, 5595, 5596, 5597, 5598, 5599

Okpalanma, L. O. 5600

Okunrotifa, P. O. 5601, 5602, 5603, 5604, 5605, 5606, 5607

Oldenski, T. E. 4796

Olina, Z. 4797, 5107

Oliveira, L. 5538, 5539, 5540, 5541

Oliver, M. 3100

O'Malley, M. P. 5256

Onasanya, K. 5608

Ophuls, W. 4798, 5108

Orion, N. 3340, 3341

O'Riordan, T. 3109, 4799, 4952, 4953

Orr, D. W. 4800, 4801, 5433, 5434

Rawling, E.  2053, 2054, 2170, 2263, 2264, 2265, 2332, 2333, 2422, 2423, 2424, 2425, 2426, 2427, 2428, 2769, 2800, 2801, 2823, 2824, 2943, 2993, 2994, 3042, 3043, 3044, 3051, 3052, 3108, 3207, 3208, 3209, 3210, 3213, 3214, 3215, 3252, 3281, 3282, 3497, 3699, 3787, 3833, 3840, 3871, 4045, 4211, 4212, 4213, 4214, 4215, 4492, 4959, 4982, 5441

Rawlings, J.  4075

Rawstron, E. M.  2115

RBP 3263, 5442

Rea, J.  5258

Regan, P.  4493

Reid, A.  2899, 4762, 4958, 4960, 4961

Rengert, A.  4170, 5396

Renner, J. M.  3266, 5259

Renshaw, P. H.  2559, 5612

Renwick, M.  2849, 3155, 3436

Revell, T.  4831

Reynolds, J.  2035, 3162, 3164, 3168, 3169, 3170, 3171, 3174, 3856

Rhodes, B.  2560

Rhys, W.  2675

Rice, G. H.  2562

Richards, P.  5578

Richardson, D.  3400, 3404, 3405

Richardson, D. M.  5260

Richardson, P.  3337

Richardson, R.  2947

Riches, M.  3516

Rickson, R. E.  4829

Ridd, M. K.  5401

Rider, C.  2802

Rider, M.  2802

Rider, M. D.  3567

Riding, R. J.  4177

Rikkinen, H.  5114, 5115, 5116, 5117

Riley, D.  3688

Riley, J.  3082, 4066

Ritchie, A. B.  3607

Ritter, F. A.  3261, 5431

Robbins, D.  4530

Roberson, B. S.  3289, 3872, 3873, 3937

Robert, B.  4962, 5443

Roberts, K. M.  5444

Roberts, M.  2429, 2430, 2742, 2770, 2771, 2772, 2995, 3091, 3608, 4531

Robertson, M.  2672, 2673, 2900, 5261, 5262, 5263

Robins, J.  4832

Robinson, A.  2561, 3640, 3700

Robinson, C.  3701

Robinson, L.  4515

Robinson, R.  2266, 2431, 2432, 3345, 3609, 4046, 4308, 4357, 4358, 4359, 4360, 4361, 4443, 4444

Robottom, I.  4588, 4704, 4833, 4834, 4835, 5222, 5264, 5265, 5266

Roe, P. E.  3874

Rogers, S.  3702, 3703, 4076

Rohwer, G.  5118

Rolfe, J.  3264

Rolfe, R.  2220

Romanova, E.  4433, 4944

Romey, W.  5267

Rosell, D. Z.  4963

Roseman, C. C.  2114

Ross, A.  3993, 3994, 4216

Ross, K. E. K.  2674

Roth, R. E.  4836

Rouncefield, J. A.  3401

Rowbotham, D.  3374, 3375

Rowles, G. D.  4191

Rowsome, W. S.  3081

Royal Society for the Protection of Birds  4837

Royal Town Planning Institute  4838

Royce, D. H.  2996

Royle, S. A.  4309

Rudd, G.  3402

Rudd, M.  3704

Ruff, T.  5445

Rupar, T.  4310

Rushdoony, H. A.  5446

Russell, J.  4532

Russell, K.  3498, 3705

Ryba, R. H.  2127, 2139, 2140, 2141, 2142

Rynne, E.  3938, 4533

Sada, P. O.  5613

Sadler, I.  3346, 3403

St John, P.  3404, 3405

St Maurice, H.  4839

St Peter, P. H.  2676, 2997

Salahie, R.  3517

Sale, L. L.  4840, 5447

Salita, D. C.  4964, 4965, 5674, 5675, 5676, 5677

Salmon, R. B.  3788

Salter, B. G.  3283, 3284

Salter, C. L.  5448, 5449, 5450, 5451, 5452, 5453

Salter, K.  5453

Sandford, H. A.  2563, 2564, 2677, 3472, 3473, 3474, 3630, 3631, 3632, 3633, 3634, 3635

Sandford, M.  4122, 4217

Sarge, A.  2601

Sarpong, E.  5614

Satterly, D. J.  3475

Saunders, M.  3234

Sauve, L.  5454

Saveland, R. N.  2565, 4841, 5455, 5456

Sawicka, E.  2743, 2998

Sawyer, K. E.  2566

Sayer, J.  4262

Scarfe, N. V.  2267, 4445

Schadler, J.  2567

Scharf, J. S.  2599

Schleicher, K.  4842

Schneider, H. J.  5544

Schoenfeld, C.  4843, 5457

Schoenmaker, G.  5132

Schofield, A.  2386, 2971, 3995

School Curriculum and Assessment Authority 2433, 2434, 2744, 2944, 2945, 3568, 3808, 3809, 3834, 3835, 3836, 3875, 3939, 4846

School Examinations and Assessment Council 3810, 3811, 3837, 3838

Schools Council 3265, 3476, 4845
Environmental Studies Project 4844
Geography Committee 3406

Schrettenbrunner, H. 2090, 5119, 5120, 5121, 5122

Scoffham, S. 3376, 3377, 3378, 3442, 3506, 3507, 3508, 3812

Scott, J. R. 4362

Scott, R. 4966

Scott, R. C. 5458

Scott, W. H. 4618, 4790, 4802, 4803, 4961

Scriven, M. 4847, 5459

Seabourne, M. 3477

Seaden-Jones, P. T. 4047

Sebba, J. 2055, 2850, 2851, 2852

Seedhouse, P. 2678

Selby, D. 4441, 4446, 4705, 4706

Self, C. M. 4178

Selkirk, K. 4018

Selmes, I. 3610

Semple, S. 4967

Senathirajah, N. 3789, 5460

Senior, D. 3611

Senior, J. 4580

Seong, K. T. 5678

Serf, J. 3003, 3612, 4110, 4363, 4396, 4444

Sewing, D. R. 4717, 5356

Shapland, H. 2773

Sharma, M. 5301

Sharma, N. P. 3347

Sharp, D. 3996

Sharp, J. G. 2678

Sharp, N. 2745, 3112

Shaw, F. 2853

Shaw, F. L. 3434

Shea, J. H. 4019

Shen, J. 5679

Shennan, M. 4263

Shepherd, I. 2746, 3082, 3113, 3114, 4066

Sheridan, P. 4494

Shevill, M. 2774

Shirley, D. 4848, 5123

Shkarban, N. V. 5124

Short, J. 4123, 4278

Shortle, D. 4968, 4969, 4970, 5268

Shuell, T. J. 2674

Shuman, D. K. 4849

Siddelley, J. 4077

Siegel, A. W. 2458, 2567

Silson, A. L. 3940

Simmons, C. M. 4851

Simmons, D. A. 4850

Simmons, I. G. 4851, 4971, 4972

Simpson, A. 4134

Simpson, J. 5157

Sinclair, S. 4363, 4447

Singh, C. P. 5680

Singh, M. 4128, 4152, 5216, 5269

Sitte, W. 5125

Skelton, I. A. N. 4048

Skelton, N. 2552

Skinner, D. 4534

Slater, A. 2803, 2804, 3997

Slater, F. 2032, 2039, 2056, 2057, 2075, 2091, 2092, 2093, 2094, 2095, 2268, 2269, 2270, 2392, 2393, 2435, 2679, 2680, 2681, 2682, 2683, 2684, 2732, 2747, 2775, 2776, 2877, 2901, 2902, 2903, 2904, 2905, 2906, 2957, 2999, 3000, 3001, 3002, 3053, 3266, 4179, 4297, 4302, 4311, 4312, 4535, 4973, 5126, 5182, 5270, 5271, 5272

Smeaton, M. 4448

Smit, M. J. 5615

Smit, T. 5616, 5617

Smith, B. 3216, 3998

Smith, B. J. 4776, 5101

Smith, C. 3693, 3941

Smith, D. L. 4135

Smith, D. M. 2907, 2908, 3115

Smith, F. 3181, 3388

Smith, G. 3348

Smith, J. H. 5273

Smith, K. 5618

Smith, M. 3054, 3116

Smith, N. 3156

Smith, P. 3098, 3813, 4078

Smith, P. L. 3349

Smith, P. R. 2271, 2436, 3350

Smith, R. 4364

Smith, R. M. 3613

Smith, S. 2854

Smith, T. R. 2633

Smyth, A. 3614

Smyth, J. C. 4593, 4852, 4853, 4854

Smyth, T. 2805

Snellock, K. 4303

Soerjani, M. 5681

Sollman, R. 2669

Sommerville, A. 4576

Souchon, C. 5061

Sparks, R. 3727, 5568

Speak, C. 2437, 2685, 2719, 4239, 4449, 4450, 5682, 5683

Spencer, C. 2462, 2463, 2464, 2465, 2466, 2467, 2468, 2469, 2470, 2471, 2472, 2473, 2474, 2475, 2544, 2568, 2569, 2570, 2571, 2572, 2573, 2574, 2575, 2576, 2686, 2687, 2688, 2689, 2690, 3411, 3423, 3424, 4855

Sperling, W. 5127

Spicer, B. 4311, 4312, 4313, 5274, 5619, 5684

Spillane, J. M. 3999

Spooner, D. 3569

Springford, A. 2777

Stainer, L. 3790

Stainton, C. 5352

Standen, J. 3615

Stander, E. 5620

Stanistreet, M. 2607, 2612, 2613, 2614, 2615, 2634, 2670, 4600, 4610, 4611, 4612, 4613, 4700, 4828, 4831

Stapp, W. 4856, 4866, 5461, 5490

Starkey, H. 4259, 4264, 4397

Stea, D. 2479, 2495, 2496, 2610, 5299, 5300, 5324, 5325

Steadman, S. D. 3283, 3284

Steel, R. W. 4365, 4366

Steer, D. 3351

Steinberg, P. E. 4974, 5462

Steinbrink, J. 2778, 3954, 5285, 5463

Steiner, M. 4424, 4451, 4452

Steinke, T. 5379

Stepans, J. 2691

Stephens, A. 2692

Stephens, P. 3217

Stephens, W. B. 2143

Stephenson, B. 2748

Stephenson, R. 4771

Sterling, S. 4740, 4857, 4858

Stevens, B. 4495

Stevens, G. 3172, 3876

Stevenson, R. B. 4859, 5464

Stewart, L. W. 5019

Stewart, R. R. 3420, 3425, 3429

Stewart-Dore, N. 2724, 5208

Stichbury, M. 4473, 4496

Stiell, B. 2589, 2590, 2591, 2592, 2709, 2710

Stillman, C. W. 4860, 5465

Stimpson, P. 2749, 3791, 4861, 5673, 5685, 5686, 5687, 5688, 5689

Stoddart, D. 4862

Stoddart, D. R. 2096

Stoltman, J. 2097, 2693, 2694, 2779, 2780, 3267, 3268, 3954, 5285, 5466, 5467, 5468, 5469, 5470, 5471, 5472, 5473, 5474, 5475, 5476, 5477, 5478, 5479, 5480, 5481, 5482, 5483, 5484, 5485

Stomp, L. 4885

Stoner, F. 3877

Storm, M. 2272, 2273, 2334, 2438, 3525, 4136, 4366, 4367, 4368, 4369, 4370, 4371, 4453

Strommen, E. 2695

Stutz, F. P. 5486

Suggate, J. 4808

Sullivan, B. J. 2696

Sumner, H. 2006, 3225, 3226, 3230, 3960

Sun Da-wen 5690

Sunal-Szymanski, C. 5487

Surrell, G. P. 2806

Sutherland, A. E. 3157

Sutton, A. 4497

Sutton, P. 4863

Swaan, M. 5042

Swain, J. R. 3942

Swan, J. 4864, 4865, 4866, 5488, 5489, 5490

Swann, A. 3792

Swee-Hin, T. 4372, 4373, 4454

Swift, D. 3003, 4347, 4498

Szekely, B. B. 5128

Szpakowski, B. 2807

Tait, N. 5621, 5622

Tamir, P. 3341

Tan, F. B. 5185

Tapsfield, A. 2274, 3499, 3669, 3706

Taylor, E. G. 3793

Taylor, J. 3352, 3643, 3943

Taylor, S. 2808, 3478

Taylor, W. H. 4265

Teather, E. K. 4000

Teh, G. 2697

Telfer, S. 3732, 3817

Terry, M. 4867, 5491

Thiel, T. 4314

Thomas, B. 3878

Thomas, C. J. 2126

Thomas, D. 2840, 4536

Thomas, G. 3407

Thomas, H. 4020

Thomas, I. 4868

Thomas, K. M. 3707

Thomas, O. G. 4315

Thomas, P. 4975

Thomas, P. A. 4577

Thomas, P. F. 5492, 5493, 5494

Thomas, P. R. 2275

Thomas, S. 2698

Thomas, T. 3292, 3353, 3379, 3393, 5077

Thornton, S. J. 5495

Thrift, N. 2617

Tickell, C. 4869

Tidmarsh, C. 3839

Tidswell, V. 2276, 3879, 3880, 4020

Tiefenbacher, J. 5375

Tierney, G. 2577

Tilbury, D. 2058, 2699, 4374, 4541, 4870, 4871, 4872, 4873, 4874, 4976, 4977, 4987, 5691

Till, E. 3443

Tilling, S. 4875

Tinline, E. 4371

Tisdale, E. G. 3218

Titman, W. 2855

Tivers, J. 4568

Tiwari, R. C. 5311

Todd, H. 2078

Tolley, H. 2035, 2049, 2059, 2659, 2765, 2986, 3162, 3173, 3174, 3881, 3944, 4079

Tomkinson, M. 2809

Tomlinson, H. 4266

Towler, J. 2671, 4978, 4979, 5414, 5440, 5496, 5497

Townley, C. 4425

Townsend, A. R. 4180

Townsend, J. G. 4180

Tracy, J. 5020

Trainer, T. 4375, 4876

Trebble, D. W. 3616

Trend, R. D. 4021, 4022, 4023, 4024, 4025

Trifonoff, K. M. 2578

Trimp, H. 2580, 2781, 5132, 5133

Troost, C. J. 4877, 5498

Troster, A. I. 2608, 4160

Trott, C. 4084

Trudgill, S. 4878

Trumman, L. J. 4776, 5101

Truper, M. 5129

Tucker, B. 3158, 3794

Tuffin, B. 4537

Turnage, J. M. 2856

Turner, A. 2277, 3435

Turner, K. 2699, 4873

Turner, P. M. 2874

Turton, D. 3055

Twells, P. P. 3708

Ugwuda, S. 5599

Underwood, B. L. 2278, 2335, 3945

Underwood, J. D. M. 2579

United Nations Educational, Scientific and Cultural Organisation 4879, 4880, 4881, 4882, 4883, 4884

Unwin, D. 3082, 4066

Unwin, T. 2439, 3117, 3118, 4538, 5499

Utgard, R. O. 3332

Uzzell, D. 4598


van der Schee, J. 2580, 4267, 4980, 5130, 5131, 5132, 5133

van der Zijpp, T. 2580, 5133

van Dijk, H. 2580, 4885

van Ginkel, H. 4136

van Hermelen, U. 5623

van Meegan, J. 5065, 5649

van Westrhenen, J. 2090, 4321, 5122, 5132, 5134

Vaughan, J. E. 2279, 2280

Vekilska, P. 5135

Velazco, G. 5692

Venness, T. 2700

Verduin-Muller, H. 2098, 4578, 5136, 5137, 5138

Verhetsel, A. 2581, 2701

Vezzosi, C. 4591

Vicars, A. 4376

Vickers, D. 4347

Viezzer, L. 4886

Villalobos, N. S. 5545

Villars, R. 4377

Villenure, M. 5313

Vining, J. W. 5500

Vivian, V. E. 4887, 5501

Vulliamy, G. 4888


Wada, F. 5671

Waites, B. 4983, 5021, 5022

Wake, R. A. 4268

Wales, R. 3146, 3853

Walford, R. 2003, 2060, 2061, 2062, 2281, 2282, 2283, 2284, 2285, 2286, 2287, 2288, 2289, 2290, 2291, 2316, 2336, 2337, 2338, 2340, 2440, 2441, 2442, 2443, 2444, 2445, 2446, 2447, 2448, 2449, 2450, 2750, 2961, 3004, 3380, 3408, 3490, 3643, 3644, 3645, 3646, 3647, 3795, 3882, 4097, 4153, 4154, 4539, 4874

Walker, A. 3444

Walker, D. 2751, 3709

Walker, G. 3119, 3445, 4026

Walker, G. T. 4981

Walker, J. M. 3159

Walker, K. 4889

Walker, M. J. 3285

Walker, R. 3147, 3278

Walker, R. J. 2582, 2583, 5275

Waller, G. 2702

Walmsley, D. J. 2703

Walmsley, F. 4499

Wals, A. 4890

Walsh, B. E. 3142, 3143

Walsh, S. E. 2532, 3420, 3421, 3422, 3425, 3426, 3427, 3428, 3429

Walton, B. 4891

Walton, M. 4317

Wang Liang-huew 5693

Waplington, A. 2006, 3225, 3226, 3230, 3960

Ward, A. 3099

Ward, C. 4996, 5023, 5024

Ward, H. 2333, 3354

Wardley, S. 5484, 5485

Wareing, H. 3437

Warn, C. 3883, 4001

Warn, S. 3884, 3885

Warner, H. 2810, 3681, 3710, 3711, 3712, 4181

Warner, P. J. 3005

Warnes, A. M. 4192, 4193

Warren, J. 3056, 3219

Warren, M. 3518

Warwick, P. 2704, 3617

Warwick, P. J. 3570

Wass, S. 3381

Waterman, S. 2909, 4378, 5139

Waters, A. 2811, 2946

Watkins, G. F. 3886

Watson, D. 3713

Watson, J. W. 2910

Watson, M. 3723

Watts, H. D. 3120

Watts, S. 3503

Weaver, R. 3796, 3946

Webb, D. 4455

Webb, G. 3947, 5546, 5547, 5548

Webster, A. 3122

Webster, P. J. 4892

Wedden, D. 4027

Weeden, P. 2584, 3636, 3839

Weetman, M. 2576

Weinbrenner, U. 4269, 5140

Weiss, J. 3789, 5460

Welch, P. 3220

Weldon, M. 2947

Wellings, P. 5624

Welsh Office 2379, 2380, 2451

Welsh, R. 4579

Wendt, N. 4893, 5276

Wenger, R. N. 5495

Wenham, P. D. 3235

Wennevold, S. 5029

Wescott, H. M. 2618

Westaway, J. 2428, 2801, 3833, 3840, 4982

Westoby, G. 2752, 2857

Weston, B. 2858

Weston, C. 3220

Weston, J. 4894

Westwood, S. 3057, 4500

Wetton, S. 3446

Wetzler, H. 4227

Wheate, R. 3627, 5310

Wheatley, A. 3160

Wheatley, D. 4895

Wheeler, J. O. 5502

Wheeler, K. 2292, 4777, 4983, 5025

Wheeler, K. S. 3355

Whiddon, K. 3714

White, G. F. 5503

White, M. 3887

White, R. 2509

White, R. T. 3331

White, S. 4580

Whiteman, P. H. G. 3618

Whitington, J. 4581

Whittall, R. 3133

Whitty, G. 4002

Wholmsley, J. P. 4517, 4540

Wiber, M. 5248

Wickert, P. J. 4318

Wicks, L. M. 4984

Wiegand, P. 2063, 2064, 2065, 2437, 2452, 2453, 2585, 2586, 2587, 2588, 2589, 2590, 2591, 2592, 2705, 2706, 2707, 2708, 2709, 2710, 2719, 2859, 2911, 2948, 3006, 3479, 3480, 3565, 3637, 3679, 3715, 3724, 3783, 3814, 3888, 3889, 3948, 4080, 4098, 4182, 4270, 4319, 4320, 4430, 4449, 4450, 5102

Wilbanks, T. J. 5504

Wilby, P. 3409

Wilczynska-Woloszyn, M. M. 2593

Wilke, R. 4741

Wilkie, M. 3648

Wilkinson, H. 5625

Wilkinson, T. 3080, 3081

Willatts, R. M. 5626

Willcocks, R. 5277

Williams, A. 4985

Williams, G. 4271

Williams, G. B. 3619

Williams, M. 2058, 2066, 2068, 2070, 2099, 2291, 2293, 2294, 2312, 2333, 2338, 2339, 2340, 2454, 2753, 2812, 2813, 2814, 3007, 3008, 3571, 3572, 4049, 4050, 4051, 4052, 4081, 4218, 4225, 4272, 4273, 4274, 4275, 4276, 4277, 4279, 4321, 4456, 4457, 4510, 4541, 4547, 4548, 4549, 4550, 4566, 4896, 4986, 4987, 5209, 5210, 5211

Williams, R. 4755, 4897, 4898

Williams, T. 2634, 4700

Williamson, D. 3716

Williamson, W. 2144

Williamson-Fien, J. 4183

Wilson, C. 2455

Wilson, P. 2505, 2711, 3628, 3868, 3869, 3890, 5180, 5183, 5212, 5213, 5278

Wilson, P. A. 4027

Wilson, R. A. 4899, 5505

Winbourne, P. 4026

Winston, B. 5506, 5507

Winter, A. 3891

Winter, C. 2456, 3189, 3573, 3574, 3965, 4238

Wisdom, J. 2575, 4855

Wise, M. 2295, 2296, 2297, 2298, 2299, 4458, 4988, 5016

Wise, N. 2594

Witney, E. 4599

Wohwill, J. F. 4586, 5279

Wolforth, J. 2100, 5141, 5313, 5508, 5509, 5510, 5511, 5512

Wong, J. Yuk-yong 5694, 5695

Wong, W. Y. 4099

Wood, D. 2596, 2597

Wood, M. 2519, 2595

Wood, P. 3064, 4057

Wood, T. F. 2712

Woodring, P. 5513

Woolway, P. 4501

World Commission on Environment and Development 4900

Worrall, L. 2601

Worster, M. 4322

Wright, D. 2300, 3481, 3509, 3575, 3576, 3577, 3578, 3579, 3580, 3581, 3582, 3583, 3584, 3585, 4155, 4156, 4157, 4184, 4323, 4324, 4325, 4326, 4366, 4379, 4380, 4381, 4382, 4542, 5514

Wrigley, K. 3966

Wurdinger, S. 3356

Wyatt, H. 3279

Wynn, M. 3892

Wynne, T. E. 2341


Xie Kun-qing 5696

Xuan, S. 5697, 5698, 5699


Yangopoulos, S. 4383, 4901, 4989

Yau, B. 5700

Yee Sze-onn 4003, 5701, 5702

Yeung, S. Pui-ming 4990, 4991, 5703, 5704

Yockney, J. 4551

Yoshida, M. 5705

Young, E. W. 3585

Young, J. E. 2725, 5345

Young, T. M. 2815, 5281

Younger, M. 2754, 3122, 3893


Zamorano de Montiel, G. L. 5549, 5550

Zhang, H. 3586

Zhang, L.-S. 5706

Zhang Ya-nam 5707

Zhu Di-chen 5708

Ziegler, D. 5403

Zin, F. D. 4459

Zoller, U. 4902